PLANNING AND ESTIMATING UNDERGROUND CONSTRUCTION

PLANNING AND ESTIMATING UNDERGROUND CONSTRUCTION

ALBERT D. PARKER

Chief Heavy Construction Engineer
Kaiser Engineers
Oakland, California

McGraw-Hill Book Company

New York St. Louis San Francisco Dusseldorf London
Mexico Panama Sydney Toronto

PLANNING AND ESTIMATING UNDERGROUND CONSTRUCTION

Library of Congress Catalog Card Number 71-90018

48487

1234567890 MAMM 7543210

Preface

The purpose of this book is to describe the procedure and methods used by heavy-construction estimators in planning and estimating the cost of underground construction.

The complexity of our civilization and our population explosion have resulted in a trend to place more and more of our industrial and transportation facilities underground. This creates a need for more engineers who understand the equipment, methods, and costs involved in constructing water tunnels, power tunnels, subways, vehicular tunnels, underground powerhouses, underground garages, and other underground facilities. In this book I have tried to provide basic information for the young engineer who is beginning to acquire knowledge in tunnel construction. Most books on heavy-construction estimating cover the field in broad generalities. I have tried to be specific in describing the information required for estimating tunnels and have presented this material in an outline form. To understand the presentation readily, a preliminary knowledge of the subject is required.

The last part of the book contains a sample contractor's estimate for a hard-rock tunnel excavated in the conventional manner of drill, shoot, and muck. Estimates are not included for driving tunnels by any other method or for the construction of underground powerhouses, but the methods and equipment used in their construction have been described. If the sample estimate for a hard-rock tunnel is thoroughly understood, the change in procedures necessary to prepare an estimate for any other method or type of underground construction is easily accomplished.

This book is intended to cover the overall scope of underground construction; if more details are required concerning equipment, construction methods, and estimating procedures, they can be found in other sources, a few of which are listed as references.

The equipment selected, the progress figures, and the crew sizes used in the sample tunnel estimate are purely theoretical and should not be considered a detailed guide for estimating other tunnels. These determinations can only be made by a man experienced in this type of estimating.

I have tried to cover in concise form the results of my construction experience. During my career I have planned and estimated over 110 miles of tunnel for which my employer, Kaiser Engineers, was a joint-venture partner on the successful construction bid.

I should like to express my appreciation to Geraldine Randall for her editorial assistance in the preparation of this book and also to Jerry Smith, Clive Williams, and Robert Snyder for their assistance.

I wish to acknowledge the help and encouragement I have received from my wife, Helen. Because of her comprehension of the subject matter she was invaluable in checking galley and page proofs.

Albert D. Parker

Contents

List of Drawings

List of Exhibits

List of Photographs

PLANNING AND ESTIMATING UNDERGROUND CONSTRUCTION

Chapter 1 Introduction

The purpose of this book is to describe the study, planning, and computations that are necessary to plan the construction and estimate the cost of any underground construction project. In order to plan the construction, the engineer must know the different types of tunneling equipment and their uses and should understand the different tunnel-construction methods. Before estimating the construction cost the engineer must first select the equipment and methods to be used on the particular project. For this reason, equipment and construction methods are described before estimate preparation is explained.

This chapter summarizes the overall scope of the book. Tunnel construction is defined and a brief history of its development is included. The different types of underground construction and their major divisions are summarized. Also discussed are the construction industry's dependence on estimating and the different uses of an estimate. Additionally the features desired in a contractor's estimator and the reasons why contractors' managerial, supervisory, and engineering personnel should have estimating knowledge and experience are presented.

DEFINITION OF TUNNEL CONSTRUCTION

Tunnel construction is the continuous excavation of one hole through the earth's crust. It presents special problems in that there is only one surface where work can be done, the end of the tunnel called the *face*. All effort is concentrated on advancing this face as fast as possible. The men at the face are called the *heading crew*. This crew's responsibility is to excavate the face day after day until the tunnel is holed through. All other men and appurtenances in the tunnel service this crew to facilitate their progress. They supply the heading with fresh air, compressed air, water, powder, drills, mucking equipment, hauling equipment, and supports, as needed. After being excavated, tunnels may or may not be lined with concrete or steel.

The construction of intake and outlet works, shafts, adits, ventilation structures, underground powerhouses, and other underground chambers utilizes similar procedures.

HISTORY OF TUNNEL CONSTRUCTION

The ancient Greeks drove tunnels by building fires against the face and then throwing vinegar against the heated rocks. This caused the rocks to cool quickly and crack off the face of the excavation. Later, tunnel excavation was accomplished by drilling holes in the face with hand-rotated drills pounded by hand-swung hammers. The rock was then broken with fuses and black powder and the broken rock mucked by hand. This method was used for centuries.

The first major improvement in tunnel driving was in the late nineteenth century when the mechanical percussion drill was developed. Photograph 1 shows a main-line jumbo used in the 1870s, equipped with Burleigh drills. At this stage in tunnel driving, dry drills were used. The large amount of dust formed in the tunnel by these drills produced silicosis—a lung disease—in the miners. Since that time, conditions have improved: wet drilling has been developed, better drills are used, mucking machines have been perfected, carbide insert bits are used, diesel equipment has been used underground, and there is greater use of rubber-tired equipment. Compare Photographs 1 and 2 for an example of the development of drilling equipment.

Tunnel construction has been aided further by the development

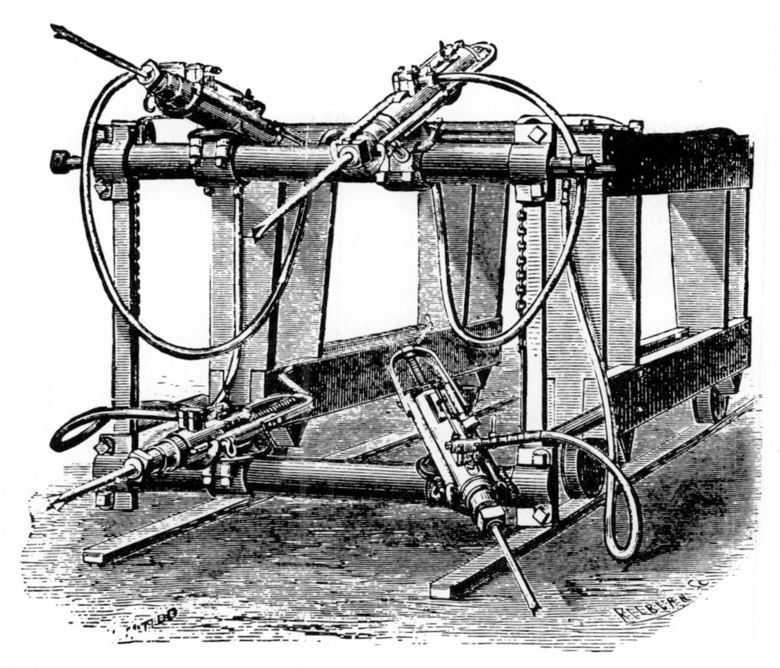

Photo 1 Burleigh drills on a main-line jumbo as used on the Hoosac Tunnel in Massachusetts and the Sutro Tunnel in Nevada in the 1870s. (Ingersoll-Rand Co.)

of tunnel-boring machines. They were first patented in England in 1856, and one of the these early machines was used in the tunnel started under the English Channel in the 1870s. This machine made a progress of approximately 40 lin ft per day, using steam for power. Modern tunnel borers are similar to this machine except that electric power is used instead of steam and bits have been improved with the development of carbide cutting surfaces. Tunnel borers fell out of use because of their unsatisfactory rate of progress in comparison with other methods; their revival occurred in 1954 at Oahe Dam, where their progress and cost were quite successful in the Pierre shale. Since that time, their use has become more widespread, and more and more companies are entering into their design and manufacture.

Most of the heavy-construction industry has experienced a sharp increase in cost in the past 20 years because of the increase in labor rates. Two types of heavy construction that have not experienced such a rapid rise in cost are dirt moving and tunneling. The reason for this is that they both have developed improved machinery and construction methods, which have resulted in increased production with a corresponding decrease in labor.

Photo 2 Modern main-line drill jumbo. (Gardner-Denver Co. and George M. Philpott Co., Inc.)

Tunnel-construction equipment is at a new threshold of development, and the future will probably see the use of tunnel-boring machines in harder rocks with the use of heat or laser beams to disintegrate the rock. Because of the wide variation of tunnel equipment now available and under development, each proposed plan for tunnel construction should be examined thoroughly to see if new methods can be used, or if different adaptations of equipment and techniques can be developed to decrease the cost.

MAJOR TUNNEL-DRIVING METHODS

The methods and equipment now in common use in excavating tunnels are briefly described here.

1. ***Conventional Tunnel Driving.*** This is the *drill, shoot, and muck* method shown in Drawing 1 and described in more detail in Chap. 2. In this method, holes are drilled in the face by air-operated drills mounted on a movable platform called a *jumbo.* After drilling is completed, the miners load the drilled holes with powder and exploders and connect all the exploders to a firing circuit. The jumbo is moved

back from the face and the men retreat to a safe distance. The firing circuit is then electrified and the charge is exploded. After the ventilation facilities have removed the powder fumes, a machine called a *mucker* is moved up to the *muck* pile. The mucker picks up this broken rock and loads it into transportation vehicles which remove it from the tunnel. After mucking is complete, the mucker is moved out, the drill jumbo is moved back in, and the process is repeated. This procedure goes on until the tunnel is completely excavated. Sometimes other operations are necessary at the face area, such as placement of tunnel supports, exploratory drilling to determine the type of formation that will be encountered, drilling and grouting which may be required in water-bearing material to reduce the water inflow, and roof bolting to support the roof and sides of the tunnel.

The major decisions that must be made by the planning engineer using this method of tunnel driving are whether electric, air, or diesel power will be used and whether the equipment will travel on rails or on rubber tires.

2. *Tunnels Driven with a Shield.* A shield is a steel plate shaped to fit the outside dimensions of the tunnel. This shield is kept with its forward edge against the tunnel face to prevent loose material from flowing or running into the tunnel in the otherwise open space between the tunnel face and the tunnel supports. It may also provide breastboard supports for the face. The front section of the shield protects the men excavating the face, and the rear section of the shield protects

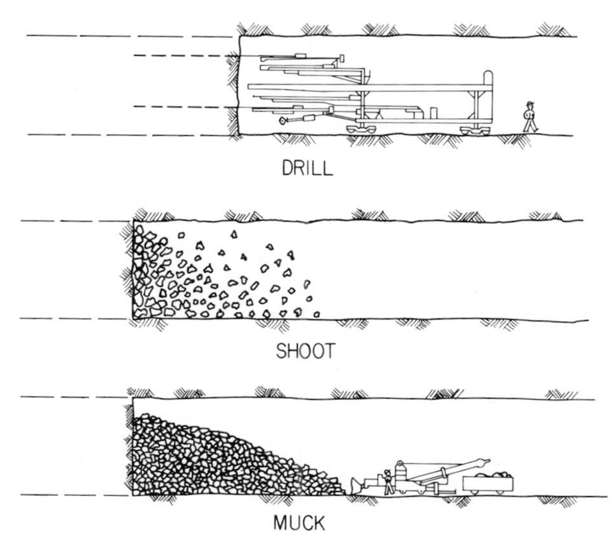

Drawing 1 Conventional tunnel driving.

the men erecting the tunnel support inside the tail of the shield. As the face is excavated the shield is jacked forward, sliding past the supports previously erected in its tail. The support of the tunnel is then transferred from the shield to the supports. Since the shield's tail is a thick plate, as the shield is moved forward it leaves behind it a space that the tail formerly occupied between the tunnel supports and the surrounding material. As soon as possible, this space should be filled with pea gravel, and the pea gravel grouted, so that the tunnel supports will restrain and take the full thrust of the surrounding material.

Shields are used in incompetent materials where temporary support is provided by the shield. Since a shield moves forward by hydraulic jacks reacting against tunnel supports, it can only be used in tunnels where supports or liner plate is necessary. The shield does not replace any equipment required in the conventional method of driving tunnels but only provides protection against running or loose materials. For a more complete description of the operation of a shield, see Chap. 5 and Drawing 2.

3. ***Tunnels Driven under Air Pressure.*** In certain soft-ground tunnels where water is a problem, the driving of the tunnel is accomplished with a shield equipped so that full or partial breastboards can be used. To prevent water and material from running into the tunnel,

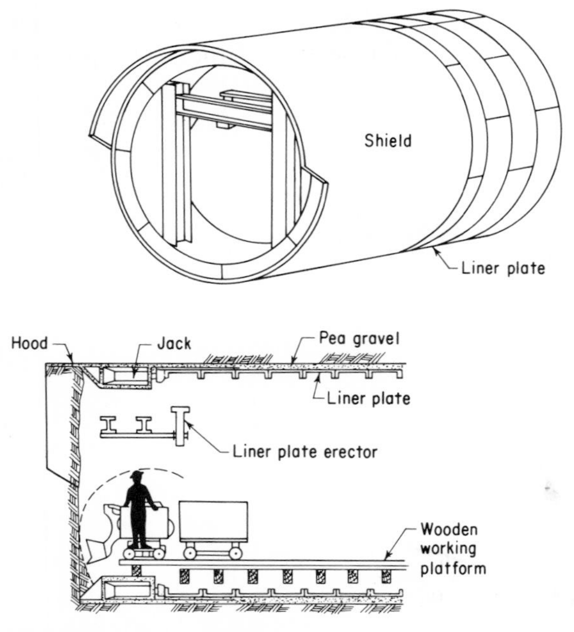

Drawing 2 Shield operation used in dry, finely particled material.

the heading is kept under air pressure sufficient to balance the hydrostatic pressure of the water. To hold this air pressure at the tunnel face, bulkheads containing air locks are provided in the rear of the shield or at the portal for both men and material passing into and out of the heading. When men work in air-pressure tunnels, the hours of work per shift are reduced in relation to the air pressure used. Essential in this operation are low-pressure air compressors, decompression chambers, and medical locks. This method of tunnel driving is further described in Chap. 5.

4. ***Tunnels Driven with a Boring Machine.*** A tunnel-boring machine replaces the drilling, shooting, and mucking operations in the conventional tunnel-driving cycle. The haulage and servicing equipment is the only equipment common to both the tunnel-boring machine and the conventional driving methods. The advantage that the tunnel-boring machine has over conventional tunnel driving is that excavation is a continuous operation compared with the cycle operation of drill, shoot, and muck used in the conventional method. This continuous method under proper rock conditions results in faster progress.

A tunnel-boring machine has a round cutterhead which operates with a rotating or oscillating motion. The action of cutter bits, chisel bits, or rotating bits mounted on the cutter face removes the material from the tunnel face. The boring machine also has provisions for picking up the cuttings from the face, conveying them from the face, and depositing them in haulage equipment located to the rear of the machine. Such machines are used without shields in competent rock and with shields in loose material. When operated in competent rock, the thrust from the jacks propelling the shield forward and furnishing the thrust required on the cutterhead is transferred to the tunnel sides. In loose material, the jacks react against the tunnel supports. To date, tunnel-boring machines have made excellent progress in soft, consistent rock. Progress has not been satisfactory when hard rock or loose material is encountered, when the tunnel passes through stratified rock layers, or when rock formations of different hardness occur along the tunnel line. A competent rock-tunnel-boring machine without a shield is shown in Photograph 3. Chapter 5 describes in detail this method of tunnel construction.

TUNNEL LINING

Certain tunnels require lining, such as water and power tunnels passing through supported ground, all tunnels in incompetent material, vehicular tunnels, and subways. In some cases ground conditions require that tunnel lining be placed as close to the face as possible in order to

Photo 3 Jarva tunnel-boring machine. (Jarva, Inc.)

furnish a strong and watertight support for the tunnel. When such support is needed, a lining of precast concrete or steel liner plate is generally installed. Additional cost occurs in both the concrete lining and the tunnel excavation operations when they must be done concurrently. This additional cost is due to the interference between the two operations caused by the limited working area in, and restricted access to, the tunnel. Thus, unless time or specifications make concurrent operations mandatory, the lining operations are not started until the excavation is completed.

When tunnels are to be lined with concrete, the following placement methods are used:

1. Concrete is placed by the full-circle method, i.e., the placement of the concrete lining in one operation. This is the method least desired by contractors since it is the most expensive. It presents numerous problems in anchoring forms and keeping them on line and grade. Full-circle or arch forms with a screeded invert may be used. Anchoring forms to prevent flotation is difficult, for there is no previously poured concrete curb or invert to which they may be anchored. In large-diameter tunnels, the concrete must flow a long distance under the invert forms, which may result in concrete deficiencies. When full-circle forms are used, the invert section of the forms should be arranged so that they can be removed as soon as possible after the pour is completed. This will allow the correction of any concrete deficiencies and permit the troweling out of air bubbles which tend to form against the invert forms.

2. The method used most in the past for pouring concrete lining is the curb, invert, and arch method. This method consists in pouring concrete curbs along each side of the tunnel outside the minimum-thickness line of the tunnel concrete. With the curbs as a reference point and as a guide and support for the invert screed, the invert concrete is then placed. Then, by using the invert to anchor the arch forms, the arch concrete is placed.

3. The curb, arch, and invert method is the same as the previous method except that the arch is poured before the invert.

4. The method now used most commonly is the invert and arch method. This method is more economical than the others because there are only two concrete placing operations instead of three. Overbreak excavation and concrete, necessary for curb installation, are eliminated. Invert concrete is placed from an invert bridge and is supported and kept on line and grade by brackets. In a supported tunnel, these brackets are stud welded to the tunnel sets. In a nonsupported tunnel. the brackets are supported by steel-pipe jacks drilled into the bottom and sides of the tunnel. The arch concrete is then poured, with the invert concrete used as a reference point and anchor for the arch forms.

5. The arch and then invert method is the same as the previous one, except for the sequence of operations.

Tunnel-concreting methods and equipment are described in more detail in Chap. 3.

SHAFT CONSTRUCTION

Shafts can be grouped into classifications of use and construction method.

Deep shafts are let as separate contracts. They are used in mines for the development of underground ore bodies or for the recovery of industrial elements such as sulfur. A modern use of deep shafts is to provide facilities for the underground testing of nuclear reactions. Such shafts are constructed by large-hole drilling operations or by excavation from the surface. Their construction is so specialized that it is usually performed by contractors who have concentrated their efforts in this field.

Small-diameter, shallow shafts are used in conjunction with other underground facilities. Examples of these are ventilation shafts for powerhouses, subways, and other underground facilities; pressure shafts for powerhouses; or gate intake and surge shafts for hydro tunnels. In soft rock formations they may be excavated with large-hole drilling equipment. If not drilled, the preferred method of construction is raising them from the bottom of the shaft. To use this construction method, bottom access must be available and the shaft must pass through competent material. In other conditions, they are constructed by sinking operations.

Large-diameter, shallow shafts are also normally constructed in conjunction with other underground work. An example of this type of shaft is a surge shaft for a hydropower tunnel. The preferred construction method, when bottom access is available, is first to raise a small-diameter pilot shaft. This pilot shaft is then enlarged with sinking operations to the full shaft diameter. Fast and efficient muck disposal for the enlargement operation is accomplished by shoving the muck down the pilot shaft to trucks waiting below. If shaft-bottom access is not available, these shafts must be sunk from the surface.

The last type of shaft to be discussed is that constructed to provide access and furnish service to tunnel headings. These are sunk from the surface to intersect the tunnel line. Two additional tunnel headings can be started at this point. Hoisting capacity is necessary both in shaft sinking and in servicing the tunnel operations. In shallow shafts, either crawler or truck cranes are used for this purpose. When shafts are excavated deeper than approximately 150 ft, more efficient hoisting capacity is required. Headframes and hoists are then erected to finish the shaft sinking and to provide service for the tunnel. If delivery of the main headframe and hoist cannot be secured in time, the shaft can be sunk with a small sinking headframe and hoist.

For more details on shaft construction, refer to Chap. 4.

LARGE UNDERGROUND CHAMBERS

Large underground chambers are currently used to house powerhouses, to store materials, and to test nuclear reactions. The future will see increased usage of these chambers for the purposes listed, and in additional applications that may be developed. To date, underground chamber experience has been gained mainly on underground powerhouse construction jobs. These will be used in the remainder of this book to illustrate this type of construction.

The use of underground locations for powerhouses is increasing because, in certain cases, the savings resulting from the elimination of long penstock runs are greater than the costs of additional excavation. Other reasons for installing powerhouses underground are to protect them from surface explosions and for esthetic reasons. Esthetic reasons have become very important along the Hudson River and in other scenic, populated areas.

Access to both the top and bottom of the powerhouse and to as many other elevations as possible is very important in powerhouse construction. This allows work to be performed on many faces with continuous operation of the drilling and mucking crew. Access to the bottom of the powerhouse permits the muck to be removed by dropping it down raises into trucks waiting below. When access is only available to the top of the powerhouse, all muck has to be hoisted, a slow and expensive operation. Rubber-tired excavating equipment is used since this type of equipment can be readily shifted from one area to another. For further explanation of powerhouse construction refer to Chap. 6.

OTHER RELATED CONSTRUCTION

In tunnel contracts, other related construction operations that may be called for are construction of roads, outside facilities, aggregate plants, concrete plants, intake and outlet structures, diversion dams, etc.

Since the purpose of this book is to explain the planning and estimating of underground construction and these related construction items cover work done on the surface, a description of construction and operation of these items will not be included in this book. If this information is desired, it can be readily found in the books listed as references at the end of each chapter.

DEFINITION OF A TUNNEL ESTIMATE

Tunnel estimating is the art of conceiving an entire job on paper and properly evaluating the cost of this planned construction. To do so, the method of tunnel construction has to be chosen, the type of plant and amount of equipment selected, progress assumed, and man-days estimated. The estimated cost of the work must include the costs of the equipment, labor, material, supplies, supervision, and escalation. Normal contingencies, interest, and profit are not included in the estimate but compose the markup which is added to the estimate by the construction company's managers to arrive at the bid price.

The estimate must be prepared in such a form that the total estimated cost of the completed work can be readily broken down to the items listed in the bidding papers furnished by the owner's representative.

PURPOSE AND SECONDARY USES OF A TUNNEL ESTIMATE

The primary purpose of a tunnel estimate is to provide the basis for the preparation of a successful bid for tunnel construction, with a bid price that will allow the contractor to make a reasonable profit. A contractor wishing to enter into or stay in the tunnel-construction field must compete in bidding with other contractors. In order to be competitive and make a reasonable profit on tunnel construction, it is necessary for the contractor's organization to prepare an estimated cost of doing the work as close as possible to what the actual cost will be. For if the contractor is the successful bidder and the estimated cost is lower than the actual cost, he will lose money on the project and would have been better off without it. Alternatively, if the estimated cost is higher than the actual cost, the contractor will have very little chance of being the lowest bidder and hence will not get the job. Therefore, his estimator must base his estimate on the best possible methods of performing the work and on the use of the most suitable equipment and, furthermore, must have enough knowledge to estimate accurately the cost of doing the work. The contractor places a great amount of confidence in the skill and integrity of his estimator since proper bidding is one of the requirements for success. This estimating requirement is not as important outside the construction industry because the contractor is the only manufacturer who prices his product before it is manufactured.

If the contractor is the low bidder on the construction project, the estimate has several secondary uses. All the adjustments made before bidding are carried back into the body of the estimate, and it is then published as a *budget* estimate. This budget estimate provides the job management with a list of the plant and equipment required to construct the job and is used as a guide in determining the methods of constructing the work. The budget estimate is an aid to job control since it offers the estimated cost for comparison with actual cost. Thus determinations can be made of those items requiring more attention by the job supervision. Cost accounting procedures and cost accounts are established in accordance with the estimate's format and the divisions of cost used in the estimate. If there are changes in the work or the job conditions extensive enough to warrant presenting a claim to the owner, the budget estimate is then used as the reference in the preparation of the claim.

If the contractor is not the successful bidder, the estimate has only one secondary use. In this case, the estimate provides the estimator with a basis for comparison with the methods, equipment, progress, and cost of the construction work performed by the successful bidder. Such a comparison will enable the estimator to incorporate any improvements developed by the low bidder into his next bidding estimate. One method of securing this information from the low bidder is to observe the number of men, pieces of equipment, and progress while inspecting his work. Several inspection trips should be made over a period of time, for a single spot check may lead to erroneous conclusions.

QUALIFICATIONS OF AN ESTIMATOR

Estimating is a very interesting field because the preparation of the estimate for each project requires the solving of different construction problems. To describe the characteristics and knowledge requisite in an estimator is difficult, for the men who are successful in this field are quite different. However, a tunnel estimator should have a majority of the following qualifications.

1. ***Temperament, Education, and Integrity.*** Since estimates have to be completed by a definite bid date, and the period between advertising and bidding is of short duration, an estimator should have a calm, controlled temperament and the ability to plan and schedule his efforts, or his work or health may suffer. He must have the ability to use figures, without confusion, as a tool of his trade. His time must be allocated in such a way that he spends as much time as possible on the major items of cost and only as much time on the minor items as their costs merit.

The estimator should have an engineering education enabling him to interpret the specifications, read the drawings, select the equipment, lay out and design the plant, and plan the construction activity. Professional integrity is necessary if he is to be respected by the owners, the owner's representative, the equipment dealers, and the subcontractors.

2. ***Knowledge of Geology.*** The estimator should develop a basic knowledge of geology, enabling him to recognize the basic rock types. Using this knowledge, he must be able to estimate drilling speeds, amount of powder required per cubic yard, how the rock will break and affect mucking capacity, supports required, amount of overbreak, water inflow into the tunnel, and excavation progress. Experience is a great help in this respect, as is the visual inspection of tunnels under construction.

3. ***Preparation of Construction Schedules.*** The ability to prepare construction schedules is important to the estimator; these schedules determine how the work should be done and the length of time required to complete the work. Moreover, the construction schedule determines how many tunnel headings are necessary and whether additional adits or shafts are required to reduce the construction time or decrease cost. The number of tunnel headings and their locations, planned in an estimate, are among the largest variables in the estimated cost of construction. This scheduling ability is one of the most difficult skills for an estimator to develop. It demands that an estimator grasp the overall scope of the project while keeping the details in focus. Details are important in estimating, for an estimate is the collection of all the details. However, the overall scope should control the details and not be controlled by them.

4. ***Knowledge of Construction Methods and Equipment.*** The estimator must be able to select the proper methods and equipment for the particular job under consideration. To make a good estimate, the work must be planned in detail before its cost is computed. It is necessary that the estimator be familiar with the methods of tunnel driving to enable him to determine when he should use the conventional method of tunnel driving, when he should plan to use compressed air on the headings, if he should use a tunnel shield, and when the use of tunnel-boring machines is economical. He should know the types of equipment available, their advantages and disadvantages, and the amount of each type required for constructing the tunnel by each method of tunnel driving. The estimator must know when to use rubber-tired equipment and when to use rail-mounted equipment. He must decide between air, diesel, or electric power units for this equipment. Finally, he must suppress his pride of authorship so that he will readily change his estimate to take advantage of new procedures or methods advanced by others.

5. ***Knowledge of Cost.*** The methods and equipment selected on any tunnel job will determine the size of crews required. All of this must then be evaluated and tabulated as cost. To do this, the estimator must know the purchase price of the equipment, the number of men required for its operation, and the cost of supplies used for operation and maintenance.

Familiarity with the cost of labor and the amount of work that will be produced in a man-day is necessary. The estimator should study labor agreements so that he has an understanding of labor classification, wage rates, fringe benefits, subsistence areas, travel time, hours of work, and overtime payments. He should know the cost of the labor burden (workmen's compensation insurance, property damage and personal liability insurance, and payroll taxes). He should study the trend of labor increases in order to estimate the amount of labor escalation during the life of the project. A study of labor classifications will acquaint him with which craftsmen are used in tunnels for specific areas. He should know the number and classifications of supervisory personnel required. By past experience or by job inspection, he should know the number of men required in a tunnel crew for different sizes of tunnels and types of tunnel operations. He must know the cost of each supply item and should secure quotations on permanent materials and the items he wishes to subcontract. Most important, the estimator should be cost conscious. He should know the range in cost of each separate operation and use this knowledge as a check on his computed cost. In observing any construction operation, he should automatically reduce this operation to cost per unit produced. When inspecting any competitor's work, he should count men and equipment and compute their progress. Cost awareness is developed by training.

6. *Estimating Format.* The estimator must be capable of preparing his estimate in a form that will allow quick review of his work by himself and others and will allow his estimate to be used as a guide for setting up the cost accounting details. Many estimates do not serve this purpose because the estimator cannot follow his own work upon completion of the estimate. The summaries should be in a form that can be understood by management and that can be compared with other estimates. As much as possible, the format should have arithmetical checks, for errors in judgment are excusable, but errors in arithmetic are not. The estimate should be in such a form that it can be readily used for preparation of bid prices and for making last-minute adjustments to the bid. The estimator should understand the principles of cost accounting so that he can arrange his estimate in the proper form and prepare the cash forecast, and he should understand the principles of job financing.

7. *Insurance and Bond.* The estimator should understand insurance coverage in order to know which equipment to insure and what the rate of this insurance will be. He must know when he should include job risk insurance in his estimate, or any other kind of insurance that may be required by the specifications. He must know the bonding capacity of his company and the bond rates for different contract sizes and lengths of contruction time.

8. *Safety Rules.* Safety rules vary greatly from state to state and country to country. They govern the kind of powder that can be used, the ventilation requirements, shaft safety rules, and the provisions that must be made for the safety of miners and for first aid.

9. *Study of Records and Inspection of Other Tunnel Projects.* The estimator should study job records and inspect other projects since the comparison of these constitutes the basis for all estimating. Records that have been adjusted for changes in physical conditions, increases in labor rates, changes in labor efficiency, and improvements in equipment efficiency can be used as a check for a new estimate. It is very seldom that past records can be used without exercising a judgment factor, for tunnel jobs are never exactly the same. Entering into the cost of construction are many variable factors, such as quality of supervision, quality of labor, weather, speed required to do the work, and the amount of winter work to be done. The generally accepted method of estimating is to determine the size of the required crew, estimate their average production, and when the estimated unit cost of an item is determined, check this unit cost against previous records and adjust as judgment dictates. It is to the advantage of the estimator to set up a record of past jobs and to become familiar with the details of these jobs in order to determine under what work conditions the cost and production figures were obtained.

An estimator should study all jobs similar to those he is estimating in order to learn the kinds and amount of equipment and methods used by other contractors and the number of personnel manning the various crews and, if possible, obtain a record of their production. One of the best ways to accomplish this is to visit projects that are under construction.

Another method the estimator can use to become familiar with tunnel construction is to read and study the methods used by different contractors in constructing specific jobs. This information can be gleaned from articles published in the construction trade magazines. These articles are quite comprehensive and illustrate the use of new equipment, new methods, and new applications of existing equipment.

One successful contractor's estimator maintains close inspection on each job that he bids on and loses in order to determine if other contractors have techniques better than his. This job inspection brings to his attention any new ideas or equipment that can be used in future planning and estimating.

10. *Trial Estimates.* If an estimator has not prepared competitive estimates, it is helpful if he prepares trial estimates on jobs that are out for bids. These trial estimates should be completed and an assumed markup added to arrive at bid prices. Then by comparing these trial estimates with the bid prices submitted by other contractors, he will have a gauge by which he can evaluate his work.

ESTIMATING EXPERIENCE HELPFUL FOR OTHER POSITIONS

There is no better way to gain understanding of all the different operations and requirements concerned with tunnel construction than actually to work on a contractor's competitive bid estimate.

If job engineers have had estimating experience, it helps them make correct decisions since they are trained to understand the importance of cost. Estimating experience is valuable when they lay out the construction plant and purchase equipment. Such experience introduces them to cost keeping and cost control and is useful in pricing change orders and claims. It is a job engineer's function to prepare at frequent intervals an estimate of cost of the uncompleted work on his project. The job engineer can prepare these estimates with greater facility if he has had estimating experience, for this experience makes him more observant of the cost of every operation being performed.

For project managers, estimating experience will teach them that not only construction progess is important, but cost is also a very important factor. It will make them realize that there is no phase of the work that can be neglected, whether accounting, engineering, or financing. By teaching them the importance of cost, estimating experience helps project managers to decide methods and crew sizes, and also helps to emphasize the importance of proper scheduling and the dovetailing of one operation into another. Many firms use the estimator as project manager, if they are successful in the bidding, because during the estimate preparation he has already studied and evaluated many of the problems the project manager will face. If the estimator is the project manager, he will also have more incentive to meet the estimate or improve on it with actual job cost.

If the manager of the construction organization has had estimating experience, it will help him in securing new business, for he will know all the steps in estimating and presenting a bid. As explained above, it is essential to secure contracts at the right price, just to stay in business. Estimating experience will assist the organization manager in determining markup, capital requirements, contingencies, and the estimated cost. Furthermore, this estimating experience will help him to advise the project managers, since he will know what to expect as the result of any major decision. It will also help him understand the problems that confront his project managers. Many executives of tunnel-construction companies have had estimating experience, and some of them still prepare estimates.

Chapter 2 Conventional Tunnel-driving Methods and Equipment

INTRODUCTION

Before one can plan the construction of a tunnel or estimate its cost, it is necessary to have a knowledge of the different equipment and construction methods that can be used. In this chapter conventional methods and equipment for drilling, shooting, and mucking will be described. Methods and equipment used in large-diameter tunnels that are excavated by the use of top and bottom headings are described in Chap. 6.

The description of tunnel excavation equipment is divided into three groups: tunnel haulage equipment; equipment unique to excavating the heading in the conventional manner—drills, jumbos, and mucking machines; and facilities necessary to service the first two groups. The method of heading excavation does not affect the haulage or servicing equipment used; therefore, descriptions of this equipment will not be repeated in the discussions of other tunneling methods.

The choice of equipment and methods for conventional tunnel excavation is influenced by the following variables: structural characteristics of the ground, length of the tunnel, diameter of the tunnel, grade in the tunnel, and the applicable laws covering the use of diesel engines underground. Descriptions of tunneling equipment are given in broad terms, but because of continued equipment development any description of equipment rapidly becomes outdated. A tunnel engineer should contact equipment manufacturers and inspect tunnels that are under construction to secure more equipment details and to keep up with improvements and new developments in this field.

HAULAGE EQUIPMENT

The type of muck haulage equipment used for any underground excavation will determine the selection of drilling and mucking methods, as the equipment for these three operations must be of the same general type. This makes the determination of the haulage method and equipment the first consideration in the planning of underground construction.

Suitable rubber-tired or rail-supported equipment is available for any size and length of tunnel or underground chamber. The development of small diesel trucks, the improvements in ventilation, the use of rubber-tired front-end loaders, and the acceptance of the use of diesel engines in underground construction has resulted in a greater use of rubber-tired equipment. Since the development of large rubber-tired front-end loaders, short tunnels and the beginnings of long tunnels of sufficient diameter to provide equipment clearance are excavated with the use of front-end loaders for both mucking and hauling. When front-end loaders are used in this manner, the only other piece of tunnel equipment necessary for performing the excavation is a truck drill jumbo. This results in a low excavation cost as crew size and equipment maintenance are held to a minimum. Except for this special use of front-end loaders, tunnel muck haulage is done with either rail-mounted or rubber-tired equipment.

Advantages of Rubber-tired Haul Units

Rubber-tired equipment can be mobilized very quickly, will operate well on grades up to 10 percent, and has restricted operation on grades between 10 and 20 percent. Rubber-tired equipment also requires less capital expense than rail-mounted equipment. For short tunnels the cost of excavation will be less with rubber-tired haulage than with rail haulage as smaller crews can be used. Furthermore, rubber-tired equipment furnishes flexibility in excavation operations. It can be readily moved from one heading to another when alternating heading crews are used. When large-diameter tunnels are excavated, it can muck and clean up any width of tunnel. When underground chambers are excavated, it is readily moved from one excavation face to another. It can also dispose of the muck at any location.

Disadvantages of Rubber-tired Haul Units

In small-diameter tunnels, rubber-tired haul units must be of small capacity because of the restricted headroom, and these small units cannot be operated up a steep grade because of their low horsepower. Rubber-tired haul units are wider than rail-mounted equipment of similar capacity, which necessitates more passing room and a wider roadbed. There is more dead weight, less efficiency, and more horsepower required per pay load, which results in greater ventilation requirements. On long hauls, this high ventilation load may make the use of rubber-tired equipment impractical. Rubber-tired units also require a well-graded, firm-surface, dry roadbed, which may be impossible to provide in a wet tunnel.

Advantages of Rail Haul Units

On long hauls, trains are more efficient than trucks since they can haul more muck with less horsepower and with fewer operators and not as much ventilation is required. Since rail haulage equipment is compact and relatively narrow, it can operate and pass in small-diameter tunnels; this compactness allows the use of rail equipment of large capacity in relatively small-diameter tunnels. Rail equipment is also more suitable than rubber-tired equipment in wet tunnels, as it can operate on flooded tracks. Furthermore, rail equipment is more adaptable than rubber-tired equipment to the conversion to concrete placing operations upon completion of the excavation. When rail equipment is operated with cables and a hoist, it can be used on any grade. Additionally, rail-mounted muckers require less maintenance than those used for loading trucks.

Disadvantages of Rail Haul Units

Rail equipment requires a longer period of mobilization than is required for rubber-tired equipment. Excavation of short tunnels is more expensive with rail units than with rubber-tired equipment as larger crews are required. If rail-mounted muckers are used in large-diameter tunnels, they must muck out one-half the tunnel at a time, or two muckers have to operate abreast of each other, as they are limited in their width of operation. Rail equipment does not give the flexibility that rubber-tired equipment does for the excavation of underground chambers as rail equipment can only operate where tracks can be installed. Rail equipment operates well on grades up to 2 percent. From 2 to 4 percent it has restricted operations. Above a 4 percent grade it must be winched up and down the slopes.

Haulage-equipment Selection

To assist in haulage-equipment selection, the types that are suitable for different diameter tunnels, different haul distances, and different tunnel grades are listed below:

1. For any length or size tunnel, first consideration should be given to tunnel equipment that is owned by the successful bidder. Contractor-owned equipment which has been partially written off on previous work has definite economic advantages. This equipment must be modern or its increased operating cost may offset the savings in equipment write-off.

2. Tunnels with a grade of over 2 percent and less than 20 percent can be excavated most efficiently with rubber-tired equipment.

3. Tunnels with a grade over 20 percent are excavated with rail equipment that is winched up and down the slope.

4. Short tunnels with a grade of up to 20 percent, a height of over 12 ft and a width that prevents the passing of trucks, and the first few hundred feet of long tunnels of similar characteristics can be driven with the least expense by the use of large, articulated, rubber-tired front-end loaders for both mucking and hauling. In this method, crew size can be held to a minimum with reasonable progress. The length of tunnel that can be economically driven in this manner increases as the amount of bucket pay load increases. The largest bucket load is secured in well-graded fine material. In ground that produces a fine, well-graded muck pile, heading distances up to 1,500 lin ft can be economically driven with one front-end loader, and if a passing niche is excavated and two front-end loaders are used, this distance can be doubled.

5. Long tunnels with a grade under 2 percent, a height of under 14 ft, and heading distances over 2,000 ft in length are, in the majority of cases, driven with rail-mounted equipment. This tunnel size does not furnish sufficient headroom for large track-mounted or rubber-tired mounted muckers to load average-size trucks. Rail equipment is used because large-capacity rail-mounted muckers and cars have lower operating heights. In some unlined tunnels with a bore 10 ft in diameter, contractors have overexcavated them to a 12-ft height in order to use the largest Conway rail-mounted mucker.

6. Tunnels over 14 ft in height with heading distances of up to 1 mile are driven most economically with rubber-tired equipment. The cost of equipping a job with rubber-tired equipment is less than that with rail equipment, and the time required for the plant erection is reduced.

7. Tunnels over 14 ft in height with heading distances over 1 mile in length require economic studies to determine the type of equipment that should be used. As the length of the haul increases in a tunnel, the number of trucks necessary to serve the mucker increases. Each additional truck in a tunnel increases the ventilation requirements, and an economic balance is reached where increase in ventilation cost will outweigh the advantage of truck haulage. Since rail-mounted equipment does not require as much horsepower as rubber-tired equipment does to move the same yardage, rail equipment can be used for much longer haul distances with less ventilation than can rubber-tired equipment. Also on long haul distances, one locomotive and one operator can haul as much as several trucks and several truck drivers, which results in a saving in manpower, equipment maintenance, and equipment write-off compared with truck haulage operations.

TRUCK HAULAGE

Gasoline trucks are not allowed in underground construction since they produce carbon monoxide in their exhaust. Therefore, all underground motors must be diesel, electric, or compressed air, and diesel trucks must be equipped with exhaust scrubbers which remove some of the engine fumes and particles.

In selecting the type of truck to be used for a particular tunnel, the following criteria should be reviewed:

1. The truck bed must be low enough that the mucker will have sufficient headroom to discharge its loaded bucket into the truck.

2. The truck must not be too wide for the tunnel. In long tunnels, the trucks must be able to pass in the tunnel, or niches must be excavated to provide passing areas.

3. The combined horsepower of the trucks that will be in the tunnel at one time, plus the horsepower of the mucker, must not exceed reasonable ventilation requirements.

A listing of the general descriptions of four types of trucks used on underground excavation haul follows. The first type described can be used in small tunnels and the last type described has been used in 50-ft-diameter tunnels.

1. Small diesel rear-dump trucks, similar to the Getman Brothers diesel truck, for small-diameter tunnels. Horsepower and dimensions

vary according to truck size as follows:

Struck capacity	½–4 cu yd
Horsepower	20–60
Width	77–96 in.
Loading height	40–56 in.
Top of driver's head	66 in.

2. Rear-dump trucks of larger capacity that have reversible driver's seats and dual controls with four speeds in either direction. An example of this type is the Aveling-Barford truck shown in Photograph 4. Another type is the Koehring Dumptor which has dimensions as follows:

	8-*ton truck*	15-*ton truck*
Struck capacity	5¼ cu yd	10 cu yd
Horsepower	109	227
Width	9 ft 2½ in.	10 ft 3¼ in.
Loading height	7 ft 8½ in.	8 ft 10⅛ in.
Cab height	9 ft 10 in.	10 ft 10⅜ in.

3. Off-highway rear-dump trucks similar to the Euclid. Reversible driver's seat, dual control, and four speeds in either direction can be installed in these trucks. Horsepower and dimensions of a 12-ton Euclid

Photo 4 Dual-control dump truck. (Aveling-Barford, Ltd., and George M. Philpott Co., Inc.)

are:

Struck capacity	8 cu yd
Horsepower	148
Width	9 ft 2½ in.
Loading height	7 ft 7½ in.
Cab guard to ground	10 ft 2 in.

4. Two-wheeled rubber-tired tractor type with rear-dump trailer, similar to Caterpillar PR 621, for use in large-diameter tunnels:

Tonnage pay load	34 tons
Struck capacity	21 cu yd
Horsepower	300
Width	12 ft
Loading height	9 ft 5 in.
Height clearance	11 ft 4 in.
Height, body-raised position	19 ft 1 in.
Nonstop-turning width	
Body up	26 ft 10 in.
Body down	33 ft 6 in.

RAIL HAULAGE

In the planning of rail haulage methods and equipment, decisions must be made on the type and size of the muck trains, size and capacity of muck cars, type and capacity of locomotives, train-switching facilities, car-changing equipment, and the size of rail.

Muck Trains with Individual Car Loading

In the majority of tunnels, muck cars that are loaded individually by the mucker are used. This provides flexibility in train operation since the cars can carry as large a piece of rock as the mucker can load and additional trains can be added or released from the operation as desired. When this type of train is used, cars must be continually and rapidly switched to the mucker so it can operate at full capacity. This requires that train-switching facilities be installed in the tunnel and that a fast car-changing method be provided for servicing the mucker. Equipment and methods that are used for train switching and car changing are described later in this chapter. With this type of train, passing clearance in the tunnel limits the width of the equipment that can be used. Drawings should be made to check the passing clearances of jumbos, muckers, locomotives, and cars.

In small, unlined tunnels, instead of using small equipment that is able to pass in the tunnel, it may be more economical to use larger equipment and overexcavate areas for passing tracks and for changing cars. In small tunnels one or two trains can usually handle the muck

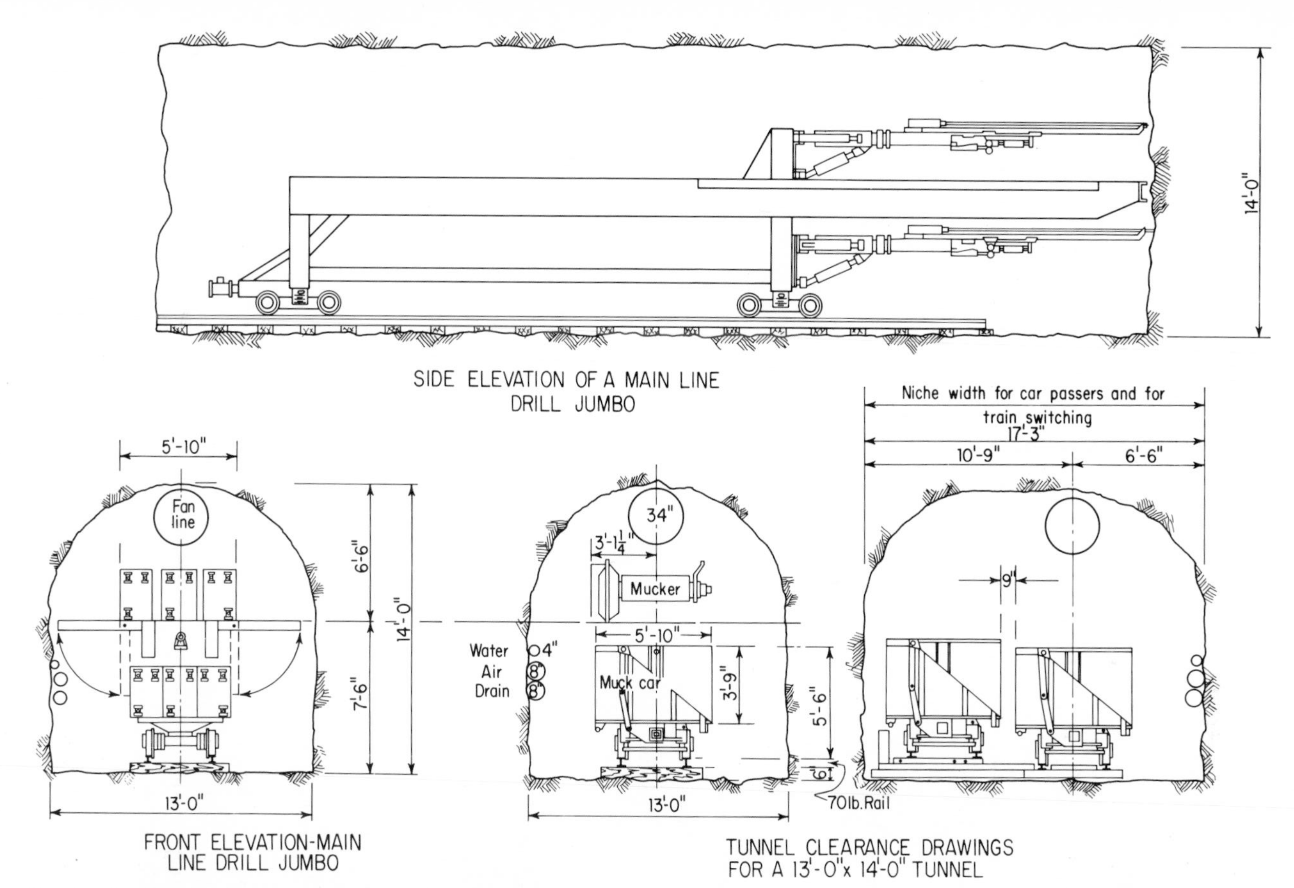

Drawing 3 **Main-line jumbo and clearance diagrams for a small tunnel.**

from one excavation round so train-switching facilities are only required at regular intervals along the tunnel line. However, to change cars at the mucker quickly, the car passer should be kept near the face, which necessitates overexcavation of car, passing niches at 150-ft spacing. The cost of the overexcavation necessary for the use of this larger equipment is generally less than the slowdown in operations caused by using smaller equipment. An example of this planned overexcavation is shown by the clearance sections illustrated in Drawing 3. When this type of operation is planned, similar cross-sectional clearance drawings should be prepared. It is also necessary to prepare plan drawings showing the length and location of the passing tracks and the length and frequency of the car-changing niches and to check the swing clearance required by the jumbo when it is switched onto a passing track.

Small concrete-lined tunnels are constructed with less cost if equipment is selected that can pass in the tunnel. In constructing these tunnels, any savings resulting from the use of large equipment is less than the extra cost of excavating and then backfilling with concrete the areas where overexcavation for this equipment is required.

Trains Loaded by Conveyor Belt

Conveyor-belt train loading is shown in Drawing 4. In this method, car changing at the mucker is not required and train-switching facilities are not necessary if each train has capacity to haul all the muck shot in one round. If the round contains more muck than can be handled by one train, then train-switching facilities are required in the tunnel. To use this method, the tunnel must have sufficient diameter to provide clearance for the belt and the belt gantry, and the muck must break fine enough for the belt to handle. These two limitations restrict the use of this type of train loading when the tunnel is excavated in the conventional manner. When the tunnel is excavated with a tunnel-boring machine, muck is removed from the face in small pieces. Since no equipment other than the tunnel-boring machine must have access to the tunnel face, the gantry for the belt causes no equipment interference. Therefore, when tunnels are excavated with boring machines, belt loading of trains is generally used. In large-diameter tunnels driven with boring machines, surge bins are located at the end of the belt to provide excavation surge storage and to increase the speed of train loading.

If belt loading of trains is used when the tunnel is excavated in the conventional manner, a main-line drill jumbo must be used since a gantry drill jumbo could not pass by the conveyor-belt gantry when the change is made from drilling to mucking. The conveyor-belt gantry must have passing clearance for the mucker and the main-line drill

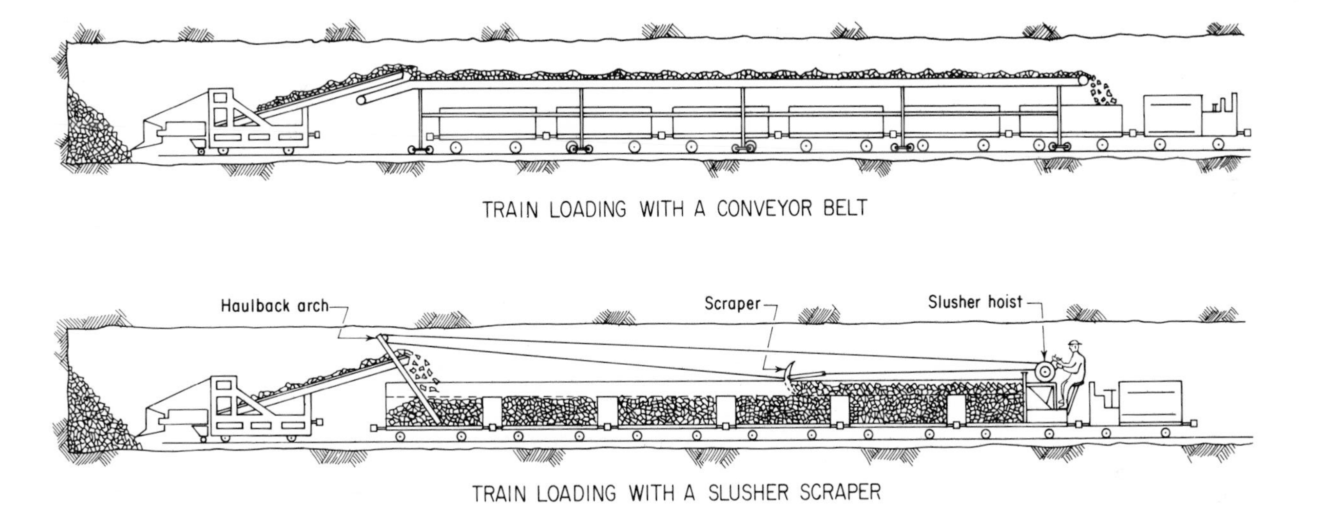

Drawing 4 Methods of loading trains without car changing.

jumbo. This limits the use of this method of train loading to tunnels over 17 ft in diameter.

Trains Loaded with Slusher Scraper

As illustrated in Drawing 4, the slusher scraper operates in a trough erected on top of and between the cars. The trough is constructed with a closed bottom between the cars and an open bottom over the cars. The lead car in the train is loaded by a mucking machine and as the muck builds up in this car it is pulled back by the scraper to load the other cars in the train. To use this train-loading method, the muck should break fine to permit efficient scraper operation and the scraper should have enough capacity to keep up with the mucker. This train-loading system has been used successfully with all sizes of cars. For example, it was used by Peter Kiewit and Sons' Company in 1959 on the excavation of a tunnel for the Western Pacific Railroad in the Feather River area of California.[1] On this project, full-sized railroad gondola cars were adapted for this method of loading. In general, however, it has been most successful with small cars used in small-diameter tunnels where the rock broke into small particles.

Conveyor-belt Trains

Literature is available concerning trains that are composed of articulated cars with a conveyor belt forming the bottom of the train. The loading procedure is to load the end car in the train with a mucker; the belt then moves the muck back over the length of the train. The train is unloaded by reversing the belt. This method has reportedly been used in Europe; I am unaware of any instance of its use in the United States.

Muck Cars

The most commonly used muck car is the non-self-dumping, side-dump type which has a low bed height and a large muck capacity. This type of car must be dumped with a car dumper as shown in Photograph 5. This method was used on a tunnel constructed by Kaiser Engineers for the Snowy Mountains Hydroelectric Authority in Australia.

The widest cars that can pass each other in a tunnel should be selected in order to reduce the number of car changes required in mucking out a round. The mucker's ability to spread out the load in the car may limit its length. Clearance under the mucker's discharge point limits the height. If the car is connected to the mucker during the mucking operation, the mucking machine's motive capacity may limit the car's loaded capacity. An example of maximum muck car selection is the use of a 15 cu yd car in a 15-ft-diameter tunnel with a 100-2 Conway.

Photo 5 Mechanical car dumper used on Eucumbene-Tumut Tunnel, Australia.

Track Gauge and Rail Size

Many contractors standardize on 36-in. gauge as this allows them flexibility in moving the equipment from one job to another. Moreover, because most equipment is 36-in. gauge, it has good resale value. Small equipment of narrower gauge may be used. On large tunnels 42-in. gauge may be used to provide a more stable track and a wider mucker cleanup width. On some tunnels equipped with specialized slusher trains or other specialized equipment, standard railroad gauge has been used. The weight of rail is determined by the maximum wheel load and the intended tie spacing. Tables 1 to 3 can be used in determining rail size in a tunnel. The larger the rail used in a tunnel, the more stable the track and the fewer the derails. It is false economy to try to use too light a rail.

Types of Locomotives

Tunnel locomotives are available with diesel engines, battery-powered electric engines, or electric engines receiving energy from a direct-current overhead trolley wire supplemented by batteries.

Battery locomotives were widely used in the past except when long hauls were required. Today, as a result of the development of the diesel locomotives, they are only used in locations that restrict the underground use of diesel engines.

TABLE 1 Dimension of Rail Muck Cars
Side-dump Cars Manufactured by Ray Moran

	Capacity of car				
	8 cu yd	9 cu yd	9 cu yd	9 cu yd	9 cu yd
Track gauge	36 in.	36 in.	36 in.	36 in.	36 in.
C_L cplg above top of rail	16 in.	16 in.	16 in.	16 in.	16 in.
Length C_L to C_L cplg	15 ft 1¼ in.	16 ft 1¼ in.	14 ft 10¾ in.	14 ft 4¼ in.	13 ft 11¼ in.
Wheel base	6 ft 0 in.	6 ft 6 in.	5 ft 11 in.	5 ft 7 in.	5 ft 5 in.
Length inside	12 ft 0 in.	13 ft 0 in.	11 ft 9 in.	11 ft 3 in.	10 ft 10 in.
Depth inside	3 ft 9 in.	3 ft 0 in.	3 ft 9 in.	3 ft 9 in.	3 ft 9 in.
Overall width	4 ft 9 in.	5 ft 0 in.	5 ft 6 in.	5 ft 9 in.	6 ft 0 in.
Overall height	6 ft 6 in.	6 ft 6 in.	6 ft 6 in.	6 ft 6 in.	6 ft 6 in.

	10 cu yd	10 cu yd	10 cu yd	10 cu yd	10 cu yd
Track gauge	36 in.	36 in.	36 in.	36 in.	36 in.
C_L cplg above top of rail	16 in.	16 in.	16 in.	16 in.	16 in.
Length C_L to C_L cplg	16 ft 2¼ in.	15 ft 7¼ in.	15 ft 1¼ in.	14 ft 7¼ in.	14 ft 3¼ in.
Wheel base	6 ft 6 in.	6 ft 3 in.	6 ft 0 in.	5 ft 9 in.	5 ft 7 in.
Length inside	13 ft 1 in.	12 ft 6 in.	12 ft 0 in.	11 ft 6 in.	11 ft 2 in.
Depth inside	3 ft 9 in.	3 ft 9 in.	3 ft 9 in.	3 ft 9 in.	3 ft 9 in.
Overall width	5 ft 6 in.	5 ft 9 in.	6 ft 0 in.	6 ft 3 in.	6 ft 6 in.
Overall height	6 ft 7 in.	6 ft 6 in.	6 ft 6 in.	6 ft 6 in.	6 ft 6 in.

	12 cu yd
Track gauge	42 in.
C_L cplg above top of rail	16 in.
Length C_L to C_L cplg	15 ft 8 in.
Wheel base	6 ft 6 in.
Length inside	12 ft 11 in.
Depth inside	4 ft 0 in.
Overall width	6 ft 6 in.
Overall height	5 ft 9 in.

In the past, battery-trolley locomotives were used when the haul became so long that the power drain on the locomotive's battery resulted in too many battery changes per shift. Trolley power was supplemented with battery power for these locomotives to provide flexibility for operation in areas where the trolley wire was not installed. Trolley wire was not installed at the heading because it would have resulted in a hazardous condition, and the continuous extension of the trolley in short

TABLE 2 Recommended Maximum Load, One Wheel, in Pounds[2]

Weight of rail,* lb/yd	Tie spacing, in.			
	24	30	36	42
8	800	600	500	400
12	1,800	1,300	1,100	1,000
16	2,700	2,200	1,800	1,500
20	3,800	3,100	2,500	2,100
25	4,700	3,800	3,100	2,700
30	6,700	5,400	4,500	3,900
35	8,100	6,400	5,400	4,600
40	9,700	7,700	6,400	5,500
45	11,300	9,100	7,600	6,500
50	13,300	10,600	8,900	7,600
55	15,300	12,300	10,200	8,800
60	17,700	14,100	11,600	10,000

* Standard lengths: 30 ft for weights up to 45 lb/yd.
33 ft for 50 lb/yd or heavier.

segments would have been required. It was not installed in dump areas because of the necessity for continuous moving as the dump expanded. Because of the hazard and expense of installing trolley wire, trolley-battery locomotives have become increasingly obsolete.

Diesel locomotives are now used in the majority of tunnels under

TABLE 3 Dimensions and Weights of Light Rail, ASCE Section[2]

Weight of rail, lb/yd	Height and width of base, in.	Width of head, in.	Section modulus	Weight of rail for 100 ft of track, lb	Weight 1 pr. splice bars and 4 bolts, lb	Size of bolt, in.	Size of spike, in.
8	$1\frac{9}{16}$	$1\frac{3}{16}$	0.32	533	2.45	$\frac{3}{8} \times 1\frac{1}{2}$	$\frac{3}{8} \times 2\frac{1}{2}$
12	2	1	0.63	800	4.24	$\frac{1}{2} \times 1\frac{3}{4}$	$\frac{3}{8} \times 2\frac{1}{2}$
16	$2\frac{3}{8}$	$1\frac{11}{64}$	1.01	1,067	5.16	$\frac{1}{2} \times 1\frac{3}{4}$	$\frac{3}{8} \times 3$
20	$2\frac{5}{8}$	$1\frac{11}{32}$	1.43	1,333	5.69	$\frac{1}{2} \times 2$	$\frac{3}{8} \times 3\frac{1}{2}$
25	$2\frac{3}{4}$	$1\frac{1}{2}$	1.77	1,667	6.56	$\frac{1}{2} \times 2\frac{1}{4}$	$\frac{1}{2} \times 4$
30	$3\frac{1}{8}$	$1\frac{11}{16}$	2.53	2,000	8.99	$\frac{5}{8} \times 2\frac{1}{2}$	$\frac{1}{2} \times 4$
35	$3\frac{5}{16}$	$1\frac{3}{4}$	3.02	2,333	9.26	$\frac{5}{8} \times 2\frac{1}{2}$	$\frac{1}{2} \times 4\frac{1}{2}$
40	$3\frac{1}{2}$	$1\frac{7}{8}$	3.62	2,667	14.33	$\frac{3}{4} \times 3$	$\frac{1}{2} \times 5$
45	$3\frac{11}{16}$	2	4.25	3,000	16.71	$\frac{3}{4} \times 3$	$\frac{9}{16} \times 5\frac{1}{2}$
50	$3\frac{7}{8}$	$2\frac{1}{8}$	4.98	3,333	19.17	$\frac{3}{4} \times 3\frac{1}{4}$	$\frac{9}{16} \times 5\frac{1}{2}$
55	$4\frac{1}{16}$	$2\frac{1}{4}$	5.75	3,667	31.81	$\frac{3}{4} \times 3\frac{1}{2}$	$\frac{9}{16} \times 5\frac{1}{2}$
60	$4\frac{1}{4}$	$2\frac{3}{8}$	6.62	4,000	35.33	$\frac{3}{4} \times 3\frac{1}{2}$	$\frac{9}{16} \times 5\frac{1}{2}$

construction. In comparison with battery and battery-trolley locomotives, they have larger engines and are capable of greater speeds, which results in the use of fewer locomotives and in lower capital expenditures and operating and maintenance costs. Besides eliminating the need for battery maintenance and the use of hazardous trolley wires, diesel locomotives make bonding of the rails and the use of rectifiers unnecessary and reduce the number of transformers required. Since they are independent of any outside power source, they allow more flexibility in operation and more constant use. The disadvantage of the diesel locomotive is that it produces fumes which increase the tunnel ventilation requirements. To reduce the amount of fumes, exhaust scrubbers are required on all diesel engines operated underground.

Locomotive Selection[3]

Preliminary selection of a locomotive can be made by determination of the weight of the locomotive required to provide traction, the maximum horsepower required to accelerate the loaded train to a reasonable speed, and the continuous horsepower required to maintain this speed. If long stretches of haulage are on steep grades, careful consideration must also be given to braking requirements. If battery locomotives are being considered, frequency of battery recharging must be determined. In every case, final equipment selection should be governed by the guaranteed characteristics stated on the manufacturer's specification sheets, with due consideration of probable loss of efficiency as the equipment ages.

The tractive effort that can be exerted by a locomotive is a function of locomotive weight and of the coefficient of friction between the steel wheels and the steel rails. Although the coefficient of friction decreases as locomotive speed increases, the decrease is not significant in the ordinary range of tunnel haulage speeds. The coefficient of friction varies from 0.15 for wet, slick track to 0.25 for dry track. The tractive force which a given locomotive can exert is stated as

$$T = W_L F \tag{1}$$

where

T = tractive effort, lb
W_L = locomotive weight, lb
F = coefficient of friction

The tractive effort required of a locomotive is a function of the weight of the train (including the locomotive) and of the resistance to be overcome. The resistance to be overcome is composed of:

1. *Rolling resistance* is caused by the deformation of rails and wheels under the weight carried by the wheels. For steel wheels on steel rails, this is approximately 20 lb per ton of train weight.

2. *Grade resistance* is the force which must be overcome in lifting the weight of the train on an uphill grade. On downhill grades, grade resistance is a negative quantity. Grade resistance is approximately 20 lb per ton of train weight per 1 percent of grade.

3. *Acceleration resistance* is the force required to accelerate the train. It is a function of the rate of acceleration. It amounts to 90 lb per ton of train weight per mph per sec. Usual acceleration rates in tunnel service are in the range of 0.1 to 0.2 mph per sec.

The tractive effort required of a locomotive may be greater to return a string of empty cars upgrade than to move loaded cars downgrade, but it will frequently be necessary in any tunnel to move loaded trains in either direction during switching, train makeup, and other operations, and locomotives should be selected on this basis.

The required tractive effort for a given train during acceleration can be stated as

$$T_T = \frac{(NW_C + W_L)(R_R + R_G + R_A)}{2{,}000}$$

where

T_T = total tractive effort, lb
N = number of cars
W_C = gross weight of 1 car, lb
W_L = weight of locomotive, lb
R_R = rolling resistance, lb/ton
R_G = grade resistance, lb/ton
R_A = acceleration resistance, lb/ton

This is restated for use as

$$T_T = (NW_C{}^1 + W_L{}^1)(20 + 20G + 90A) \qquad (2)$$

where

$W_C{}^1$ = gross weight of 1 car, tons
$W_L{}^1$ = locomotive weight, tons
G = grade, percent
A = acceleration, mph

The required tractive effort after acceleration is stated

$$T = (NW_C{}^1 + W_L{}^1)(20 + 20G) \qquad (3)$$

The foregoing remarks and formulas pertain only to the weight requirements for locomotives. The second factor in selecting a locomotive, whether diesel or electric, is the peak power requirement for accelerating the train. The formula is derived in many texts from mechanics and is stated as

$$P_P = \frac{T_T S}{375E} \tag{4}$$

where

P_P = required peak power, hp
E = efficiency of locomotive
S = speed after acceleration, mph

The final factor applicable to all types of locomotives is the sustained power requirement necessary to keep the train moving at a constant speed. This is considered separately because diesel engines and electric motors are not capable of delivering power continuously at peak output. Attempting it will cause early failure of locomotive components.

The required continuous power is stated as

$$P_C = \frac{T_R S}{375E} \tag{5}$$

where

P_C = required continuous power, hp
T_R = tractive effort for rolling resistance and grade resistance applied to train weight
E = efficiency of locomotive
S = speed, mph

Formulas (1) to (5) are adequate to determine the power and weight requirements for locomotives. For example, it is required that a locomotive be selected to handle muck trains under the following conditions.

Problem

Tunnel, 16-ft horseshoe, neat line
Pull, 8 ft of tunnel per round
Maximum grade, 0.4 percent adverse
Muck cars, 12 cu yd, weighing 13,800 lb empty
Desired acceleration, not less than 0.10 mphps
Tracks damp, but no slippery clay; assume $F = 0.20$
Desired train speed, 10 mph

Solution

Determine the volume of muck from one round:
Neat-line 16-ft horseshoe
Use 17-ft horseshoe; area, 240 sq ft

Volume of 8-ft round, 240 × 8 ÷ 27 = 71 cu yd of rock
Volume of muck, 100 percent swell, 142 cu yd

Determine the number of cars required and the loaded weight:
Number of 12 cu yd cars required, 142 ÷ 12 = 12 cars
Weight of muck of one car, 12 × 2,600 = 31,200 lb
Weight of one empty car, 13,800 lb
Weight of one loaded car, 45,000 lb = 22.5 tons

First trial, a 15-ton locomotive capable of delivering 225 hp intermittently or 175 hp continuously:

Tractive effort available:

$$T = W_L F \qquad (1)$$
$$T = 30{,}000 \times 0.20 = 6{,}000 \text{ lb}$$

Required tractive effort:

$$T_T = (NW_C{}^1 + W_L{}^1)(20 + 20G + 90A) \qquad (2)$$
$$T_T = [(12 \times 22.5) + 15][20 + (20 \times 0.4) + (90 \times 0.10)]$$
$$T_T = 10{,}545 \text{ lb}$$

Compare available tractive effort with required tractive effort: 6,000 lb available, 10,545 lb required. Not acceptable, but proceed.
Determine the peak power requirement, assuming 80 percent locomotive efficiency:

$$P_P = \frac{T_T S}{375E} \qquad (4)$$

where

$$P_P = \frac{10{,}545 \times 10}{375 \times 0.80} = 352 \text{ hp}$$

Since the 15-ton locomotive has peak power capacity of only 225 hp, it is apparent that one might operate 6-car trains with 15-ton locomotives or 12-car trains with 25- or 30-ton locomotives. Because the smaller locomotives are more generally useful, assume 15-ton locomotives hauling 6 cars and recompute (2) and (4).

$$T_T = (NW_C{}^1 + W_L{}^1)(20 + 20G + 90A) \qquad (2)$$
$$T_T = [(6 \times 22.5) + 15][20 + (20 \times 0.4) + (90 \times 0.10)]$$
$$T_T = 5{,}550 \text{ lb} \qquad \text{Acceptable; 6,000 lb available}$$
$$P_P = \frac{T_T S}{375E} \qquad (4)$$
$$P_P = \frac{5{,}550 \times 10}{375 \times 0.80}$$
$$P_P = 185 \text{ hp} \qquad \text{Acceptable; 225 hp available}$$

Determine the tractive effort required after the train has been accelerated:

$$T_R = (NW_C{}^1 + W_L{}^1)(20 + 20G) \qquad (3)$$
$$T_R = [(6 \times 22.5) + 15][20 + (20 \times 0.4)]$$
$$T_R = 4{,}200 \text{ lb}$$

Determine the power requirement after acceleration:

$$P_C = \frac{T_R S}{375E} \tag{5}$$

$$P_C = \frac{4{,}200 \times 10}{375 \times 0.8}$$

$P_C = 140$ hp Acceptable, since the 15-ton locomotive is rated 175 hp for continuous operation

A 15-ton diesel locomotive, or an electric locomotive of equal capabilities, will be able to meet the stated conditions. However, the 15-ton battery locomotives available are found to be rated at only 90 hp. A 30-ton battery locomotive is available which is rated at 250 hp for continuous duty. It is immediately evident that the heavier locomotive will be capable of the required tractive effort, but it is necessary to check on the horsepower requirements for the heavier train.

The required tractive effort to start and accelerate the train is

$$T_T = (NW_C{}^1 + W_L{}^1)(20 + 20G + 90A) \tag{2}$$

$$T_T = [(6 \times 22.5) + 30)][20 + (20 \times 0.4) + (90 \times 0.10)]$$

$$T_T = 6{,}105 \text{ lb}$$

The required power to start and accelerate the train is

$$P_P = \frac{T_T S}{375E} \tag{4}$$

$$P_P = \frac{6{,}105 \times 10}{375 \times 0.80} = 204 \text{ hp}$$ Acceptable; 250 hp available

Since the battery locomotive can start the train without exceeding the continuous-duty rating, it is evident that it will easily handle the line haul. It is then necessary to consider the frequency of battery recharging. Assume a 3-mile haul and two batteries of 121.6 kwhr per battery, or 243 kwhr total.

The weight of the loaded train is $(22.5 \times 6) + 30 = 165$ tons
The weight of the empty train is $(6.9 \times 6) + 30 = 72$ tons

Work Performed per Round Trip

Condition	Grade %	Weight, tons	Resistance, lb/ton	Tractive effort, lb	Distance, ft	Work ft-lb
Loaded.....	+0.4	165	28	4,620	15,840	73,180,800
Empty.....	−0.4	72	12	864	15,840	13,685,760
Subtotal....						86,866,560
25% Acceleration for spotting, switching....						21,716,640
Total....						108,583,200

The number of kilowatt hours of energy required to perform a given amount of work is derived in standard texts. It can be stated as

$$K = \frac{F}{2,654,155E} \tag{6}$$

where

K = kwhr
F = ft-lb
E = efficiency

Assuming an overall efficiency of 0.63, the power required per round trip is

$$K = \frac{108,583,200}{2,654,155 \times 0.63} = 65 \text{ kwhr}$$

Thus, the 243-kwhr battery set provides sufficient power for three round trips. To reduce the time lost in changing batteries, one might consider the use of a direct-current trolley system and using battery power only at the face and in other areas not serviced by the trolley wire.

TRAIN SWITCHING

To prevent delays in the tunnel-driving operations, it is necessary to have double trackage near the heading for switching trains and also space both for parking the mucking machine when it is not in use and for storage of cars loaded with drill steel, supports, powder, vent pipe, and other supplies. If a main-line jumbo is used, it is necessary to provide a parking place for it also during the mucking cycle.

In tunnels that are too small for trains to pass, this double trackage must be installed at intervals along the tunnel line that are overexcavated to provide the clearance required. As an example of this, refer to Drawing 3, which shows the amount of overexcavating required in a 13- by 14-ft tunnel.

In larger tunnels that have sufficient space to enable equipment pieces to pass each other, portable passing tracks can be used. Two portable passing tracks are needed near the heading; the first one is used for train switching, and the second one is used for storing the mucker, drill jumbo, and cars loaded with supplies. Other portable passing tracks are kept along the tunnel so trains can pass each other on the trip from the portal to and from the heading. These portable passing tracks are called *California switches,* and a detailed description of them is included under the following section on car changing.

Car Changing

When the mucking method used requires that the mucker load individual cars, a fast car-changing method is used for removing the loaded car from the mucker and replacing it with an empty car. This can be done by one of the following five methods of changing cars.

1. ***California Switch.*** The California switch consists of a portable combination of a double siding and switches constructed on a structural mat which is laid over the main track and can be readily moved forward without disturbing the main track. Not only does the California switch allow train switching, but it can be used for switching cars to the mucker. Car changing can be done faster with a California switch than by any other method since fewer moves are involved. Other methods of car changing require the use of only one locomotive at the face, but the fastest use of the California switch for car changing requires two locomotives.

When cars are changed by a California switch, one switch is located close to the face directly behind the mucker for car changing, and one switch is located a short distance down the tunnel for train switching, the parking of jumbos, muckers, etc. When used for changing cars, the loaded car is pulled away from the mucker by a locomotive working on one siding, and an empty car is then coupled onto the mucker by a locomotive operating from the other siding. When enough cars are loaded to constitute a train they are hauled away and replaced by a train of empty cars. An illustration of this use of a California switch is shown in Drawing 5.

The California switch is built on a structural frame which limits its use to straight tangents in the tunnel. The width of the tunnel must be of sufficient size to allow two trains to pass and to allow the California switch to be moved forward as the heading advances. The California switch is a rigid structure, so it has to be dismantled to take it around short-radius curves. During this dismantling, moving, and erecting operation, car changing is done by the use of car passers.

2. ***The Floor.*** Floors are used for train switching, car passing, and track laying. They contain mucking tracks and a storage siding for the mucker, provide a smooth, slick mucking surface, and have gantry trackage so that the gantry drill jumbo may be advanced to the tunnel face for drilling and powder loading and then can be moved to the rear of the floor during the shooting and mucking cycles.

Jacobs floor. The Jacobs floor, shown in Drawing 6 and in Photograph 6, is suitable for the operation of one mucking machine. It is a three-section California switch, approximately 400 ft long, equipped with hydraulic jacks installed where the sections join. In moving the floor, first the front section is jacked forward approximately 3 ft at a time with the two rear sections used as dead weight anchors; then the remaining sections are jacked forward individually with the other sections used as anchors. The floor is maintained in elevation by the

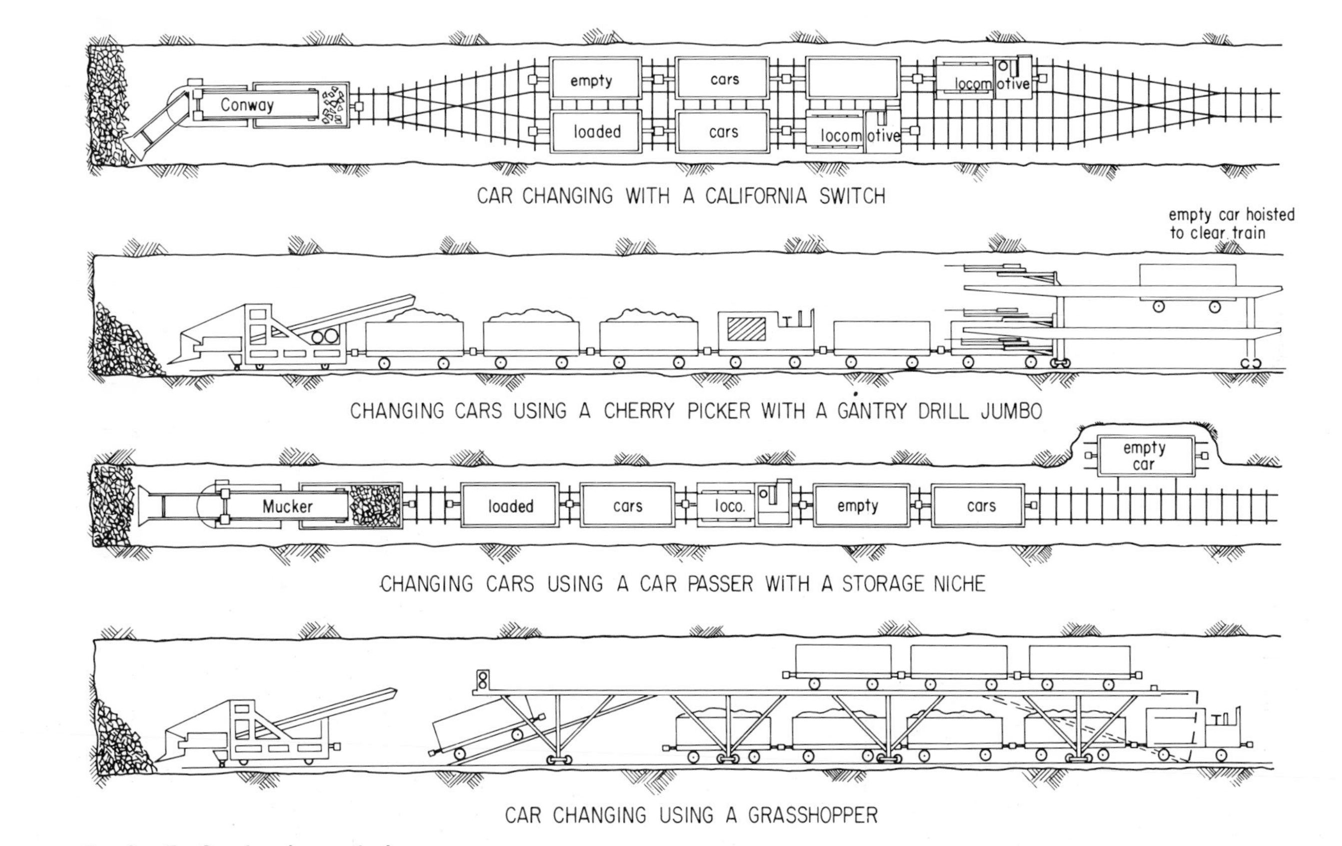

Drawing 5 **Car-changing methods.**

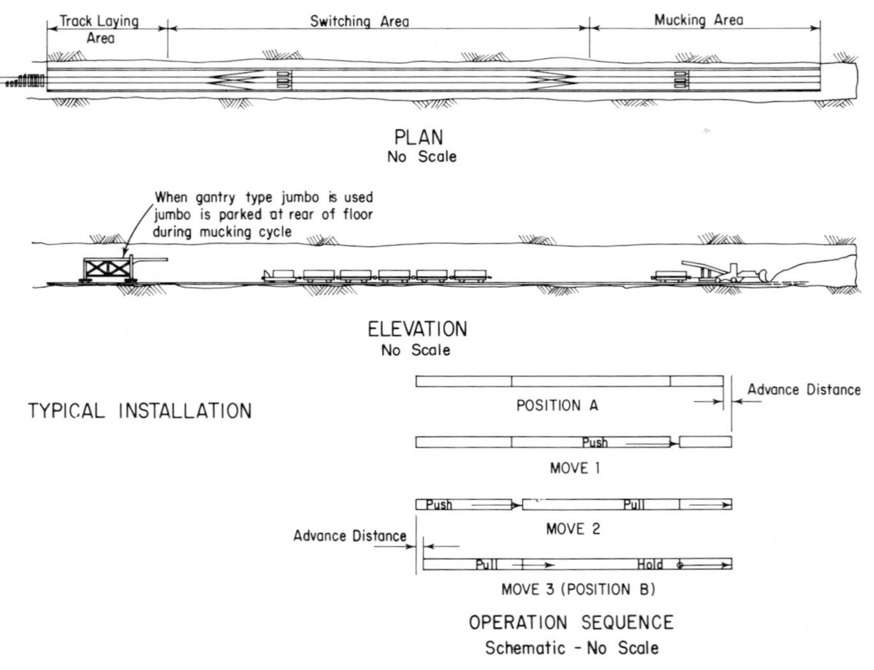

Drawing 6 Sliding tunnel floor. (Jacobs Associates)

depth of cleanup ahead of the front section and the position of the mucker on the first section during its forward movement. When the floor gets below grade, it is raised by placing the mucker in the back of the first section as it is moved. When the floor starts above grade, it is dropped by keeping the mucker in the front of the first section during its moving operation. When the floor gets off line, it is brought back on line by jacking from the tunnel wall. Excavation of the bottom of the tunnel must be watched so no high spots are left, or the floor will ride up the high spot and continue to rise in elevation as the excavation proceeds.

The floor is equipped with one track entering it from the rear and one track in the front that is used by the mucker. The remainder of the floor is equipped with four rails, each set on gauge and equipped at the ends with triple switches so that together they form one main-line track down the center or two passing tracks. The gantry drill jumbo also travels on the two outside rails, so they are run the full length of the floor to permit the jumbo to be stored at the rear during the mucking operation and moved to the face for the drilling operation.

The forward part of the front section where the mucker works is covered with closely spaced rails which provide a smooth, slick bottom for the mucker bucket to slide on while it is being filled with muck.

The single track at the rear of the last section consists of a supported steel plate on rail gauge with space under the plate so that standard lengths of rail can be placed under these plates and left in position as the floor is moved forward. Ties can then be slipped under these rails, tie plates placed, and the rail spiked as required.

Standard operation with this floor is to do final cleanup with the mucker and one car. Meanwhile, the jumbo is pushed by a locomotive astride the mucker. After cleanup, the mucker moves the jumbo to its final location and drilling is started. After drilling and loading the holes, the drill jumbo is moved to the back of the floor, the round is shot, and the mucker is moved up to the muck pile and mucking commenced. The mucker mucks off the slick-plate section of the floor, and the only bottom cleanup is underneath the round shot.

Empty cars are stored on one of the passing tracks with one locomo-

Photo 6 Sliding floor used by Walsh Construction Co. for the railroad relocation tunnels, near Libby Damsite, Montana. (Jacobs Associates)

tive to shove them to the mucker. Another locomotive pulls the loaded cars from the mucker onto the other passing track. As empty trains are brought in, the locomotives change tracks and the loaded trains are taken out of the tunnel. As mucking is being carried forward, the floor is moved toward the face. When the mucker is cleaning up, the drill jumbo is again moved to the face and operations are repeated.

Advantages of this operation.

1. Quick car changing is provided so the mucker is not delayed.
2. Neither mucker rails nor gantry rails have to be laid at the heading, which saves time.
3. The jumbo can be moved to the heading while the mucker is cleaning up.
4. The mucker does most of the mucking on a slick plate, which reduces both cleanup and mucking time.
5. The mucker operates from a firm track instead of from an unstable temporary track, which improves mucking operations.
6. The only track laying required is bolting up, placing ties and tie plates, and spiking standard length rails at the rear of the jumbo, which cuts time and labor in the heading.

This floor works best where a gantry jumbo can be used and the bottom of the tunnel is over three times the gauge of the track.

Jacobs floors have been developed for use in tunnels of such widths that two Conway muckers can operate alongside each other. These floors contain three passing tracks which switch into two mucking tracks in the front of the floor and into the main-line track at the rear. This allows each Conway mucker to have one locomotive servicing it during the mucking cycle. These locomotives operate on the two outside tracks and each outside track is equipped with a car passer. Both car passers shift empty cars to and from the center track. With a separate car-changing arrangement for each mucker, and with each mucker loading a car in less than 4 min, the total mucking capacity of the floor is one car in less than 2 min.

Navajo carpet. This is a floor designed and built by Ray Moran for use in small tunnels that have only enough width for two passing tracks. The track arrangement is similar to the track arrangement on a California switch. There is one track in the front of the floor on a slick plate which is used for mucking operations and by a main-line jumbo during the drilling operations. The passing tracks are used for switching the mucker and the main-line jumbo between the drilling and mucking operations. These passing tracks are also used for car changing during the mucking operation. A stub track is used for drill-jumbo and mucker storage; it incorporates the same track-laying facilities as the Jacobs floor except that rails are fed into the track in the front of the floor rather than in the rear. The floor is fabricated in one piece and jacks itself forward, as the heading advances, with jacks reacting against the main-line track.

3. ***Car Passers.*** To maintain production in small-diameter, unlined tunnels, equipment is selected that cannot pass other units except at overexcavated, double-tracked train-switching areas. This requires that car changing be done with car passers, and it is necessary to cut niches in the tunnel wall to allow storage of the empty cars at the car-passing locations. Car passers are also used around short-radius turns in large-diameter tunnels that ordinarily change cars with a California switch. Another use for car passers is on a California switch when two muckers are used as described above. A minor use is in the outside yard area where they are used to store specialty cars such as powder or timber cars and thus reduce the number of sidings required.

A car passer consists of a sufficient length of track to support one car, with short, knife-edged lead tracks in both directions. This track section is supported on rollers which travel on members perpendicular to the main track and enable the car to be pushed to the side to give clearance for passage of the train. When car passers are used at the heading, the locomotive's position in the train at the start of the mucking cycle is on the tunnel-face side of the empty cars. One car is attached to the mucker. When the first car is loaded, the train travels forward past the car passer to pick up the loaded car attached to the mucker and drops an empty car on the car passer. This empty car on the car passer is then pushed to one side to clear the track. The train in the meantime connects to and removes the loaded car from the mucker and then travels back to the tunnel past the car passer. The empty car is pushed back on the main-line track and the train moves forward shoving the empty car to connect it to the mucker. At the same time it drops another empty car on the car passer. This process is repeated until the last empty car is connected to the mucker. At this point, the loaded cars are located in the train between the locomotive and the mucker. The loaded train travels out the tunnel past a siding where a train load of empty cars is waiting. This empty train then moves in to the heading and the process is repeated. This car-changing method is shown in Drawing 5.

To maintain a good rate of mucking production, car changing must be done in as short an interval as possible. For this to be accomplished, train travel must be held to a minimum by locating the passing niches at frequent intervals. Preferable spacing of these niches is every 100 ft; maximum spacing is 200 ft.

In small-diameter, concrete-lined tunnels the car-passing niches and the overexcavation required for train switching will result in a large amount of overbreak concrete. This added concrete cost may be more than the savings in excavation cost resulting from the use of large equipment. When this is so, the tunnel should be excavated with equipment small enough to pass in the tunnel.

4. ***Cherry Pickers.*** If a tunnel has sufficient diameter that a gantry jumbo can be used, car changing may be done with a *cherry picker* located on the rear of the drill jumbo. Sufficient hoisting space must be provided in the jumbo to hoist a muck car clear of the train passing beneath it. The jumbo must also be equipped with hoist, cables, and hooks for raising the car. This cherry-picker arrangement on a gantry jumbo is shown in Drawing 5. The operation is similar to that of a car passer with the exception that the empty car is hoisted instead of being moved to one side.

5. ***The Grasshopper.*** This method of car changing has not been used in recent years because of its bulk and the necessity for extra rails. It requires the use of a steel frame about 150 ft long, traveling on separate rails set on each side of the main-line track. There are hinged ramps at each end of the framework, which are operated by an air hoist. Tracks are laid up these ramps and over the deck of the framework. Six to eight empty cars are pulled up the rear ramp by a hoist and held on the top deck, and the rear ramp is then raised. After the mucker has loaded a car, the loaded car is pulled away from the mucker by a locomotive to a position clear of the front ramp of the grasshopper. The front ramp is lowered and an empty car is let down the ramp and coupled onto the mucker. This method of changing cars is shown in Drawing 5.

EQUIPMENT UNIQUE TO THE CONVENTIONAL METHOD OF EXCAVATING TUNNELS

Drills

The tunnel planning engineer has a wide range of choices in drill types and methods of mounting drills on the drill jumbo. Literature from drill manufacturers can be secured to gain specific information on the various drills, so only overall concepts will be discussed in this book.

Most of the drilling in tunnel construction is done with the following drills:

1. *Percussion drill with rifle-bar rotation.* This is the most common type of drill and is used in all types of rocks. It is the most satisfactory drill for work in hard rock.

2. *Percussion drill with separate positive method of drill rotation.* This type of drill is used in soft rock to get greater penetration than the straight percussion drill with rifle-bar rotation can give. When used in hard rock, bit cost may become excessive.

3. *Rotary drill.* This drill gives a high penetration in extremely soft rock, such as shale.

4. *Auger drill.* This is suitable for use in very soft rock of a hardness similar to coal, such as some volcanic tuffs.

All underground drilling is done wet to reduce the amount of rock dust breathed by the miners. Wet percussion drills are the same as the outside dry percussion drills except that water rather than air is used for clearing the cuttings out of the hole to prevent dust formation. The use of water has a secondary result in reducing the amount of compressed air required per drill.

In selecting the size and type of drill for short tunnels, consideration should be given to the possibility that the lowest total cost may be the combination of lowest capital cost with a higher direct cost. For short tunnels, capital cost may be reduced, with an increase in direct cost, by selecting light, hand-held drills or air leg-support jack hammers. Although these drills do not obtain as fast a penetration as the larger drills, they use smaller bits, require less capital outlay, and use less air.

In soft rock, a drill should be selected that furnishes good penetration but will also hold the capital cost to a minimum. As an example, the penetration rates of 3½- and 4½-in.-size drifters in soft rock are quite similar; the smaller drifter is therefore used as it costs less and uses less air. Or rotary drills may be selected as they are less expensive than percussion drills.

In determining the size and type of drill to be used in hard-rock tunneling, selection should be based on the fact that excavation progress is directly proportional to the time required to drill out a round. The fastest penetration in hard rock is secured by using the largest drill that can be used with standard-size bits without having excessive steel breakage. However, the larger the machine, the greater the steel breakage, the more air consumed, and the greater the capital cost; so all factors must be weighed in selecting the size of drill.

Drills are commonly identified by the size of the cylinder bore. Those now used in tunnel driving vary from 1⅞ to 5½ in. Percussion drills are classified as follows:

1. *Sinkers and jackhammers, designed primarily to be hand held.* They may also be mounted on a feed leg by an adaptor bracket. These drills are generally classified by weight and vary from a light drill of 30 lb to a heavy drill of 65 lb or more. Feed legs are air-activated,

long-pipe jacks which can be used to position the drill and maintain pressure on it during drilling.

2. *Feed legs and jack legs, which consist of sinker drills attached in a readily demountable manner to an air feed leg.* They are used for both lateral and overhead drilling. Sizes most generally are:

Bore of air feed cylinder. . . . . 1⅞–2⅝ in.
Length of feed travel. . . . . 3–6 ft
Weight of sinker. . . . . 30–70 lb

3. *Drifters.* The drills are of the self-rotating type which are usually screw fed by a gear or reciprocating piston motor on a steel or aluminum shell, or chain fed by a vane or piston motor on a heavy steel channel frame. Sizes most generally used are:

Light. . . . . Up to 3-in. bore
Medium. . . . . 3½–4-in. bore
Heavy. . . . . . . 4½-in. bore

4. *Burn-hole drills.* These are drifters of 5½-in. bore or over, used to drill the large holes required for relievers on a burn-cut pattern of shooting. The number of holes varies from one to three, and the holes are generally 5 in. in diameter. The steel used is generally 1⅞ in.

5. *Stopers.* These are drills with an air feed which is usually designed as an integral part of the drill. Stopers are used on up hole drilling and are classified according to weight from a light drill of 75 lb to a heavy drill of over 100 lb.

Sinkers or jackhammers can be hand held on the work platforms on the jumbo. Air legs can be used on these platforms or can be mounted on steel ladders which provide some of the advantages of the jib and drill positioners used with drifter drills.

Drifter drills are mounted on a horizontal support composed of three adjustable arms, called *jibs,* which are bolted to the jumbo. These jibs allow mechanical positioning of the drill at the tunnel face, and jibs are available which will rotate the drill for ease in drilling side holes and lifter holes. Also available are controls for these jibs, called *drill positioners,* which enable the miner to control the position of the drill in regard to the tunnel face. The jibs are mounted on the drill jumbo so that one or more drills will be able to drill any spot in the tunnel face. The use of rotating jibs and drill positioners eliminates the need for chuck tenders and thereby reduces the size of the drilling crew.

Number of Drills. To determine the number of drills required at the heading, in general it may be assumed that for 12- to 14-ft-diameter standard horseshoe tunnels in granite, one hole will be required per 5 sq ft of face area.

In smaller-diameter tunnels, the number of holes per square foot will increase to possibly one hole per 2½ sq ft. In larger-diameter tunnels the number of holes per square foot will decrease to possibly one hole per 6 or 7 sq ft. The use of a burn cut in the smaller-diameter tunnels will reduce the number of holes per square foot. Other factors that influence the number of holes required for a specific-diameter tunnel will be the type and general formation of the rock (e.g., heavily jointed, blocky, or massive). For example, tunnels driven through certain granites will require as many as twice the number of holes as those driven through softer rocks. After the number of holes required for any tunnel is determined, it should be compared with the number required on previous tunnels of similar size and with similar rock conditions.

The number of drills is determined by furnishing enough drills so each driller will drill from seven to nine holes. The actual number of holes per drill will vary depending upon the rock formations. The type of hole pattern to be used will also determine the type of drills and length of steel changes on the drills.

A common practice in hard rock is to use large-diameter burn-cut holes which necessitate the use of one large drill per heading. These burn holes furnish relief for the explosion (space for the rock to expand when an explosion occurs). This burn cut does away with the requirements for a relief action on the face furnished by the short diamond-cut or V-cut holes and allows each hole to be drilled the full length of the rounds. Furthermore, long feeds can be used on each drifter. Since the feed can be as long as the round, steel changes will not be required for individual holes, which reduces the labor requirements and decreases the actual drilling time but increases the cost of drill steel. The longer the steel, the more the breakage, and the broken steel cannot be reworked for shorter steel changes as when diamond cuts or V cuts are used. When large drills are used, steel breakage can be reduced by using upgraded hardened steels with traveling centralizers and long feeds.

In closely supported ground, the rounds used are generally much shorter and often a diamond or V cut is used instead of the burn cut. In this case, the drifters should have shorter steel changes, such as a 6-ft change, so that they can drill the angle holes required for the diamond or V cut.

Drill Jumbos. The tunnel face is drilled with drills suspended from jibs, or booms, and these jibs are mounted on movable frames called *drill jumbos.* Jumbos are equipped with work platforms to give access at a sufficient number of levels to cover the tunnel face and they contain all facilities required for drilling a round, such as hydraulic pumps, air and water connections to the drills, lights, and equipment for auxiliary face ventilation. Besides being used while drilling out the round, drill jumbos are used as work platforms for loading the holes with explosives, for setting steel and placing timber supports, for drilling and placing rock bolts, and for supporting breastboarding in soft ground. The jumbo may also be equipped with a hoist (a cherry picker) for raising an empty car to a height that clears the train so that cars can be switched during the mucking cycle. The drill jumbo can either ride on rail, be equipped with crawler tracks, or be mounted on a diesel truck. Drill jumbos are of the gantry or main-line type or in large tunnels may be designed to cover one-half the face.

A gantry jumbo rides on wheels supported near the sides of a tunnel and is designed so that the center work platforms may be collapsed to allow the mucker and haul units to pass to and from the tunnel face through the jumbo. Photograph 7 and Drawing 7 illustrate this type of drill jumbo. The gantry jumbo shown in the drawing is equipped with a cherry picker. Rail-mounted gantry jumbos are supported on special rails laid along each side of the tunnel. While at the face, the jumbo is used for drilling and for loading the holes. Before the charge is exploded, the gantry jumbo is moved back from the face a sufficient distance to protect it from the explosion. It is moved up again to the face for drilling after the mucking cycle.

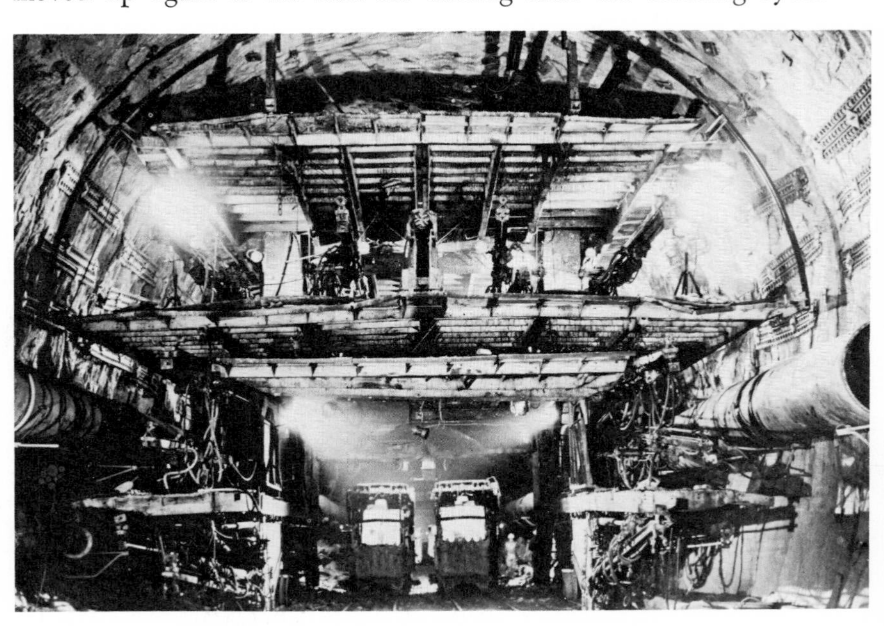

Photo 7 Gantry drill jumbo used on Mont Blanc Tunnel.
(Ingersoll-Rand Co.)

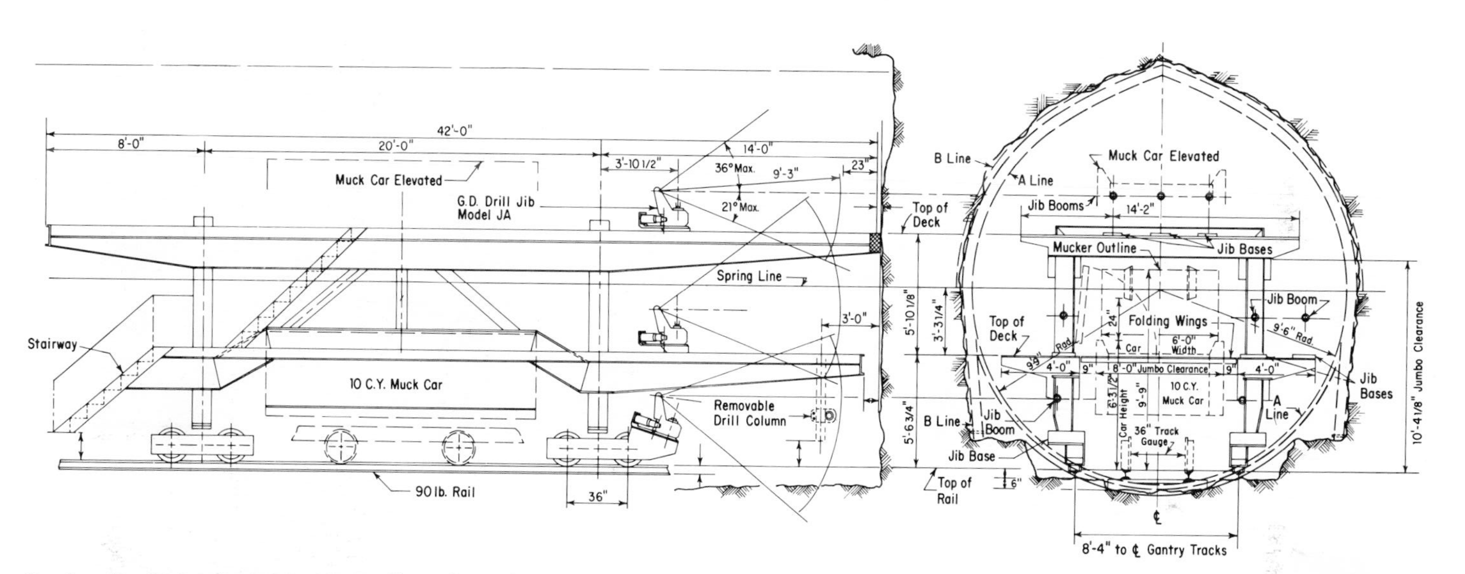

Drawing 7 Gantry jumbo used on Clear Creek Tunnel.

A main-line jumbo (so called because it rides on the main rail line) is shown in Drawing 3, page 25, and in Photograph 2 in Chap. 1. It has collapsible man platforms on the sides that are raised into position for use in the drilling, hole loading, and tunnel support setting operations. The man platforms are dropped along the jumbo sides to allow space for car passing when it is moved back from the face and parked at a siding during the mucking cycle (done to allow access to the face for the mucker and haul units). After the mucking cycle is completed, the mucker then must be moved back to a siding before the main-line jumbo can be moved into the drilling position at the face.

Clearance restrictions dictate that only main-line jumbos be used in tunnels that are less than 17 ft in diameter. For tunnels over 17 ft in diameter, either gantry or main-line jumbos may be used. Some superintendents favor gantry jumbos since they can be moved into the face more quickly than main-line jumbos. They may prefer to set steel, timber, and rock bolts from this type of jumbo. Other superintendents prefer main-line jumbos for any size tunnel since gantry rail is not required and they prefer changing cars with a California switch.

Truck drill jumbos are generally of the main-line type with collapsible side work platforms. On short tunnels, the truck jumbos may have

Photo 8 Truck-mounted drill jumbo. (Gardner-Denver Company and George M. Philpott Co., Inc.)

fixed platforms which necessitate that they be removed from the tunnel after each drilling cycle to furnish access for the other equipment. On large-diameter tunnels, truck jumbos are often made to cover one-half the tunnel face. Two jumbos are then used side by side during the drilling cycle, and they can be parked end-to-end during the mucking cycle to allow passage of the mucking and hauling equipment. A truck jumbo is shown in Photograph 8.

Specification Requirements. Specification requirements for drilling should be checked closely. Some specification writers, because of specific design requirements calling for smooth and sound excavated rock surfaces, call for the *long-hole* technique or for the drilling and blasting procedure known as *smooth, shear, cushion, or periphery* blasting. These methods ensure that a shear plane is established between the periphery holes, which minimizes strain or cracks in the strata beyond the blasting perimeter.

Long-hole technique. Under this method, a minimum heading is driven down the center of the tunnel. Then, at approximately 100-ft intervals, the excavation is enlarged to the full diameter of the tunnel. From these enlargements, holes are drilled to the next enlargement on the periphery of the tunnel, and also sufficient holes are drilled in the face to break the rock properly. Diamond drills are often used to drill the periphery holes. Another type of drill used successfully with the long-hole drilling method is the drifter drill with independent rotation equipped with drill guides. The holes are loaded and shot; the center excavation provides relief for the explosion. Holes can be shot the full length between the enlargements but are generally plugged and shot in 20-ft sections.

Periphery blastings. This method is similar to the predrilling, presplitting method used on open-cut work. Periphery holes are drilled at the face on approximately 20-in. centers and shot with light charges before the remainder of the face is shot. This procedure gives a shear plane which results in a smooth surface at this line.

Mucking Machines

The many different types of mucking machines suitable for tunnel excavation allow the construction planner a wide range in selection of this equipment. Before a choice is made, state laws should be reviewed to see if there are restrictions on the use of diesel engines underground. The type of muck haulage and the diameter of the tunnel will be the other important factors in mucker selection. The capacity, horsepower, and dimensions of various muckers are presented in Table 4. To assist in mucker selection, suitable muckers for various tunnel sizes and methods of muck transportation are described on pages 54 through 57.

TABLE 4 Underground Excavating (Mucking) Machines*

	Bucket size	Power	Type of power	Tramming width	Relation of cleanup width, operating height, tramming height, and track gauge				Belt width	Minimum-radius curve	Weight	Maximum car height	Maximum car length
					Cleanup width	Heights above top of rail		Minimum gauge					
						Tramming height	Operating height						
Rail-mounted mucking on rubber belts													
Conway 100-2	1½ cu yd	1–125 hp	Electric	6 ft 2 in.	17 ft 0 in.	8 ft 2½ in.	12 ft 0 in.	30 in.	42 in.	25 ft	55,000 lb		
		1–40 hp			18 ft 6 in.	8 ft 6½ in.	12 ft 9 in.	30 in.					
					20 ft 0 in.	9 ft 3¼ in.	13 ft 5 in.	36 in.					
					21 ft 6 in.	9 ft 10½ in.	14 ft 5 in.	39⅜ in.					
					22 ft 4 in.	9 ft 10½ in.	14 ft 8 in.	39⅜ in.					
					23 ft 0 in.	10 ft 3 in.	15 ft 0 in.	42 in.					
Conway 100-1	1¼ cu yd	1–100 hp	Electric	6 ft 2 in.	16 ft 6 in.	8 ft 2 in.	11 ft 8½ in.	30 in.	38 in.	20 ft	50,800 lb		
		1–30 hp			18 ft 0 in.	8 ft 7 in.	12 ft 6 in.	30 in.					
					19 ft 6 in.	9 ft 4 in.	13 ft 4 in.	36 in.					
					21 ft 0 in.	9 ft 10 in.	14 ft 3 in.	39⅜ in.					
					21 ft 6 in.	9 ft 10 in.	14 ft 3 in.	39⅜ in.					
					23 ft 0 in.	10 ft 8½ in.	15 ft 1 in.	42 in.					
Conway 100	1 cu yd	1–100 hp	Electric	5 ft 5½ in.	14 ft 10 in.	8 ft 0 in.	11 ft 4 in.	30 in.	38 in.	20 ft	48,500 lb		
		1–30 hp			16 ft 0 in.	8 ft 3 in.	11 ft 7 in.	30 in.					
					18 ft 0 in.	8 ft 6 in.	12 ft 5 in.	30 in.					
					19 ft 6 in.	9 ft 3 in.	13 ft 3 in.	36 in.					
					22 ft 0 in.	10 ft 2½ in.	14 ft 9 in.	36 in.					
Conway 75	¾ cu yd	1–75 hp	Electric	5 ft 5½ in.	13 ft 0 in.	7 ft 6¾ in.	9 ft 7 in.	24 in.	28 in.	.....	42,000 lb		
		1–25 hp			15 ft 0 in.	7 ft 6¾ in.	10 ft 7¾ in.	24 in.					
					17 ft 4 in.	8 ft 1 in.	11 ft 9 in.	30 in.					
					19 ft 0 in.	9 ft 1 in.	12 ft 11 in.	36 in.					
					22 ft 0 in.	10 ft 6¾ in.	14 ft 14 in.	36 in.					

Conway 50	⅝ cu yd	1–50 hp 1–25 hp	Electric	4 ft 3½ in.	11 ft 4 in. 13 ft 3 in. 15 ft 0 in.	6 ft 6 in. 6 ft 6 in. 7 ft 0 in.	8 ft 1 in. 9 ft 1 in. 10 ft 2 in.	24 in. 24 in. 28 in.	28 in.	.....	27,000 lb		
Eimco 40 H	½ cu yd	635 cfs	Air or electric	6 ft 0 in.	12 ft	5 ft 10 in.– 6 ft 10 in.	....	28½ in.	.....	.....	19,000 lb	4 ft 9 in.– 7 ft 2 in.	9 ft 6 in.– 15 ft 0 in.
Eimco 40 W	½ cu yd	635 cfs	Air or electric	6 ft 0 in.	15 ft	5 ft 10 in.– 6 ft 10 in.	....	28½ in.	.....	.....	19,300 lb		
Rail-mounted mucking into haul unit													
Eimco 12 B	4½–6 cu ft	....	Air	34 in.	75–83 in.	48–51 in.	78½–83 in.	15 in.	.....	.....	4,200 lb	46–59 in.	
Eimco 25	8–13½ cu ft	....	Air	43⅞ in.	96–118 in.	52–72 in.	91–112 in.	18 in.	.....	.....	12,000 lb	52–72 in.	
Crawler-mounted mucking into steel flight conveyor belt													
Eimco 635	12½ cu ft	....	Air or electric	6 ft 0 in.	....	4 ft 10 in.– 8 ft 8 in.	5 ft 0 in.– 8 ft 8 in.	45 in.	.....	.....	15,000 lb	7 ft	11 ft
Crawler-mounted mucking into haul unit													
Eimco 631	12½ cu ft	....	Air	5 ft 8⅝ in.	....	6 ft 5 in.	11 ft 2⅜ in.	......	.....	.....	13,000 lb	8 ft	
Eimco 630 E	8–14 cu ft	....	Electric	5 ft 8⅝ in.	....	4 ft 11½ in.	6 ft 8 in.– 10 ft 7 in.	......	.....	.....	11,300 lb	3 ft 9 in.– 7 ft 2 in.	
Eimco 105 or 115	1½ cu yd	143 hp	Diesel	7 ft 8 in.	....	9 ft 6 in.	14 ft 0 in.– 17 ft 8 in.	......	.....	.....	42,500 lb	9 ft 6 in.– 11 ft 3 in.	
Caterpillar 977 w/Libu bucket	54–68 cu ft	150 hp	Diesel	9 ft 3 in.	....	....	17 ft 6 in.	......	.....	.....	41,290 lb		

* Information abstracted from catalogues furnished by the Goodman Division, Westinghouse Air Brake Company; The Eimco Corporation; The Caterpillar Tractor Company.

Photo 9 Eimco 635 mucker. (The Eimco Corp.)

1. For a truck haulage setup
   a. In small tunnels between 6 and 12 ft in height, Eimco 635 crawler type of loaders may be used for loading small trucks. See Photograph 9.
   b. Medium tunnels between 12 and 18 ft in height have suffi-

Photo 10 Eimco 115 mucker. (The Eimco Corp.)

cient headroom for the use of the Eimco 115 crawler type of overshot loaders. See Photograph 10.

c. In tunnels over 18 ft in height, Traxcavators with Libu side-dump buckets or Eimco overshot loaders can be used.

d. For tunnels over 28 ft in diameter, large front-end loaders can be used. Also these tunnels have sufficient clearance for the use of a crawler type of power shovel. Depending on local laws, these shovels are equipped with diesel engines or adapted for electric drive.

2. For a rail haulage setup

a. A rocker type of rail-mounted air-operated overshot loaders produced by Eimco and other firms is used in small tunnels. See Drawing 2, Chap. 1.

b. Eimco 40 H muckers are used in tunnels from 9 to 14 ft in diameter. The 40 H mucker has a bucket loading a mucker belt. See Photograph 11.

c. Conway muckers are used in tunnels from 10 ft in diameter to tunnels with a cleanup width of 23 ft. When the tunnel has a larger cleanup width than 23 ft, two Conways are generally used abreast. The Conway mucker consists of an electric-powered shovel loading a short muck belt. Photograph 12 shows two Conways working abreast in the Mont Blanc Tunnel in France.

Photo 11 Eimco 40 H mucker. (The Eimco Corp.)

d. Any type of mucker can be used with a slusher train, depending on clearance height. When a crawler type of loader is used with a slusher train and when it is necessary to move this mucker in and out of the tunnel, it is generally transported on a specially built flatcar.

3. Combination excavating and hauling machines
   a. Rubber-tired front-end loaders are used to *portal-in* long tunnels, to drive adits, and to drive short tunnels. The mucker in this application both loads and hauls muck out of the tunnel or adit.
   b. Low-profile rubber-tired front-end loaders (similar to the Eimco 916) are used when headroom is restricted to perform the same work as other front-end loaders. Photograph 13 is of an Eimco 916.
   c. Self-propelled scrapers are often used in large-diameter tunnels to remove the bottom heading. In large-diameter tunnels

Photo 12 Two Conway 100-1 mucking machines working abreast in the Mont Blanc Tunnel, France. (Goodman Division, Westinghouse Air Brake Company)

Photo 13 Eimco 916 low-profile front-end loader. (The Eimco Corp.)

driven with multiple drifts, after the center steel has been set, these scrapers are used to remove the remainder of the excavation. An example is their use in the construction of the Waldo Tunnel in Marin County, California.[4]

SUPPORTING EQUIPMENT AND FACILITIES NECESSARY FOR TUNNEL EXCAVATION

Tunnel Ventilation

The increasing underground use of diesel equipment has resulted in a large ventilation load. The amount of underground ventilation required is almost directly proportional to the amount of diesel horsepower used underground. The larger the tunnel, the more haulage units are required and hence the more horsepower; therefore, as the tunnel length increases, larger pipe and fans are required. State requirements on the number of cubic feet of ventilation air per diesel horsepower used underground varies between 50 and 100 cu ft per min; these rules should be reviewed for each job.

The following computations of ventilation requirements are based on the use of axivane fans exhausting air from the tunnel. These axivane fans are the same diameter as the ventilation pipe and can be mounted directly into the pipeline. To assist in the selection of ventilation equipment, the number of cubic feet of air that can be exhausted from a tunnel for different diameters of pipe, different fan spacing, and different fan horsepower is listed in Table 5.[5] Table 6 gives the reduction in fan horsepower for increases in elevation.[5]

TABLE 5 Size of Pipe and Fans for Air Requirements at Sea Level

Air volume, cfm	Pipe size, in.	Fan, bhp	Fan, nominal bhp	Maximum spacing, ft	
				First fan	Others
80,000	48	117	125	120	720
75,000	48	120	125	320	960
70,000	48	95	125	320	960
65,000	48	100	125	640	1,280
60,000	48	100	100	520	1,120
55,000	45	90	100	720	1,320
50,000	42	75	75	440	960
45,000	42	120	125	1,720	2,240
40,000	42	100	100	2,120	2,680
37,500	38	106	125	1,240	1,680
35,000	38	90	100	1,520	2,000
30,000	38	86	100	2,560	3,000
27,500	36	92	100	2,040	2,480
25,000	36	75	75	2,640	3,080
22,500	34	48	50	1,800	2,200
20,000	32	45	50	1,440	1,800
17,500	32	38	40	1,940	2,300
15,000	30	30	30	1,760	2,080
12,500	26	29	30	1,520	1,800
10,000	24	40	40	3,000	3,240
7,500	24	28	30	4,960	5,200
5,000	18	18	20	1,920	2,120
4,000	18	15	15	3,040	3,240
3,000	18	10	10	4,320	4,480

TABLE 6 Reduction in Fan Horsepower Requirements with Increase in Elevation

Elevation	Horsepower factor
1,000	0.979
2,000	0.944
3,000	0.910
4,000	0.876
5,000	0.845
6,000	0.813
7,000	0.782
8,000	0.755

Following are two examples of how Table 5 can be used in selecting ventilation pipe and equipment:

EXAMPLE 1 *Ventilation for a Tunnel Driven with Diesel Equipment:*

Assume that three 109-bhp Koehring Dumptors will be in the tunnel at one time and that mucking will be done with a 143-bhp Eimco 105 overshot loader. Also assume state ventilation requirements are 75 cfm per bhp. Then the required ventilation in cubic feet per minute is $(1 \times 143 + 3 \times 109)75 = 35{,}250$ cfm. From Table 5 this requires the use of a 38-in.-diameter pipe, with a 100-hp fan at the portal, the second fan spaced 1,520 lin ft from the portal, and the spacing of all additional fans at 2,000 lin ft intervals.

EXAMPLE 2 *Ventilation for a Tunnel Driven with Battery- and Air-operated Equipment:*

Since there is no diesel equipment used underground, the ventilation requirements are set by providing 50 cfm per sq ft of tunnel-face area. If we assume a 14-ft-diameter horseshoe tunnel, the ventilation requirements are $14^2 \times 0.8293 \times 50$ cfm $= 8{,}127$ cfm. On referring to Table 5, this requires a 24-in.-diameter pipe, a 40-bhp fan at the portal, a spacing of 3,000 lin ft to the second fan, and a spacing of 3,240 lin ft for each additional fan required.

Table 6 is used when the purchase of the fans is to be made.

Vent Pipe. Selection of vent pipe can be made from the following types:

1. Collapsible plastic tubing used on short tunnels when the capital cost is a large factor in the total cost. With this tubing, ventilation has to be a pressure system which blows air into the tunnel.

2. Plastic vent pipe which is extruded on the job. This is a comparatively new product and its suitability has not as yet been proved.

3. Steel pipe with quick-connecting couplings secured from pipe vendors.

4. Pipe fabricated on the job with airtight clamping rings for quick connections. This pipe fabricated with special machines that make pipe of various diameters from coils of steel strip. In order to use a lighter gauge, pipe is made with corrugations which give it extra strength. Fabrication of pipe on the jobsite greatly reduces freight costs as the charge for hauling steel strip is determined by weight and the charge for hauling fabricated pipe is by volume. See Photograph 14, which illustrates the machine making small-diameter pipe.

Savings in Length of Vent Pipe. In tunnels that have connecting shafts, it is possible to exhaust air through these shafts to save vent pipe. In tunnels that have a shallow cover, it may be economical

Photo 14 Machine for fabricating pipe from steel strip. (George M. Philpott Co., Inc.)

to drill special vent shafts so that vent lines can exhaust into them, which will reduce the total length of vent pipe required.

Secondary Ventilation System. The end of the main ventilation pipe is kept 200 ft from the tunnel face to protect the pipe from blasting damage. This results in a dead-air space between the end of the pipe and the tunnel face. To obtain proper ventilation at the face, small fans are set up on the jumbo with short sections of pipe which extend back past the end of the main vent pipe.

Air Compressors and Piping

Air-compressor capacity should be provided for:

1. Primary drilling
2. Roof bolting
3. Winches
4. Sump pumps powered by air
5. Any air-operated equipment such as air-operated muckers
6. Shops
7. Air leaks

Air pressure required at the tunnel face is 100 psi, and any drop in this pressure will decrease the drilling speed and thus decrease production. To maintain the air pressure at the face, air lines and air receivers should be sized so there will be only a small pressure drop in the air system. The pressure at the compressor plant should be set to take care of the pressure drop in the system.

In computing the capacity of the compressor plant, the amount of air required per drill, based on sea-level operation, is as follows.

5½-in.-bore burn-cut drill......600 cfm/drill
4½-in.-bore drifter drill........330 cfm/drill
4-in.-bore drifter drill..........250 cfm/drill
3½-in.-bore drifter drill........225 cfm/drill
3-in. drifter drill................150 cfm/drill

Increased air consumption caused by increased elevation is as follows.[6]

Altitude	*Correction Factor*
0	1.0
1,000	1.03
2,000	1.07
3,000	1.10
4,000	1.14
5,000	1.17
6,000	1.21
7,000	1.26
8,000	1.30
9,000	1.34
10,000	1.39
12,000	1.52
15,000	1.67

On tunnel jobs where a large number of drills are used, the estimated total consumption of air can be reduced because all the drills will not be working at one time. Tables covering this reduced consumption have been given in various publications. These tables were completed before the development of modern jibs and drill positioners which reduce nondrilling time, so the reduction factors shown in these tables should be weighed for any particular job.

Stationary electric compressors should be selected except for short tunnels since electric power is cheaper than diesel fuel and the maintenance cost for electric compressors is less than for diesel-powered ones. Air handbooks give tables listing the factors to be applied to the air produced by single-stage compressors to get their true production at different elevations. Since the majority of air compressors now used are two-stage compressors, these tables no longer apply. Two-stage compressors are very slightly affected by altitude up to an elevation of 3,300 ft. If they are to be operated above this altitude, the same air production can be maintained by enlarging the first-stage cylinder.

EXAMPLE *Compressor and Pipe-line Selection:*

If the compressed-air requirements are to be determined for a heading 20,000 ft long at an elevation of 5,000 ft, with the use of one 5½-in.-bore burn-cut drill and five 4½-in.-bore drifters, the computations are:

1 5½-in.-bore drill............	600 cfm
5 4½-in.-bore drifters at 330...	1,650 cfm
Subtotal....................	2,250 cfm
Shop and miscellaneous consumption...............	500 cfm
Total...................	2,750 cfm
Altitude correction 1.174 × 2,750 =	3,229 cfm

If a 1,100-cfm two-stage compressor is selected, four machines will be required. These machines should be purchased with enlarged first-stage cylinders to compensate for this elevation.

To determine the size of air line required to provide 2,640 cfm at the face, by referring to tables of friction loss in pipe lines,[7] the use of 6-in. pipe will give a pressure drop of 1.76 lb per 1,000 ft, or 35 lb in 20,000 ft. An 8-in. pipe will give a pressure drop of 0.41 lb per 1,000 ft, or 8 lb in 20,000 ft. Therefore, the 8-in. pipe will be used.

Water Supply

Water forced through the drill steel is used to wash the cuttings out of the drill holes. Water is also used for wetting down the muck pile to prevent dust while mucking, for invert cleanup, for concrete cleanup, and for grouting. The main water line should be of a size to supply water to a ½-in. water-hose connection to each drill. Concrete cleanup requires more water than drilling, so this requirement determines the minimum-size water line. Water lines vary in size from 3 in. in small tunnels to 8 in. in large ones. Couplings should be of the quick-connection type for ease in installing the pipe.

Electric Supply

Blasting Circuits. Single-phase either 220- or 440-volt circuits are used for blasting. Using higher voltages decreases misfires in rounds that require a great number of detonators. The blasting circuit should be separate from all other circuits so that fluctuations from motor start-ups will be at a minimum.

Lighting Circuits. The method of lighting tunnels is to space 100- or 150-watt bulbs 50 ft apart on one side of the tunnel. Lines of 110 or 220 volts are normal.

Power Circuit. The main tunnel power transmission lines must be sized to carry power for the muckers (if required), drill-jumbo motors, ventilation fans, pumps, and locomotives if trolley locomotives are used.

A general procedure for the utility centers is to locate them at specified stations in the tunnel. If these stations are designed at spacings in multiples of 500 or 1,000 ft, there is less waste of parkway cable. Fewer splices will be required and fewer scattered installations will be made. Fan stations, pump stations, transformer stations, and passouts may all be located together, which will give better access for repairs and replacements.

Light-circuit transformers are normally a 5-kva one-phase dry type in circuits between utility centers.

The blasting circuit transformer is normally a 5-kva one-phase dry type on a separate circuit from that for the portable heading center.

In estimating transformer requirements, the lower constant temperature normally encountered underground should not be overlooked. This may give a substantial savings in that a much higher overload for short periods may be possible, which will allow use of a somewhat smaller transformer. This should be checked with the transformer manufacturer.

Light fixtures and sockets must be waterproof. All major circuits must be grounded by a ground wire and not by rail or piping.

Drag Cable. When electric-powered muckers are used, it is necessary to purchase drag cables which allow both freedom of movement for the muckers and spacing of the outlets required for these muckers.

Power requirements are quite high in some tunnels; therefore, careful consideration must be given the total power required, the length of transmission, and the voltage to be used. Power cable may be obtained for underground conditions in voltages ranging from 600 to 6,000 volts. The area or size of the cable decreases as the load decreases; thus, the greater the voltage carried, the lower the load. It is advisable to use 2,240-volt or in longer tunnels 4,480- or 6,000-volt lines. Either copper or aluminum parkway cables are available; however, in estimating comparative costs, it must be noted that aluminum cable must be two sizes larger than copper cable for equal conditions. For preliminary purposes, until the power load is set, a main power circuit of three-conductor, 350 MCM, 5-kv armored cable should be used.

Underground Transformers. Underground transformers must be either the *dry* type or the *noninflammable* type. The selection of the proper transformer requires an estimate of power requirements as outlined below. Transformers will be located at utility centers spaced through the tunnel and at a portable heading center which is kept as near the tunnel face as practical.

The portable heading center will supply power to the mucker, lights at the face, miscellaneous motors (jumbo), and pumps. Transformers used should be a portable, noninflammable type.

The transformer power requirements for one utility center are those for the fans, pumps, and lights served from that center. Transformers used should be a portable, three-phase noninflammable type.

Tunnel Drainage

It is standard to allow for a small amount of pumping and drain lines in a tunnel estimate. However, owing to the uncertainty of the exact volume of water to be handled, this portion of the estimate depends on judgment or past experience in similar type of rock; on some wet tunnels it may be a major cost factor. If there is any question concerning the amount of water to be handled in any tunnel esimate, it is wise to get advice from a structural geologist.

Drainage lines and pumping are required in flat tunnels or in headings driven down a slope. In the latter case, all water runs to the face, which slows progress and necessitates pumping to keep the lower part of the face free from water.

If a heading is driven up a definite slope, ordinary flows of water can be handled in a ditch alongside the track. When the water flows become excessive, pumps and drainage lines must be installed. On some wet tunnels that are driven with a shallow cover, pumping stations have been installed with discharge pipes extending through holes drilled from the tunnel to the surface. This cuts down on the amount of pipe required and also may save in pump head capacity and power.

Special Vehicles

Besides muck cars, it is necessary to supply the following special cars or their equivalent in truck-mounted equipment if truck haulage is used:

1. Man cars for hauling the tunnel crews inside the tunnel
2. Flat cars for hauling timber, pipe, and miscellaneous supplies
3. Steel car which carries drill steel and bits in and out of the tunnel
4. Powder cars or prill cars or a combination of the two, complete with prill pots and hoses for loading the holes
5. Vent-line car outfitted with an overhead template for carrying one section of vent pipe and with two hydraulic jacks for lifting this vent pipe in place and positioning it
6. Car with built-in cradle for hauling steel sets into the tunnel

Outside Facilities and Equipment

These include:

Yard grading

Trackage to the dump, shops, powder house, concrete-mix plant, and sidings for the storage of spare cars, muckers, and other rail-mounted equipment. If a rail-mounted car dumper is planned, trackage for this is required paralleling the car dump trackage.

A powder magazine and cap house conforming to the local safety laws are required of bullet-proof construction.

Warehouse, electric shop, repair shop, pipe shop, bit and steel shop, and a compressor house are required. These shops necessarily have to be complete with the proper equipment. Shops can be built separately or included under one roof to get more efficient use of personnel.

If rubber-tired equipment is used on the job, a tire shop is required.

A separate office is required for the supervisory and engineering personnel.

Depending on the location, camp facilities and a mess hall may be required.

Also depending on the location, it may be necessary to construct access roads.

Besides office, shop, and engineering equipment, it is necessary to provide the following:

1. Pickups
2. Crane for handling lifts, such as a small hydraulic crane, or a front-end loader equipped with a fork lift which furnishes a dual-purpose rig, or a truck crane
3. Bulldozer for shaping muck pile
4. Flatbed truck for miscellaneous haulage
5. Change house.

REFERENCES

1. King Size Muck Cars Speed Tunnel, *Western Construction Magazine,* April, 1959, page 34.
2. Harold W. Richardson and Robert S. Mayo, *Practical Tunnel Driving,* copyright 1941 by the McGraw-Hill Book Company.
3. Locomotive Selection Procedure, Technical Report from Plymouth Locomotive Works, Division of the Fate-Root-Heath Company, Plymouth, Ohio.
4. They Drove This Tunnel Inside Out, a Construction Methods and Equipment reprint, copyright 1955, McGraw-Hill Publishing Company.
5. Information secured from the Joy Manufacturing Company, 1956 W. Harris Avenue, P. O. Box 2148, South San Francisco, California 94100.
6. *Rock Drill Data,* copyright 1960 by the Rock Drill Division of Ingersoll-Rand Company.
7. F. W. O'Neil, ed., assisted by the technical staff of Ingersoll-Rand Company, Compressed Air Data, copyright 1939, *Compressed Air Magazine.*

ADDITIONAL READING

Blasters Handbook, 15th ed., copyright 1966, E. I. du Pont de Nemours & Co. (Inc.), Wilmington, Delaware.

Compressed Air and Gas Institute, *Compressed Air Handbook,* 2d ed., copyright 1954, McGraw-Hill Book Company.

Frank W. Stubbs, Jr., ed., *Handbook of Heavy Construction,* copyright 1959 by the McGraw-Hill Book Company.

C. A. Pequignot, ed., *Tunnels and Tunnelling,* copyright 1963, Hutchinson & Co. (Publishers), Ltd., London.

Chapter 3 Methods and Equipment Used for Lining Tunnels

INTRODUCTION

The purpose of this chapter is to describe the construction methods and equipment necessary for the installation of permanent linings in tunnels. Transportation and utility distribution facilities, compressors, shops, and other outside facilities involved in the excavation operation and used to service the lining operations were described in Chap. 2. Descriptions of equipment included in this chapter are limited to additional equipment necessary for the tunnel lining operations and unique to this operation.

Although the majority of tunnels constructed have permanent lining installed before they are placed in service, some tunnels are left unlined, e.g., those constructed in sound, hard rock which are to be used for the conveyance of water under a low hydraulic head.

If short sections of these bare-rock tunnels require steel supports, these sections are then lined with concrete to protect the steel sets and to assist in providing permanent support. Some unlined hydraulic tunnels have paved inverts to prevent uneven erosion of the invert; such uncontrolled erosion may cause dams and eddies and restrict the flow. Other unlined hydraulic tunnels have paved inverts to facilitate motor vehicle operation when tunnel inspections are indicated in later years. Tunnels for vehicular traffic may be left unlined if they are on secondary roads and have an alignment suitable for the daylighting of ventilating notches at regular intervals along one wall of the tunnel. Yet another use of unlined tunnels is to provide access to a powerhouse or other underground facility when these access tunnels pass through suitable rock.

The type of tunnel linings used varies with the competency of the ground and the purpose of the tunnel. Poured in place concrete lining is used for hydro, highway, and subway tunnels. Tunnel linings composed of precast concrete sections or heavy cast-iron or steel liner plates are commonly used in subway tunnels located in metropolitan areas where incompetent ground is encountered. These liners, installed within the tail of the excavation shield, restrict ground subsidence and minimize building foundation underpinning requirements. The increased use of shotcrete lining for all types of tunnels driven in incompetent material is due to its ability to provide both temporary and permanent support. Other linings used for special conditions are precast concrete or steel pipe, where the space between the lining and the tunnel surface is backfilled with concrete.

When a concrete tunnel lining is used, its thickness is often determined by the "rule-of-thumb" method: 1 in. of thickness per ft of diameter of the tunnel.

CONCRETE LINING

Terminology

The concrete lining of a tunnel is divided into two general areas. *Invert concrete* comprises approximately the bottom 90° of the concrete lining of a circular tunnel, the bottom and a short distance up each side wall in a horseshoe tunnel. This "wall distance" in a horseshoe tunnel must be of sufficient height to anchor the arch forms. *Arch concrete* is simply the remainder of the concrete in the tunnel's lining (i.e., the top of the arch and the rest of the sides). Some concrete lining operations include the pouring of *curbs*. Curbs are continuous concrete walls poured along each side of the tunnel. Specifications usually require that the surface of these pours be set back from the finished tunnel surface. Thus, all finished surfaces in the tunnel are made on either the invert or arch pour. Because of limitations of the placing equipment, *tunnel concrete* should have more plasticity than concrete ordinarily placed in open forms. To achieve this plasticity and workability, this concrete has a higher cement and sand content and the mixing size aggregate is usually under 2½ in. Gravel is preferred to crushed rock as an aggregate. Before the concrete is placed, forms must be erected in the excavated tunnel. There are several types of forms that can be used in this operation. *Telescopic forms* are either full circle or arch forms which can be stripped, collapsed, and moved through the center of other forms previously erected and which can then be erected in front of the concrete pour. *Nontelescopic forms* are constructed so that they cannot be moved through the center of other similar forms and are used only when noncontinuous pours are made. They are less costly than telescopic forms. *Bulkhead forms* are forms placed between the arch forms and the tunnel rock to give a vertical construction joint at the end of any pour. A *form traveler,* a traveling jumbo equipped with hydraulic cylinders, is used to strip, collapse, transport, and erect the full circle or arch forms.

Concrete is placed in "pours." In a *full-circle pour,* the concrete is placed completely around the tunnel in one operation. A *continuous pour* is concrete placement that continues 24 hr a day for the entire work week. Bulkhead forms are installed at the end of the work week only, after the weekly pour is stopped. When a continuous pour is made, only one construction joint is formed per week. *Bulkhead pours,* with bulkhead forms and vertical construction joints, are made at definite intervals along the tunnel line. They are made when specifications limit the length of pours or when nontelescopic forms are used, which results in a cyclical operation of concrete placing. (This cycle consists in concrete placing, form stripping, form setting, and the resumption of concrete placing.)

The concrete placement operation requires specialized equipment. A *concrete placer* is a pump or air gun used to force concrete through a pipe embedded in the fresh concrete being placed between the form and the tunnel surface. That length of pipe that transports the concrete from the placer to pour area is called the *slick line.* The slick line must be embedded in the fresh concrete to prevent segregation of the concrete as it is discharged from the pipe. The traveling frame that supports the slick line is known as the *pipe jumbo.*

Another traveling frame, used in tunnels with a large diameter, provides a working platform for the finishers. This frame is called the *finish jumbo.* From its platform the finishers correct any deficiencies in the fresh concrete after the forms are removed and apply curing compounds if required.

After the concrete is placed, *low-pressure grout* is placed between the concrete lining and the excavated tunnel surface. The purpose of the grouting is to fill any voids left after the concrete placing operation.

Concrete Lining Sequence

If a tunnel is to be lined with concrete, the construction planner must first decide whether the tunnel lining operation is to be done concurrently with the excavation or whether lining is to be installed upon completion of the excavation. Concrete lining and tunnel excavation are done at the same time when specifications make it mandatory or when tunnels are driven in mud, soft ground, or sand, which requires that the lining be placed as close to the heading as possible. Concurrent lining and excavation operations are sometimes used in subways constructed in material other than competent rock, in a downtown area where any ground subsidence would effect building settlement. When concreting and excavation operations are performed at the same time, the resulting interference between the two operations slows the progress and increases the cost of both. Therefore, when concurrent operations are necessary, the engineer should make allowances for this increased cost and the increased construction time required.

The preferred method of placing concrete lining is to complete the tunnel excavation before lining operations are started. Tunnel excavation is generally done by personnel who have only worked on tunnel excavation in the past, and who move on to the next job when the excavation is completed. Different superintendents and different labor crews trained in concrete placement then move onto the job to line the tunnel. Thus, completing excavation before lining is begun provides each crew with total access to the tunnel and allows management and personnel to give full attention to the operation under way.

Concrete-placing Methods for Completely Lined Tunnels

When a tunnel is to be completely lined with concrete, it is placed by one of five methods. Descriptions of these methods are as follows:

1. ***Full-circle Method.*** The full-circle method involves the placement of the complete circumferential concrete lining in one operation. This method is used when specification requirements or job conditions make its use mandatory or when restricted concrete placement makes its use economical. Either full-circle forms or arch forms with a screeded invert may be used. The most difficult aspect of this placement method is the work required to keep the forms on line and grade

and prevent their flotation. Most of the other concrete-placing methods have previously poured concrete that can be used both as a line and grade reference point and as an anchorage for the arch forms. In the full-circle method, the forms must be set to line and grade by the use of bottom jacks. Flotation can be prevented by blocking from the tunnel roof. This blocking is removed as the pour is made.

The full-circle method of concrete placement may be the most economical method when production is not critical; for concreting can be done by a small crew. Cleanup is done directly ahead of the pour, and the lineal feet of concrete poured per day is often determined by the amount of tunnel that can be cleaned up in one shift. Working procedure is to assign one shift to cleaning up, one shift to moving forms, and one shift to pouring. With this method of operation, all labor is worked as efficiently as possible, with crew sizes restricted to the number required for each task, on each particular shift.

When full-circle pours are made, the design of the form traveler presents problems since the surface on which it must travel will vary from concreted invert, to the top surface of the invert forms, and finally to the surface of the unpaved invert. To travel on these three surfaces and support the forms in a level condition, jacks must be provided over both the rear and front wheels. A preferred form-traveler design, for use with telescopic forms, is one designed to travel only on rails mounted on top of the invert forms. In order to restrict the form traveler to this area, cantilever beams, capable of supporting a length of forms, must be provided on the rear and front of the form traveler. Facilities for sliding the forms from the rear cantilever over and under the jumbo, to the front cantilever, must also be incorporated in the form traveler. Form moving procedure consists in backing the form traveler up to the last section of forms and raising the invert form by the rear cantilever arm. This form is then moved forward so that it is supported by the front cantilever arm. The form traveler is then moved forward in the tunnel, and the invert form is set on jacks by the front cantilever arm. The traveler then goes back and picks up the arch form with the rear cantilever arm. The arch form is then slid forward so that it is over the main section of the form traveler. The traveler then moves forward and sets it in place. The arch forms can be held in position by blocking from the tunnel roof. As the concrete is placed around the form, the blocking is removed.

In large-diameter tunnels when full-circle forms are used, the invert section of the full-circle forms should be designed so it can be lifted from the invert shortly after the pour is made in order that air bubbles can be troweled out and any concrete deficiencies can be corrected. Concrete deficiencies may occur in the invert section of large-diameter tunnels because of the long horizontal distance the concrete must flow across the invert to fill the form properly.

2. ***Invert Pour and Then Arch Pour.*** Invert pour and then arch pour is the method of concrete placement in most common use. It does not have the problem of form referencing and form flotation encountered in the full-circle method since the arch forms can be firmly secured to the previously placed invert concrete. This method has a cost savings over the curb, invert, and arch method because the lining is poured in two operations instead of three.

In this method, the invert is poured first by using a slip-form screed to form the invert. After all the invert concrete is placed, the arch pour is started with the arch forms bolted to the previously placed invert. Continuous pours are made, and as the arch concrete develops strength, telescopic arch forms are continuously stripped from the fresh concrete and erected in front of the concrete pour. With this placement method and the proper selection of equipment, rapid, continuous pouring of both invert and arch can be made.

3. ***Arch Pour, Then Invert Pour.*** If specifications permit the leveling of tunnel muck to provide a foundation for the invert concrete, then invert cleanup and the placement of invert concrete can be done concurrently by the "retreat" method of invert placement. With this invert-cleanup method if low-pressure grouting and final cleanup are done with rubber-tired equipment, it will not be necessary to relay track, provided the arch concrete is poured before the invert concrete. However, since there is no previously placed concrete that can be used for arch-form anchorage, there will be added cost and time required to anchor the arch forms and hold them to line and grade. The added time and cost required for form anchorage often surpass the savings that result from not relaying the track. For this reason, this method of concrete placing is seldom used.

4. ***Curb, Invert, and Arch Method.*** The curb, invert, and arch was the method most popular in the past because of the simplicity of having the curb concrete in place to provide a reference and a firm anchorage for both the invert and the arch pours. This method is becoming less popular because it is more expensive than the invert and arch method. When the curb, invert, and arch method is used, there is a tendency to overexcavate to allow for the curb pour. This overexcavation increases cost by increasing the nonpay yardage of both the excavation and the concrete per lineal foot of tunnel. Another reason for increased cost is that the concrete lining is placed in three operations instead of two and invert cleanup must be done in two operations instead of one.

With this method, the procedure is to clean up under the curb pour, place curb forms, and then pour the curbs. To save time, these curbs can be placed while excavation is being performed without too much interference with excavation. After the curbs are poured, the remainder of the invert is then cleaned, and with the curbs for anchorage and grade reference, the invert is placed. The arch pour is then made in the same manner as in the invert and arch method.

When the concrete lining must be placed concurrently with excavation, this is the method most commonly used. It has the advantage, under these condtions, of giving less interference with the excavation operations than other methods do, while affording constant access to the tunnel heading during all concreting operations. Such access can be maintained during the curb and arch pour by using California switches. Similarly, when the invert is cleaned and the concrete is placed on this prepared area, the main-line travel to the excavation heading can be preserved. The curbs, previously placed, provide a simple method of supporting a bridge, necessary for this main-line access and in the clear of the concreting operation.

5. *Curb, Arch, and Invert Method.* The curb, arch, and invert method is used for the same purpose, and under the same conditions, as the arch and invert method described as Method 3. As with that method and under the right conditions, track relaying will not be necessary. This saving of track relaying can be accomplished when concrete and invert cleanup are done concurrently, when low-pressure grouting and final cleanup are carried out with rubber-tired equipment, and when arch is poured before invert. The difference between this method and Method 3 is that the arch forms can be anchored to the curbs; however, additional expense is involved in curb placement.

Concrete-placing Methods for a Partially Lined Tunnel

When specifications require only a paved invert, the invert is placed by methods similar to those used in the invert, arch lining method, which will be described in detail below. On tunnels where cleanup is required to bare rock, the large amount of nonpay overbreak concrete in the invert will affect cost, production, and the capacity of the equipment required.

If a tunnel has only a few areas where concrete lining is required, bulkhead pours are made with nontelescopic forms. These pours can be made while excavation is being performed by using the curb, invert, and arch method. Placing time and cost are high, relative to the amount of concrete poured, because the operations are intermittent. Transition forms are required at the start and stop of each concrete section, and because of limited yardage, the equipment write-off will be high. Concrete placement in the arch section is done by pumping methods or by use of *pots*. These pots are large-capacity air guns used to transport the concrete into the tunnel, where they are connected to the slick line and air supply in order to shoot the concrete into the forms. Pots serve a dual purpose since they replace both the concrete agitators and the air guns.

Detailed Description of the Invert, Arch Concrete-placing Method

The invert, arch method is the only concrete-placement method that will be described in detail. If this method is understood, the requisite changes in procedure for using other placement methods can be readily made. For descriptive purpose, the invert, arch placement method is separated into work and cost divisions.

1. ***Removal of Fan Line.*** Often, after the tunnel is holed through and there is an uninterrupted passage of air from one tunnel portal to the other, the natural flow of air through the tunnel will satisfy ventilation requirements. If this natural ventilation is not adequate, ventilation requirements can be met by placing bulkheads equipped with exhaust fans over one end of the tunnel. These exhaust fans will then draw fresh air through the entire length of the tunnel. Automatic opening and closing doors can be installed in the bulkhead to provide access for men and equipment.

Since ventilation requirements can thus be met by other means and because the large-diameter vent pipe will interfere with the concreting operations, the first step in preparing the concrete lining is the removal of this vent pipe. The pipe can be uncoupled and lowered by cranes and the vent-pipe car by which it was placed. But because it will be removed much faster than it was placed, the vent car will not provide sufficient transporting equipment. To provide sufficient pipe-hauling units, special cradles can be mounted on some of the haul units that were used for muck disposal in the excavation operation.

2. ***Reset Steel Sets, Retimber, Remove Tights—Arch Cleanup.*** First, surveyors run templates down the tunnel line, marking all sets that encroach on the minimum-clearance line and all rock that projects past the minimum-excavation line. The sets that encroach must be reset, the excavation tights removed, and the lagging and blocking removed, rearranged, or replaced to conform to the specification requirements. No special equipment is needed for this operation, for it can be performed with some of the equipment used for tunnel excavation.

The concrete specifications should be checked for any special requirement affecting this work. For example, some specifications state that lagging and blocking can only cover up to 50 percent of the surface area to be concreted.

3. ***Invert Cleanup.*** Specification requirements influence invert

cleanup more than any other step in the lining procedure. This is due to wide differences among specifications on the type of tunnel cleanup required.

When specifications do not require cleanup to bare rock, invert cleanup can be combined with invert concrete placing, which eliminates a separate invert-cleanup operation. Concurrent invert cleanup and concrete-placing operations result in a savings to the owner. (Many designers believe that this procedure produces as competent a concrete lining as any constructed under the bare-rock cleanup requirement.) Under this type of specification, the only cleanup required is the removal of loose material that is unsatisfactory for backfill, the leveling of the remainder to tunnel grade, and the removal of track. Cleanup operations required by this type of specification can be combined with the "retreat" method of placing invert.

A separate cleanup operation completed before the invert pouring can begin is necessary when the specifications require that the smallest particle of loose material must be removed from the tunnel invert and the invert surface must be free of all water. Because of the additional time and man-hours required for such cleanup, the added amount of excavated material to be handled, and the increase in overbreak concrete, this type of cleanup amounts to a large percentage of the concrete cost. Cleanup operations are started at one end of the tunnel and are carried through to the other. As the cleanup progresses, the track must be lifted, and track materials hauled out of the tunnel or hung on the tunnel sides. All muck must be removed and the rock surface cleaned with air and water jets. Provisions must be made for surface drainage and all surface water must be removed.

Under bare-rock cleanup requirements, some contractors have obtained a cost savings, after rock cleanup is completed, by installing drainage systems in preference to hand mopping the surface water (required to keep the invert dry ahead of the concrete pour). The type of drainage system used is a well point system of drains, which is covered with gravel to the concrete pay line. Plastic is placed over the gravel before the invert concrete is placed. Suction is maintained on the drain pipes while the invert concrete is placed and cured. After the invert concrete has strengthened, the gravel under the plastic is grouted.

Much of the equipment used for the tunnel cleanup is available from that used for tunnel driving, such as the muckers, muck cars, locomotives, drills, and air facilities. This equipment may be supplemented by the following specialized units:

Tractor-mounted front-end loaders
Gradalls or backhoes for removing the tunnel muck, used in conjunc-

tion with protective shields which have ahead of them air and water jets for final cleanup of the tunnel

Conveyor belts for transporting the muck from the excavating equipment to tail cars

4. ***Placing Reinforcing Steel.*** Reinforcing steel is often installed by a subcontractor. In this case, the prime contractor transports the invert steel into the tunnel for the subcontractor before the invert cleanup is started, and the steel is hung from the sides of the tunnel until the invert cleanup is completed. The subcontractor then places the steel in the invert ahead of the concrete placement. Reinforcing steel for the arch is taken into the tunnel after the invert pour is made and is placed prior to the arch concrete.

In some pressure tunnels with low cover, the designers often call for heavy mats of reinforcing bars of large diameter, such as number 18 bars. This reinforcement causes unique problems and increases the cost of tunnel concrete. If the invert is poured separately from the arch, the steel must be spliced above the invert pour and the bars must be lapped or coupled together. Specifications should be checked to see if the steel in the laps is a pay quantity. When the arch is poured, the reinforcing steel may interfere with retraction of the slick line as the pour advances, which will require that either intermittent pours be placed with the slick line located above the reinforcing steel or the slick line be lodged in a concrete dimple in the tunnel arch. If a dimple is used, the designers may allow this extra concrete in the arch to remain; in other instances the dimple must be removed and the concrete ground to a polished surface.

The vibration and flow of the concrete also becomes more of a problem in a reinforced tunnel, and this factor should be reflected in the estimated cost.

5. ***Panning and Care of Water.*** If the tunnel has water inflow in the crown and sides, it may be necessary to guide this water down the sides of the tunnel to discharge pipes placed in the bottom. Such guidance is accomplished with light-gauge metal or metal foil placed between the supports or pinned to the rock. The drainage system in the bottom may have to be as extensive as a modified well point system, with pumps exhausting the bottom drainage system to the main discharge pipe. Main drainage pipe of large diameter should be installed along the sides of the tunnel so that all water will be removed. This drainage system must be maintained until the completion of the arch concrete. The bottom drainage system can then be grouted or, in some cases, left as a permanent drainage system with flap valves on the exit pipes. The main drainage pipes should then be removed from the tunnel.

6. *Pouring Invert Concrete.* There are two main methods of placing invert concrete. One is the "advance" method, the other the "retreat" method. The following description of the two methods of placing invert concrete is for a tunnel excavated with track-mounted equipment. If the tunnel were driven with rubber-tired equipment, the procedure would be the same except that there would not be any track to take up and relay.

"Advance" method. The advance method of placing invert concrete, schematically shown by Drawing 8, because it is more complicated than the retreat method, is normally only used when specifications require that the invert surface be cleaned up to bare rock and be free of water. With the advance method, the cleanup operations are done well in advance of the invert placing operation. If a tunnel has two open ends, or portals, the cleanup is started at one portal. Track, muck, and other material from the cleanup operation are hauled out the other end of the tunnel, with concreting operations following the cleanup. In a tunnel which has only one portal, cleanup is started at the blind end and carried back to the portal before the concrete invert is started.

The key piece of equipment with the advance method of placing concrete is an invert traveling bridge supported from the sides of the tunnel and of such length that the concrete at the rear of the bridge has sufficient strength to support the railroad track. A cross section taken through an invert bridge at the screed location is depicted by Drawing 9. The bridge must be suspended high enough so that space is available beneath it for finishing the invert concrete and for relaying the track. One method of support and travel for this bridge is to support it on rails that run on wheels located on each side of the tunnel. The wheels are supported and kept on line either by brackets which are attached to the steel sets or if the tunnel is unsupported, by brackets which are supported by pipe jacks inserted in holes drilled in the bottom and sides of the tunnel. If desired, the wheels can be installed in the bridge and the rail on the brackets. If this type of bridge support is used, rail is hung from the sides of the tunnel when the track is removed for invert cleanup. The rail is then installed on the brackets shortly ahead of the invert pouring operation.

After the bridge passes, the rail is taken off the brackets and used for track installation on the invert. The brackets are then taken off and rehung in front of the bridge. A traveling screed is mounted in front of the bridge, with independent travel on duplicate wheels so it can be more easily held to line and grade and so its movement is independent of the main bridge movement.

A conveyor belt is mounted on the bridge, running from the track in the rear of the bridge to the front of the bridge, where it terminates

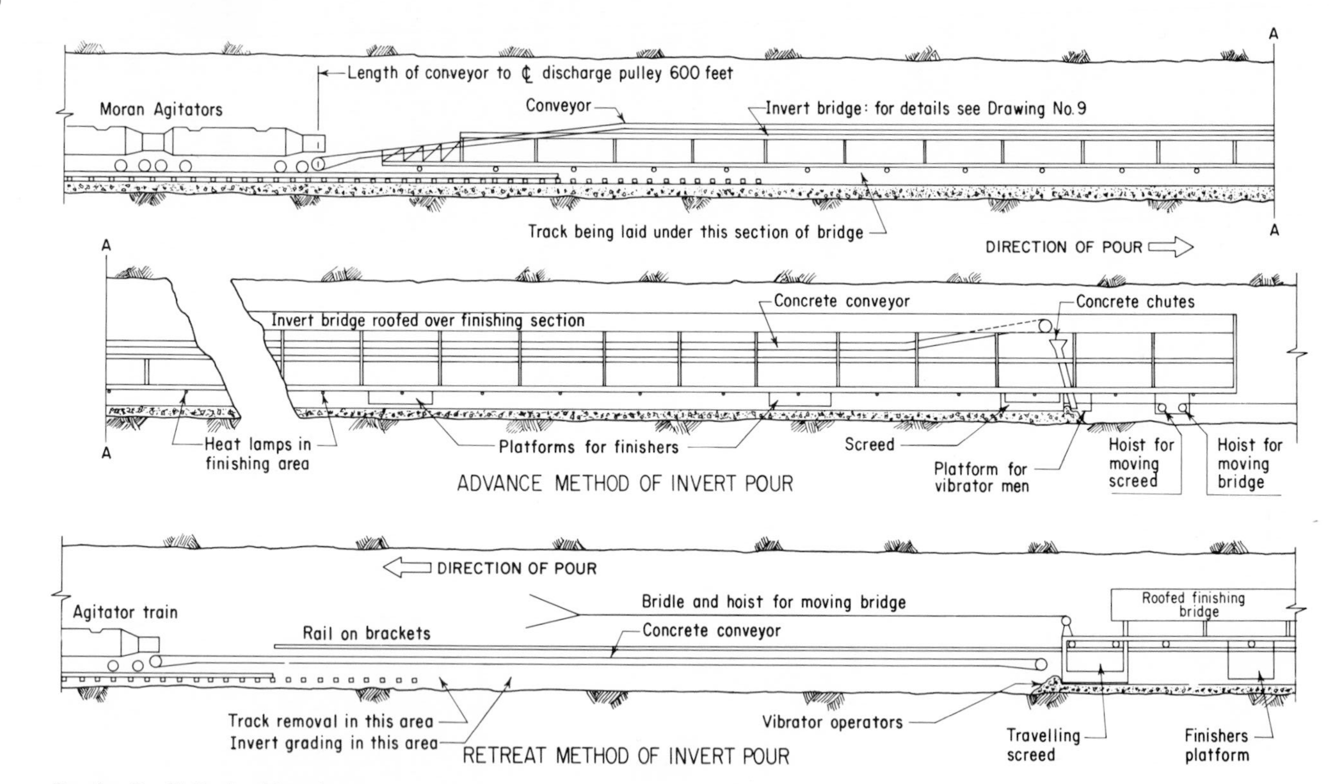

Drawing 8 Methods of invert pour.

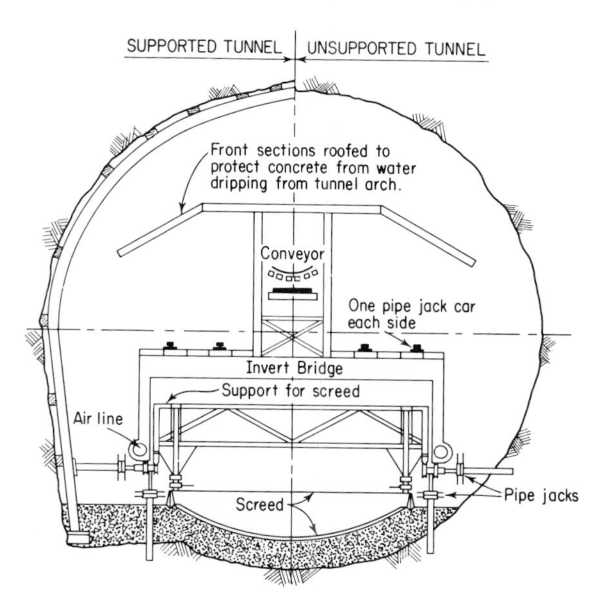

Drawing 9 Section through invert bridge and invert screed for the advance method of invert pour.

over a hopper connected to a three-barrel chute. Concrete placement is performed by delivering the concrete to the rear end of the bridge by trains of agitator cars. The trains are discharged onto a conveyor belt that runs the length of the bridge and deposits the concrete in a hopper. A gate at the bottom of the hopper directs the concrete into one of three pipe chutes by which it is deposited on the invert ahead of the screed. Concrete is switched from pipe chute to pipe chute to deposit it evenly across the invert. On platforms in front of the screed ride men who vibrate the concrete so that it is forced under the traveling screed. As the screed advances, the bridge advances and the whole operation moves down the tunnel.

Concrete finishing is performed under the bridge with heat lamps to hasten the curing time. Under the rear of the bridge, first paper, for concrete protection, then longitudinal stringers, ties, and rail are laid on the concrete so that as the bridge advances, there is always rail connection to the bridge. The paper is placed to aid in curing as well as to protect the concrete. The longitudinal stringers are laid under the ties to give firm support to the ties on the curved surface of the invert. Ties and rail are brought in from the portal as required, and the ones taken up during cleanup operation are reused. In a two-portal tunnel where cleanup and concrete are carried on at the same time it is generally necessary to truck the rails and ties from the cleanup portal to the concreting portal. If track material was hung on the tunnel sides during the cleanup operation, it is only necessary to reclaim this material.

On some tunnels, the specification requirements are so strict that mopping up water is more expensive than installing a well point system, covering the aggregate with plastic, and after the concrete invert is placed, grouting this aggregate. If this method of invert drainage is used, the aggregate is brought in by concrete agitators, unloaded, and transported in the same manner as the concrete. However, the aggregate is discharged ahead of the concrete pour by a special belt provided for this purpose.

Special equipment required for the advance method:

Bridge—complete with guides, conveyor belts, brackets, power drum for moving, power, heat lamps, etc.
Invert screed—complete with guides and power drum for moving
Concrete vibrators
Agitator trains

"Retreat" method. The retreat method of concrete invert placing, as shown in Drawing 8, is used when tunnel cleanup specifications allow leveling the tunnel muck for invert support. This type of specification greatly reduces the cost of invert concrete and invert cleanup and allows the cleanup operation to be done along with the retreat method of invert pouring.

The first operation is to excavate all excess tunnel muck from both sides of the track with the mucking machine. The invert pour is then started at one end of the tunnel and progresses toward the other. This invert pouring method uses a bridge and a screed, but the bridge can be very light since it is only used to provide the concrete invert with protection from water dripping from the roof of the tunnel and to furnish suspended supports for the concrete finishers.

Concreting operations are started backing up from one end of the tunnel where lengths of rail, sufficient to support the bridge, are removed from the track and then fastened to brackets along the sides of the tunnel. The rails must be set to line and grade since they are used for guides and support for the screed and the bridge. The ties are then removed and hauled outside the tunnel, the tunnel invert is graded, and the bridge and screed are erected into position. Concrete is transported into the tunnel by agitator trains and discharged onto a conveyor belt which deposits it in front of the screed. Vibrator then consolidate the concrete as the screed is pulled forward. As the screed and bridge advance with the concrete pour, other sections of rail are taken up and placed on the sides, and the invert is prepared for concrete.

Mechanized screed units can be used which perform the same function as the vibrator operators; this reduces the manpower required but increases the equipment cost.

Behind the bridge, paper is laid on the invert, stringers and ties are hauled into the tunnel and laid on the paper, and rail is taken off the brackets and relaid on the ties. The brackets that supported the rail are taken off the sides of the tunnel and carried forward to be rehung. Finishing and curing are performed under the roofed bridge. With this method of invert placement, the invert cleanup and invert pour are carried on concurrently.

Special equipment required for the retreat method:

Bridge—riding on rails supported on the sides of the tunnel or steel sets (when available); designed to support a roof and to carry the finishers; for some contractors, equipped with heat lamps to hasten the curing time

Traveling screed—riding on the same rails as the bridge

Short conveyor belt—used for transporting concrete from the agitator trains to the screed

Agitator trains

The advantages of the retreat method over the advance method are:

a. There is less tunnel cleanup cost, due to specification requirements and the fact that cleanup is not a separate operation.

b. A lighter and shorter invert bridge is required since the bridge supports only the roof and the finishers. (Under the advance method, the bridge must both support a conveyor belt and be long enough to allow track to be erected under it on concrete that has sufficient strength for its support.)

c. Less overbreak concrete is necessary since the tunnel floor can be graded to proper elevation instead of being excavated to solid rock.

d. With a graded bottom (retreat method), water handling is less expensive than it is when cleanup is to bare rock (advance method).

7. *Placing Arch Concrete.* The following is a description of the only method in common use for the placement of arch concrete. This method is schematically shown in Drawing 10. A length of telescopic arch forms, sufficient to maintain a continuous pour, is erected at one end of the tunnel. These forms are fastened to the invert concrete either by the use of Richmond screw anchors, installed in the invert concrete when it was placed, or by anchor bolts, installed in holes drilled later in the invert concrete. Concrete is transported into the tunnel by agitator trains and is then discharged onto a short transfer belt. This transfer belt elevates the concrete and deposits it in a hopper located

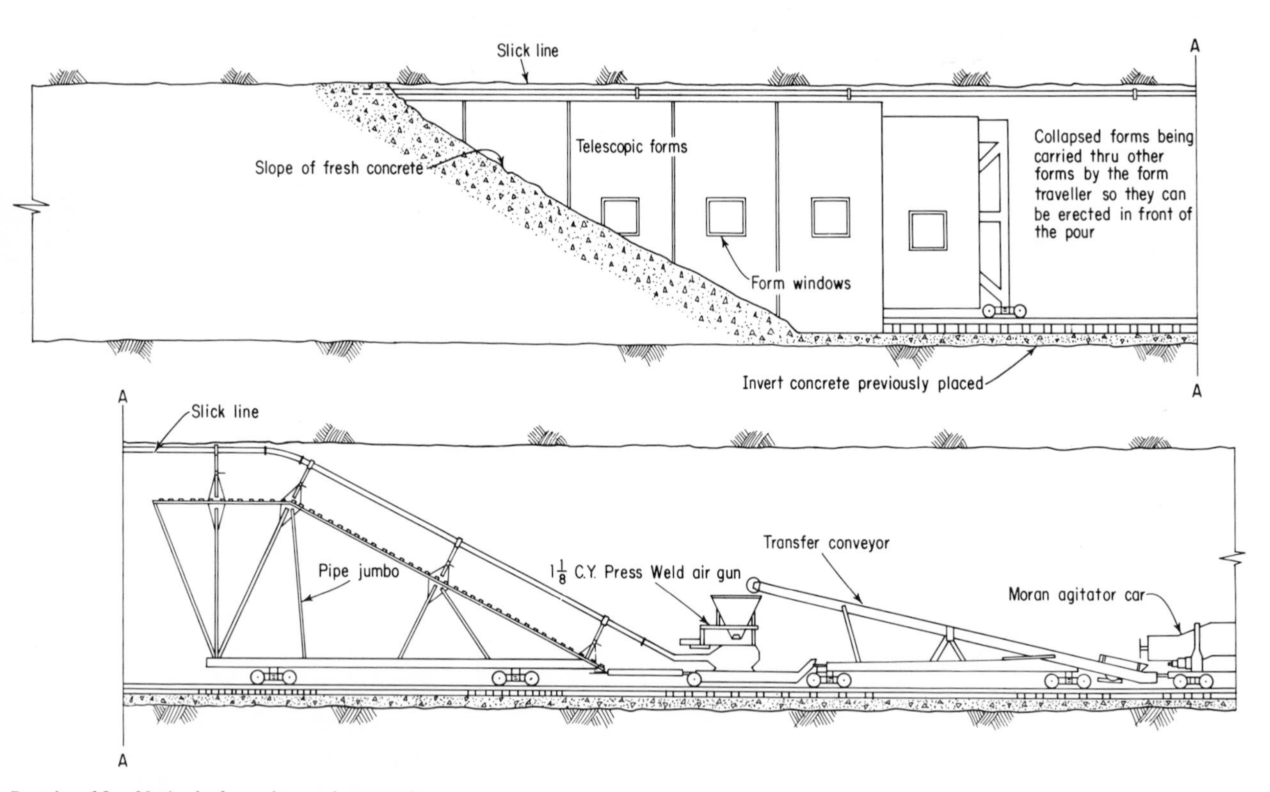

Drawing 10 Method of pouring arch concrete.

above the concrete placer. The concrete is then batch fed from the hopper into a concrete placer[1] which forces the concrete into the crown of the arch and in back of the forms through the slick-line pipe. This pipe is supported by a pipe jumbo, and after the pour is started, the discharge end of the pipe is kept embedded in the fresh concrete. Embedding the end of the pipe is necessary to prevent segregation of the concrete. The concrete placed in the arch flows down the sides of the tunnel and connects with the invert concrete.

As the pour is made, the belt, placer, and pipe are moved backward at the same speed at which the concrete fills the forms. When the concrete has set sufficiently behind individual lengths of forms, these forms are stripped, collapsed, and carried through the other forms. The collapsed forms are then erected in front of the forms still in position. This stripping, collapsing, transporting, and erecting of the forms is done with a form traveler jumbo. Concrete haul, concrete placing, and form moving are synchronized so that the arch concrete can be placed continuously (except for shut downs over the weekend). At the end of the week, bulkhead pours are made, which form a vertical construction joint.

On small tunnels, only one slick line is used, which discharges into the crown of the arch. On large tunnels more discharge pipes are used, located at various points in the tunnel circumference, and they are connected in rotation to the placer. These additional pipes reduce the distance that the fresh concrete must flow around the sides of the tunnel. On tunnels that have a large volume of concrete per lineal foot of tunnel, two or more placers may be used and the mixing and transporting equipment must be sized for their capacity. When placement rates, equipment capacity, and cost are estimated, the amount of nonpay overbreak concrete must be taken into consideration.

The arch forms can be either telescopic or nontelescopic. Telescopic forms are used for continuous pouring, and enough forms should be provided for 16 hr of concrete placing, taking into account the front slope of the concrete inside the form. Nontelescopic forms are used for short pours, and the form covers the length of tunnel to be poured at one time. After curing, the forms are stripped, moved, and erected for the next pour. Forms are moved by a form traveler riding on railroad track or on rubber tires and containing jacks for collapsing and setting the forms.

Forms should be provided with windows through which concrete placing can be watched and the concrete vibrated. On large tunnels, concrete distribution pipes may be carried down the inside of the forms to these windows. They should also be equipped with form vibrators.

There are three types of concrete placers: concrete pumps, air guns, and pots. Concrete pumps force the concrete through the discharge pipe by mechanical means. Pumps are used when the specifications limit the use of air guns. They are also used to pump concrete long distances since they can pump concrete approximately 1,200 lin ft, while a gun operates best at a distance of 200 ft. Finally, pumps are used for placing short pours since it is easier to start and finish pours with a pump than with an air gun.

Pneumatic placers or air guns force batches of concrete through the discharge pipe by the use of air pressure. Their placement capacity exceeds that obtained with pumps. Operating and maintenance cost of air guns is less than for pumps because they have fewer moving parts. Space occupied by this placer is smaller than that necessary for a pump. For these reasons contractors prefer placing concrete with air guns rather than pumps. Most pneumatic placers operate on the same principles as the Press Weld, an all-air-operated concrete gun shown in Photograph 15. These units are large steel containers equipped with a discharge nozzle and a sliding door mounted on top of the container. The unit is charged with batches of concrete by opening the sliding door and dropping concrete into the container. The sliding door is then closed, air pressure is applied, and the concrete is forced through the nozzle. The unit requires a single operator. This man operates a quick-acting valve controlling air to the back of the container and an-

Photo 15 Press Weld placer. (George M. Philpott Co., Inc.)

other quick-opening valve controlling air to the nozzle. When both valves are opened together, concrete starts out of the container through the nozzle in a steady stream. As concrete travels through the 6-in. discharge pipe and reaches the forms, a quick drop in pressure results. Both valves are then closed and the machine is ready to recharge and place another batch of concrete. An upper automatic charging gate is almost always used with Press Weld units. This is a small hopper which mounts on top of the Press Weld unit and holds one charge of concrete. As the sliding door opens on the Press Weld, a sliding gate in the bottom of the charge gate opens and drops a charge of concrete into the Press Weld. The upper automatic charge gate is necessary for the most efficient operation of Press Weld units.

Listed below are dimensions and capacities of various sizes of Press Weld placers:

Size	*Height*		*Width*		*Length*		*Approximate Hourly Capacity,*
cu yd	*ft*	*in.*	*ft*	*in.*	*ft*	*in.*	*cu yd*
1⅛	4	0	3	8	9	0	60–100
¾	3	6	3	1	9	0	45–60
½	3	0	2	8	9	0	34–45

Pots are constructed so that they will hold up to 8 cu yds of concrete. They are charged with concrete outside the tunnel and then travel on rail to the point in the tunnel where the concrete is being poured. At this point they are connected to a concrete discharge pipe and the air supply. Thus, pots act as air guns, shooting the concrete into the forms. Pots are used in small tunnels that have restricted working area or in large tunnels which have intermittent pours. The advantage of using pots is that they replace the agitators, transfer conveyor, hopper, and placer. They are disadvantageous in that the amount of concrete placed per day with this operation is comparatively small unless a large number of pots are purchased.

A summary of the special arch concrete equipment would include:

Arch forms
Form traveler
Slick line
Slick-line jumbo to support the pipe
Concrete placer
Concrete-charging hopper
Concrete-transfer conveyor belt
Agitator trains
Vibrators, both form and wiggle-tail

8. ***Low-pressure Grouting.*** After the concrete is placed in the tunnel, any voids left between the concrete lining and the tunnel surface must be filled with low-pressure grout. Specifications should be checked to see if this is a pay item, or if the contractor must include the cost of this operation in the concrete pay item. Grout pipes are installed in the lining as it is poured. These pipes must be cleaned out and connected to the grout pump. Grout is then pumped as required.

Equipment essential to the grouting operation includes:

A grout pump serviced with air, water, and electricity and equipped with a grout mixer to feed the pump (a grouting setup is shown in Photograph 16.)

Equipment to haul cement and sand to the grout mixer

9. ***Final Cleanup.*** Final cleanup involves the removal of track, pumps, pipe, electrical facilities, and all other items of plants and equipment. The operation further entails being certain that all loose material has been removed from the tunnel after grouting operations, and includes the cleaning and patching of all concrete.

Photo 16 Grouting equipment. (Gardner-Denver Co. and George M. Philpott Co., Inc.)

CONCRETE-SERVICING EQUIPMENT

Compressed Air

More compressed air is used for one concrete setup than for one excavation setup, but since most jobs have several excavation headings and only one concrete setup, the air provided for excavating the tunnel generally takes care of the concreting. This may not be the case when only one heading is driven, and additional air may then be required for concreting. Air required for concreting is used for:

1. Drilling out tights: Allow about 100 cu ft per min per drill.
2. Air and water cleanup: Allow 1,000 cu ft per min for each ¾-in. nozzle.
3. Air-operated sump pumps: Allow about 40 cu ft per min for every 100 g per min pumped.
4. Air-operated concrete placers: For Press Weld placers it takes an average of 800 cu ft of compressed air at 100-lb pressure to deliver 1 cu yd of concrete 100 ft and lift it 20 ft. For greater distances add 1 cu ft of air for each additional foot of horizontal pipe and 5 cu ft for each foot of additional lift.
5. Air-operated vibrators: Allow 25 cu ft per min each for light-duty vibrators, 80 cfm each for medium-duty vibrators.
6. Miscellaneous small tools and air leaks: Allow 200 cu ft per min.

Aggregate, Concrete-batch, and Concrete-refrigeration Plants

The aggregate and refrigeration plants, if required, as well as the concrete-batch plant, are in most cases located near the tunnel portal. Since these plants include the same equipment that can be used on any type of construction, a description of this equipment will not be included. However, capacity of these plants must be balanced with the placing equipment.

Concrete Haulage

If the tunnel muck was removed from the tunnel with rubber-tired equipment, then diesel-driven agitator trucks are generally used to haul the concrete from the batch plant into the tunnel.

If the tunnel muck was removed from the tunnel with rail-mounted equipment, then rail-mounted agitator trains are used to transport concrete into the tunnel. These agitators are of two types, standard and tubular agitators. Standard agitators are located on cars so that they will be able to side-dump onto a conveyor belt. This conveyor belt is located along the tunnel wall and is used for transporting the concrete to the concrete placer. Tubular agitators discharge into each other. The front agitator discharges directly onto a belt which conveys the concrete to the concrete placer. With tubular agitators, a full train load of concrete can be discharged at one point. This is very important in a small tunnel that does not have clearance for a conveyor-belt installation along the side of the train.

SHOTCRETE LINING

Shotcrete is a term used to describe pneumatically placed concrete. It differs from gunite in that a coarse aggregate is used in shotcrete. During the last 10 years, shotcrete lining has been used successfully to provide temporary support for tunnels during excavation, and when later increased in thickness, to provide the permanent lining. It is economical when it can be used in this dual capacity.

As a temporary support, a thickness of approximately 2 in. of shotcrete is applied to the excavated surface immediately after the round has been exploded and the surface has been scaled. Thickness depends on the diameter of the tunnel and should be established by field test for any tunnel job. To furnish this temporary support, a high-early-strength shotcrete is of greatest importance. This can be secured by the use of a hardening-acceleration admixture. The shotcrete placed in the Tehachapi Tunnels included a German Tricosal admixture; the amount used was from 5 to 7 percent of the weight of the cement. Since this admixture reacts quickly with the concrete, it is necessary to apply the shotcrete in the dry-process manner, i.e., by mixing the ingredients and water at the nozzle. This 2-in. lining of shotcrete is later increased to 6 or 8 in. to serve as a permanent lining. These additional applications of shotcrete can be delayed so they will not interfere with the tunnel excavation.

Temporary support by shotcrete is dependent on its interaction with the rock surface. A shotcrete layer applied immediately to a new rock face acts as a tough surface, by means of which a rock of minor strength is transformed into a stable one. The shotcrete absorbs the tangential stresses which build up to a peak close to the surface of a cavity after it is opened up. As a result of the close interaction between the shotcrete and rock, the rock retains almost all of its original strength and is able to supply arch action. The effective thickness of the zone of arch action is in this way increased to a multiple of that of the shotcrete. In this way tensile stresses due to bending are diminished, and compressive stresses are easily absorbed into the surrounding rock. The zone of arch action can be increased with rock bolting.

Shotcrete also prevents rock disintegration, which always starts by the opening of a minute surface fissure. Since shotcrete prevents this initial movement, the rock behind the shotcrete remains stable.

The use of shotcrete as a temporary and permanent lining has had wide application in countries that have a low labor cost permitting more delay in the excavation cycle. Because of high labor cost in the United States, the use of shotcrete here is not so advantageous, unless its application can be made without slowing the mucking cycle. Slowing the mucking cycle can be prevented if there is enough room in the heading to allow a shotcrete jumbo to be used to support the nozzlemen without interfering with the mucking operation. If mucking is delayed until the shotcrete is applied, the extra excavation cost plus the cost of the shotcrete lining has to be balanced against the cost of the tunnel supports and concrete lining that would otherwise be used, to determine the economical procedure for any given tunnel. One minor problem in its use is that the admixture now used has a caustic action and may remove skin upon lengthy contact.

The equipment used in the application of shotcrete is in the development state. In the future, this equipment will undoubtedly show great improvements in its production rates. At the present time the production rate for one setup is approximately 10 cu yd per hr. Equipment needed for shotcrete application consists of a gun, material hose, air and water hoses, nozzle, and sometimes a water pump. Jumbos are used to suspend the nozzlemen over the muck pile. These can be simple platforms suspended on drill jibs which are mounted on rubber-tired, self-propelled units, or more elaborate jumbos as necessary. A supply of compressed air is required, and equipment is needed to supply aggregate, sand, and cement to the gun.

TUNNELS LINED WITH LINER PLATE

Preformed steel liner plate or heavy liner plate of cast iron, fabricated steel, or precast concrete is often used under bad ground conditions. Any of these types of liner plate may be used for temporary support, and then reinforced with concrete for the permanent lining. Heavy fabricated steel liner plate was used for temporary support on the Carley V. Porter Tunnel, which was part of the Tehachapi crossing of the California aqueduct. Liner plates have a wide use for permanent linings when job or ground conditions require the placement of the permanent lining immediately after excavation. Tunnels to be driven under air pressure are generally designed for this type of lining, and it is frequently used for free air tunnels driven with a shield. For example, liner plates are used for lining subway tunnels driven in metropolitan areas through incompetent ground, in order that the permanent lining can be installed close to the excavation face to ensure that the risk of ground subsidence is held to a minimum.

As a shield advances, the liner-plate sections are transported into the tunnel and placed in position by an erector arm incorporated into the shield design. Then pea gravel is blown through hoses connected to liner-plate openings, to fill the space outside the liner plate section formerly occupied by the shield's skin. After this void is filled with pea gravel, it is grouted. To prevent deflection of liner plates, horizontal tie rods are temporarily installed and then removed after the pea gravel has been placed and grouted. After grouting, the liner-plate joints are caulked with lead. Special equipment required for liner-plate installation is equipment to hauld the liner-plate sections into the tunnel, erector arm assemblies used for erecting the liner plate, tie rods to keep the liner plates from deflecting before they are backfilled, pea-gravel-blowing equipment, and grouting equipment.

CONCRETE PIPE LINING

This lining is used for sewer tunnels and for some types of low-head hydro tunnels. Its installation involves transportation into the tunnel, placing in position, making connections, and backfilling the space between the pipe and the tunnel wall with gravel or concrete. The special equipment required is a carrier to haul the pipe and locate it in position and equipment for placing the backfill or concrete.

STEEL LINER AND BACKFILL CONCRETING

This type of tunnel lining is used on pressure shafts and on high-head hydro tunnels under light cover. The steel penstocks are fabricated outside the tunnel, transported into the tunnel, and then welded together. Concrete is then pumped around them to fill the space between the steel liner and the tunnel wall. On pressure shafts, prepacked concrete is often required by the specifications. When the tunnel is lined with steel liner and backfill concrete, low-pressure grouting must be done in two operations. First, grouting is done between the steel liner and the concrete and then between the concrete and the rock.

REFERENCES

1. Reginald W. Rhein, Assistant ed., Concrete Placers, When and How to Use Them. What's Available, a reprint from *Construction Methods and Equipment,* June, 1965, copyright 1965 by McGraw-Hill.

Chapter 4 Shaft Construction

INTRODUCTION

Shaft construction is the excavation and lining of a near-vertical tunnel. It differs from other types of underground construction because excavation is performed either downward, from the excavation surface that also supports the men and equipment, or upward, from platforms suspended underneath the face of the excavation. This type of excavation requires the use of special shaft equipment not used in other types of underground excavation. It is preferable to use experienced shaft-excavation personnel for this type of work; if unavailable, allowances must be made for job training.

TYPES OF SHAFTS

There are three types of shafts: deep shafts, shafts incidental to other underground construction, and shafts for servicing tunnel driving. Deep shafts are usually advertised as separate contracts. They are constructed for the development of ore bodies, for the recovery of industrial elements such as sulfur, or to provide space for the underground testing of nuclear reactions. Recent years have seen the introduction of shafts sunk to form silos for housing ballistic missiles and shafts sunk to serve as vessels for the storage of natural gas and liquified petroleum gas. Since access to the bottom of these shafts is seldom available, they are constructed by large-hole drilling methods or by excavation downward from the surface.

Shafts incidental to other underground construction are usually advertised in conjunction with tunnel, subway, or underground powerhouse contracts. Examples of this type of shafts are ventilation shafts for subways, vehicular tunnels, or powerhouses; gate shafts, inlet shafts, or surge shafts for hydro tunnels; and access shafts, penstock shafts, or elevator shafts for underground powerhouses. Since access is usually available to either the top or bottom of these shafts, they can be constructed by large-hole drilling,[1] sinking from the surface, raising from the bottom, or any combination of these methods.

Shafts necessary to service tunnel driving are constructed by the tunnel contractor. These shafts are used when tunnel driving cannot be performed through the tunnel portal and the topography prevents the construction of short construction adits. Such shafts are also utilized on long tunnel projects to divide the tunnel into shorter distances that can be excavated from each heading. Since access is not available to the bottom of these shafts, they must be constructed by sinking from the surface. Their large diameter makes the excavation of these shafts unsuitable for large-hole drilling methods.

SHAFT CONSTRUCTION METHODS

Five main methods are employed in the construction of shafts: sinking the shaft from the surface, raising from the bottom of the shaft, large-hole drilling, pilot-shaft enlargement methods, and long-hole raising methods.

Shaft Sinking

Limitations. Shafts are sunk when access is not available to the bottom of the shaft or when the shaft passes through incompetent material which would cause a hazard in shaft raising operations. Production is limited in this process by two conditions: the restricted working area in the shaft, and the necessity that all movement in the shafts must be vertical with slow, hoisting methods.

The only space available for men to work in the shaft is on the rock face that they are excavating or on work platforms. If work platforms are used, these platforms must be suspended by cables anchored to the sides of the shaft or by cables from the hoisting equipment. This restricted working space limits the number of men, the number of drills, and the size of the pieces of equipment that can be used in the shaft.

The hoisting capacity provided for shaft sinking limits the weight of the individual pieces of equipment that can be used in the shaft. Hoisting capacity further limits the speed of mucking, since the rope speed controls the number of buckets of muck that can be hoisted out of the shaft per unit of time.

Equipment and Procedures. All methods of shaft sinking use drilling, mucking, and hoisting equipment. Some of the differences among the methods of shaft construction lie in the type of equipment used in these three operations and other differences lie in whether working platforms are used and if used, in the platform arrangement. A discussion of the basic equipment and procedures, common to all shaft sinking operations, will precede a detailed discussion of the operations themselves.

1. *Hoisting service.* Progress in shaft sinking is controlled by the main hoist since the length of the mucking cycle is dependent on the speed of muck removal. Hoisting service in shallow shaft construction can be provided for a short distance, approximately 100 ft, by crawler cranes or truck cranes. The limit on this type of hoisting service is the cranes' hoisting-cable-drum capacity. When this capacity is exceeded, headframes and hoist are required.

When headframes are used, the headframe must be strong enough to resist the stresses caused by the line pull and tall enough that the longest lift can clear the shaft opening. The main sheave must be of sufficient diameter to prevent excess wear on the main hoisting cable. If the shaft is to be equipped with a permanent headframe and hoist, these may also be made available for shaft construction. If the shaft is not to be so equipped, a sinking headframe and hoist are required. Skid-mounted portable sinking headframes and hoists are available from equipment manufacturers.

The main hoist should have a cable drum of sufficient diameter and capacity to hold all the cable required to reach the shaft bottom. The hoist motor must be of sufficient size to furnish the line pull necessary to lift the heaviest load and to furnish a rope speed adequate to prevent the hoisting of the muck buckets from delaying the mucking cycle.

In addition to the main hoist, two or three smaller, air-operated hoists are used. Cables from these hoists pass over secondary sheaves, and these cables are used to move and control muckers, platforms, forms, etc.

2. *Other surface facilities required for shaft sinking.* A variety of additional surface facilities are needed at the construction site. A list of these facilities would include a shaft door, ventilation equipment, a water supply, power supply or distribution, and concrete production facilities. For the proper disposal of muck, it is essential to provide a muck bin equipped with automatic shaft-bucket-dumping facilities, and truck-loading gates. Provision should also be made for a hoist house, a change house, a shop and warehouse, a place for powder storage, a cap house, and office facilities. Finally, it is often necessary to construct a concrete collar around the shaft opening, and this possibility should not be overlooked.

3. *Drilling.* Drilling in the shaft can be done with hand-held drills, with drills mounted on a collapsible, shaft drill jumbo, or in large shafts, with air-propelled drill units. A shaft drill jumbo has arms like umbrella ribs that are used to support either air-leg jackhammers or jib-mounted drifter drills. The jumbo frame is equipped with an index for orientation of the arms so that the drill pattern can be mechanically set. When the shaft drill jumbo is located on the excavation face and the umbrella-

Photo 17 Collapsible, shaft drill jumbo. (Shaft and Development Machines, Inc., Salt Lake City, Utah)

like top deck of the jumbo is expanded, it can be plumbed and held rigidly in position by jacks which react against the sides of the shaft. Photograph 17 is of this type of drill jumbo.

4. *Mucking.* Shaft mucking is done by hand, with a clamshell, by the use of mechanical muckers such as the Cryderman or the Riddell, or by a crawler type of front-end loader. If a clamshell is used, remote controls for its operation are available for use in the bottom of the shaft. The Cryderman mechanical mucker is air operated. It has a sliding boom which activates a positive-action grab bucket that picks up material and deposits it into skips. The mucker is supported and controlled from the work deck of a platform. Cryderman muckers are available in sizes that have ½ and 3⁄16 cu yd bucket capacity. The manufacturer rates the production capacity of the ½ cu yd machine at 40 to 50 cu ft per min and the 3⁄16 cu yd machine at 20 to 30 cu ft per min. The Riddell mucker is a movable bridge which supports and controls a cable-operated clamshell. The bridge rides on rails laid on a work platform. Both the Cryderman and the Riddell mucker platforms contain openings for muck-skip passage. Crawler front-end loaders are used in shallow shafts which have a diameter in excess of 17 ft. They vary in size depending on the diameter of the shaft. The smallest unit in common use is the Eimco 630 with an 18 cu ft bucket capacity. Front-end loaders with a greater capacity are available up to the size of the Caterpillar 977, which has a 3 cu yd bucket. Mucking skips are required for hoisting the muck out of the shaft. These vary in size depending on the shaft hoisting capacity and the shaft diameter. Free-swinging muck skips are used on shallow shafts. On deeper shafts, the muck skips are equipped with crossheads and have safety dogs on either side for engaging guides in the event of a cable failure. The crossheads and bucket ride on cable guides or fixed guides installed on the shaft sides. If muck bins are used, the skips are equipped with dumping rollers which engage the dumping scrolls in the headframe, which results in automatic dumping of the skip into the muck bins. Shallow shafts are excavated with one muck skip, but as the shaft deepens, two or more muck skips are used to expedite the mucking cycle. While one is being loaded, the other or others are hoisted, dumped, and returned.

Safety codes often require that men cannot work below a free-swinging bucket.

5. *Work platforms.* The use of work platforms and the number of decks required on these work platforms depend on the method of shaft construction and on the depth of the shaft. In shallow shafts that are completely excavated before the concrete lining is placed, work decks are not required during the shaft excavation, and only a simple

work deck is necessary during the concrete-placing operations. In deep shaft construction, when concrete is placed directly behind the excavation and work is done by the cycle type of operation (to be later discussed in detail), additional work platforms are required. These may be separate platforms that are removed from the shaft when the change over from excavation to concrete is made, or they may be multideck platforms which remain in the shaft and are used for both excavation and concrete. If multideck platforms are used, the bottom deck supports and contains the mucker controls and the upper decks are used for form moving and for concrete pour. The platforms contain openings for the passage of muck skips and drill jumbos.

In deep shaft construction, when concrete is placed directly behind the excavation and work is done by the concurrent type of operations (to be discussed in detail later), multideck platforms are required and they are not removed from the shaft. In South Africa, where shafts are sunk with greater rapidity than in any other country, five-platform jumbos are used. Passageways are provided through the platform for the muck skips. Since all drilling is done by hand-held drills, the bottom platform contains ladders for access to the excavation face and is equipped with piping manifolds for servicing the drills. The bottom platform also suspends the mechanical clamshell mucker and contains the mucker controls. The second platform is used for setting the curb, or blast ring (see below), and contains hydraulic jacks which react against the shaft sides for stabilization of the platform. The third platform is movable and is used as a work deck for setting forms and pouring concrete. The fourth platform contains blocks for movement of the total platform. The fifth, or top, platform is used for adjusting the suspension, stabilizing the platforms, and as a work platform for setting eyebolts in the concrete lining. These eyebolts are used for platform suspension during the greater part of its use. When movement of the multideck platform is required, it must be moved with the main hoist cables.[2]

6. *Placement of concrete.* Concrete lining operations within the shaft require facilities for transporting the concrete to a central container on the concrete work deck and for then distributing it behind the forms. Concrete can be lowered and discharged into the central container by concrete buckets or by a vertical slick line. Concrete can then be distributed around the inside of the forms with hoses or swing spouts. If the shaft excavation is completed before concreting is started, concreting is done from the bottom of the shaft upward. Slip forms are often used under these conditions. If the shaft lining follows along with the excavation, then concreting is done downward in progressive pours, and a heavy bottom bulkhead form called a *curb* or *blast ring* is installed

at the bottom of every pour. Forms are then erected to connect this blast ring to the previously placed concrete. Ventilation pipes, compressed air pipes, drain lines, water lines, and electrical service lines are required in the shaft. When concreting follows excavation, these temporary lines are frequently embedded in the concrete lining. Providing multilift pumping for proper drainage in deep shafts necessitates the excavation of booster-pump stations in the sides of the shaft, at approximately 200-ft intervals.

When excavation must pass through a water-bearing rock stratum, drilling and grouting equipment is required to grout ahead of the excavation in order to cut off water flow into the shaft. Freezing has also been utilized for this purpose.

7. *Shaft supports.* When shafts are constructed in incompetent material, supports are required to restrain the sides of the excavation. Supports used may be steel-ring beams, wood sets, blocking between beams or sets and the excavated surface, solid-steel or wood lagging, gunite, or rock bolts.

Methods of Shaft Sinking. As suggested above, there are different methods of sinking shafts. These methods are three: completing excavation before concreting is started; employing an alternating method of operation; or excavating and concreting at the same time.

1. *Shaft sinking by completing excavation before concreting.* In shallow shafts and some medium-depth shafts passing through competent material, the shafts are constructed by completing the shaft excavation before the concrete placement is started. One advantage of this method is that better progress can be obtained by performing only one type of operation at a time. Another advantage is that the concrete lining can be placed by starting at the shaft bottom, with slip-form pouring to the surface. The disadvantage of this construction method is that there is more exposure to rock falls, and if incompetent rock or water is encountered, temporary bracing and construction drainage become both extensive and costly.

This method of shaft excavation is a drill, shoot, muck, and support type of operation. First the drilling equipment and personnel are lowered to the face of excavation. If hand-held drills are used, 5-ft lifts are excavated. If drilling is done with a drill jumbo, the lifts are increased to approximately 10 ft. When a drill jumbo is used, it is lowered to the bottom of the shaft where the center leg is placed on the exact center of the shaft. The jumbo is then plumbed and anchored by jacking against the sides of the shaft. The drill pattern is then drilled out, the drilling equipment is removed from the shaft, and the holes are loaded with explosives. After removing all personnel from the shaft, the holes are exploded. The shaft is ventilated until all fumes are removed, and then the mucking equipment is lowered into the shaft. In shafts of less than 17 ft in diameter, mechanical shaft muckers like Crydermans may be used. In larger shafts, mucking may be done with front-end loaders. In shafts with very large diameters, when the crawler type of mucker is used, only half of the shaft area may be drilled and shot at a time, while the mucker is placed on the other half and covered to prevent damage from the shot rock. On shallow shafts, when the hoisting time is of short duration, only one muck bucket may be used. On deeper shafts, two or more are used. In this case, while one is loaded, the other or others are hoisted out of the shaft and dumped. Upon completion of the mucking cycle, supports are placed and the mucking equipment is removed from the shaft. Then the drilling equipment is again lowered and the cycle repeated.

Upon completion of all excavation, the shaft is checked for tights, and these being removed, the concrete operations are started. Slip forms are installed in the bottom of the shaft, and concrete is placed from a work platform suspended from the shaft sides. Concrete may be lowered to the work platform in buckets or by use of a vertical standpipe. The concrete is then distributed from the central container by either swing spouts or flexible hoses.

2. *Shaft sinking by the alternating method of excavating and concreting.* In the alternating method of shaft construction, after three rounds (or approximately 30 ft) of shaft excavation are completed, excavation is stopped, and an equal distance of the shaft is concreted. This method is preferred in incompetent rock, where temporary support for the shaft walls would present a problem. The cycle method is also preferred in all deep shafts since the hazard of rock falls is eliminated. This method is widely used in the United States for deep shafts, since crew size can be held to a minimum by using the same crew to excavate and concrete. Separate equipment units may be used for excavation and for concreting. This necessitates that each type of equipment be removed from the shaft before the next type is lowered. Other setups use a three-deck jumbo with the mucker supported and controlled from the bottom deck and the other decks used for concreting. If hand-held drills are used, they can be carried on the bottom deck. If a shaft drill jumbo is used, it can be raised and lowered through the muck-skip passages.

In this method of shaft sinking, the third round exploded is not mucked out. Instead, the broken rock is used as an additional working surface in the concreting operations. The other working surfaces for concreting may be a separate two-deck platform or a combination multi-deck platform used for both excavation and concrete. First, the curb ring, or as it is often called, the *blast ring*, is stripped from the previous pour and anchored in position at the bottom of the new pour. This curb ring supports the bottom of the pour and also protects the concrete from blast damage when excavation is resumed. The remainder of the forms are then stripped from the previous pour and erected in position. Concrete is lowered in the shaft to a central container by buckets or a vertical pipe. From this central container, concrete is deposited behind the forms by a swing spout or by flexible hoses. Upon completion of the concrete pour, the excavation cycle is resumed by mucking out the broken rocks left from the last round and then drilling the next round.

3. *Shaft sinking by the concurrent method of excavating and concreting.* The concurrent method of shaft sinking requires that excavation and concreting be performed at the same time with separate crews. Production by the crews and the crew size are balanced so that the concrete lining is always maintained at the same distance from the excavated face. Faster progress is obtained with the concurrent method of shaft construction than with the alternating method, but a larger crew is required, there is more interference between the two operations in the shaft, and a more complicated equipment setup is required. The procedure for both excavating and concreting operations is the same as in the alternating method, except that both are done at the same time. This method definitely requires a multideck work platform.

Using the concurrent method of shaft sinking, a progress rate of 8 lin ft per shift on a 24-ft-diameter shaft has been made in South Africa.[2] Similar shaft-sinking methods and equipment have been used in the United States, but the African production rates have never been equalled. This high production rate in South Africa may be attributed in part to the availability of economical labor which permits use of large crews. The shaft-sinking platforms used in Africa were described under shaft-sinking equipment on p. 96. The construction procedure used in Africa is to lower access ladders from the bottom platform to the bottom itself. After the bottom is cleaned, the shaft centerline is marked, the drill-hole pattern laid out, and the round drilled out by hand-held drills. The holes are then loaded, the platform is hoisted clear of the shot, and the personnel is removed from the shaft. The round is shot, the shaft is ventilated, and the platform is again lowered to a mucking position. The majority of the muck is loaded into skips with a mechanical mucker and the final cleanup done by hand mucking. The excavation process is then repeated.

Concreting operations are carried on at the same time and are timed so that three shifts of work will result in the same lineal-foot production as was accomplished in shaft excavation. The first shift strips the pour ring, or curb ring, and prepares it for lowering. Then all protruding concrete is chipped away and the various utility lines, such as compressed air, water, and electrical service, are extended. The second shift lowers and sets the curb ring, lowers and erects the forms, and starts the concrete pour. On the third shift, the remainder of the forms are erected and the concrete pour is completed. The top forms are placed last to facilitate the concreting operations.

Shaft Raising

The most economical method of constructing small shafts or pilot shafts for large shafts is the raising method, providing that access is available to the bottom of the shaft or that it is feasible to delay shaft excavation until such access is available. However, shaft raising should not be planned unless the shaft passes through competent material, for a raising operation in incompetent rock is a hazardous one. Shaft raising is economical because mucking time is eliminated; the shot rock falls directly away from the excavation face. Another cost advantage in shaft raising is the fact that air, water, and power services can usually be taken off the tunnel-driving service lines, which eliminates the duplication of these services. Some of the disadvantages of this method are that all excavation must be done overhead from platforms suspended beneath the rock surface and that the movement of men, equipment, and materials for shaft raising is slower and more complicated than that in a shaft sinking. Shaft raising can be done in a variety of ways and new methods are constantly being developed. To date, the three most successful methods of raising small shafts are described here.

1. ***The Manway and Muckway Method.*** The manway and muckway method is shown in Drawing 11. As the shaft excavation is carried upward from the bottom of the shaft, the excavated space is timbered off into two compartments. One compartment is used as a muck chute, and the other is outfitted with platforms and ladders and used to provide access to the face. On pilot shafts, the overall dimensions are held to a minimum of approximately 6 by 8 ft. If it is permissible to obstruct the area under the shaft, the muck chute can be left open at the bottom and the muck allowed to drop on the tunnel floor. Since only a small amount of muck is produced, a day's production can then be loaded out, on one shift a day, with a front-end loader.

If it is necessary to keep the area under the shaft clear, the shaft muck can be retained in the chute by hydraulically operated gates located at the bottom of the muck chute. Then, if a siding for muck cars is installed underneath these gates, car loading is easily and rapidly accomplished. If the shaft is over a small-diameter tunnel, it may be necessary to widen the tunnel at this point to furnish room for the siding.

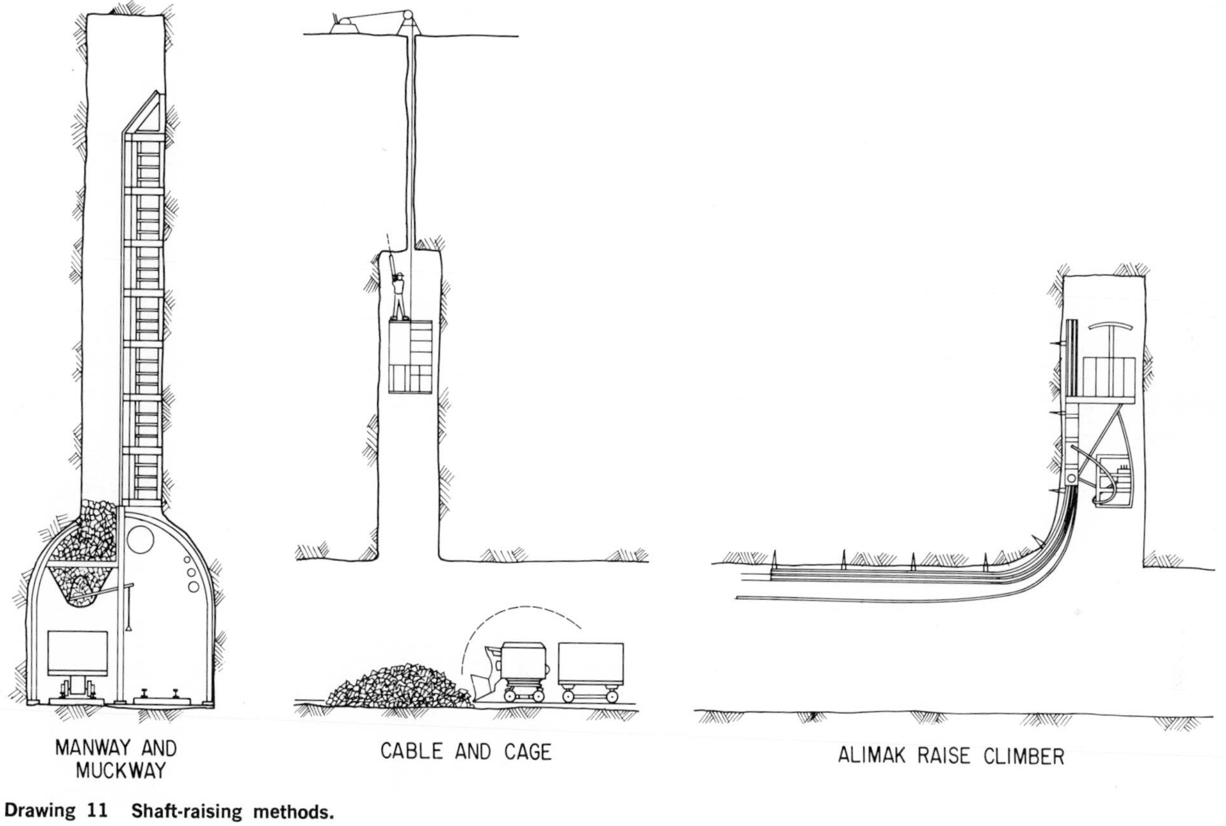

Drawing 11 Shaft-raising methods.

Excavating procedure requires that miners stand on a platform covering the top of the manway and drill out the round with stoper drills, After loading the holes, they climb down the manway and explode the shot. Ventilation removes the powder fumes, and they climb back up the manway to clean the muck off the platform and scale the sides and the new rock face. Next, the timbering is extended so that the miners can drill the next round. This process is then repeated.

On small, inclined shafts, where the angle of inclination is great enough to cause the muck to slide down the shaft, the shaft is divided into upper and lower compartments by heavy timbers spanning the shaft and pinned to the wall surface on each side. The space under the timbers supplies a muck chute. Ladders are constructed above and on the dividers to provide access to the face. In order to furnish mechanical transportation to the face, a track is built on these dividers and a small car is moved up and down this track by an air hoist located near the face.

On inclined shafts where the angle of inclination is such that the muck will not slide on the rock surface, generally less than 40 percent, slick plates are installed on the bottom wall to decrease the friction. The slick plates should be spaced at intervals that will reduce friction enough for the muck to maintain motion in the chute. If the shaft is so inclined that the muck will not slide even when the entire shaft bottom is covered with plate, then a shaft division is not used, slick plates are not installed, and instead, the muck is pulled down the slope with a slusher scraper.

2. *The Cable and Cage Method.* A sketch of the cable and cage shaft-raising method is shown in Drawing 11. When shafts are raised by this method, a hole approximately 6 in. in diameter is drilled from the surface down the centerline of the shaft. A hoist is erected over this hole, and a hoisting cable is passed through it. A man cage is attached to the cable underneath the shaft. The miners are then hoisted in the cage to the shaft face. There, they stand on the cage roof while scaling the face and drilling out the round. The cage is then lowered, explosives and powder are picked up, and the cage is again raised so that the men can load the holes with explosives. Again the cage is lowered to the bottom where it is this time unhooked from the cable and moved back a safe distance to be clear of the falling rock. In the meantime the cable is hoisted up the hole clear of the shot. The charge is exploded and the shot rock falls down the raise. After ventilation has removed the fumes from the raise, the cable is lowered and the cage is moved under the cable and reattached to it. The cage and men are hoisted to the excavation face, and the process is repeated. As the men drill out the next round, the muck at the bottom of the raise can be removed.

3. *The Alimak Raise-climber Method.* The Alimak raise climber consists of a working platform and a man-cage elevator that travels on a rail fastened to the side of the shaft on a vertical shaft or the top side of the shaft on an inclined shaft. Different-sized Alimaks can be purchased with cage capacities varying from one to six men. The rail that the cage rides on is a pin-rack track fastened to four pipes which provide the face with ventilation, compressed air, water, and electrical service. The rail weighs approximately 33 lb per ft and comes in short sections. As the excavation advances, the rail can be extended by bolting these sections onto the end of the rail and onto the shaft sides. The excavation procedure itself, with this method, is quite similar to that used in the cage and cable method. A schematic layout of the Alimak raise-climber method is shown in Drawing 11.

Shafts Excavated by Large-hole Drilling

When access has not been available to the bottom of the shaft, large-hole drilling methods have only been successful on shafts up to 8 ft in diameter. On shafts larger than this, the removal of cuttings from the hole has presented a difficult problem.

When access has been available to the bottom of the shaft, shafts up to 17 ft in diameter have been drilled. This operation entails drilling a pilot hole of approximately 12 in. in diameter, the length of the shaft. The main function of this hole is to furnish a method of disposal for the cuttings from the reaming operations. This hole can be reamed out to a 17-ft limit in progressive steps. Two methods are used in the reaming operation. One is to ream downward, and the other is to take the reamer to the bottom of the shaft and, with hoisting equipment located over the pilot hole, to ream upward.

When a large shaft is to be excavated by the pilot-shaft-enlargement method, large-hole drilling is often used to furnish a pilot shaft of 60-in. size.

In the construction of silos to hold missiles, large-diameter augers were successfully used in excavation through loose material.

Shafts Excavated by the Pilot-shaft-enlargement Method

The pilot-shaft-enlargement method of shaft excavation is used for large-diameter shafts when access is available to the bottom of the shaft. First, a small-diameter pilot shaft, located on the centerline of the main shaft, is raised to the surface. The shaft-raising method may be any of those previously described. Depending on the type of rock encountered, it may be more economical to drill a large-diameter hole from the surface for the full shaft length than to construct a raise. After the pilot shaft is finished, it is enlarged to the full shaft diameter, with the pilot shaft or drilled hole used as a means of muck disposal. This is the most economical method of large-shaft excavation, for it utilizes the force of gravity to provide a fast and efficient method of muck disposal.

This shaft excavation method was used to construct the surge shaft located over the Angeles Tunnel in southern California. A schematic layout of this operation is shown in Drawing 12. After the top heading of the tunnel was driven and a 6-ft pilot shaft was drilled, excavation for shaft enlargement was started from the surface. This rock was soft enough to be loosened by ripping and then shoved down the hole with bulldozers. At the bottom of the shaft it was loaded into Caterpillar 619 rear-dump haulers by a belt loader. The sides of the shaft were supported with 14-in. WF ring beams in various spacing, with gunite applied between the rings.

In some cases the rock must be drilled and shot. In this situation, air-propelled drill units or hand-held jackhammers can be used for the drilling for the shaft enlargement.

On shafts where diameter limits the use of standard-size tractors,

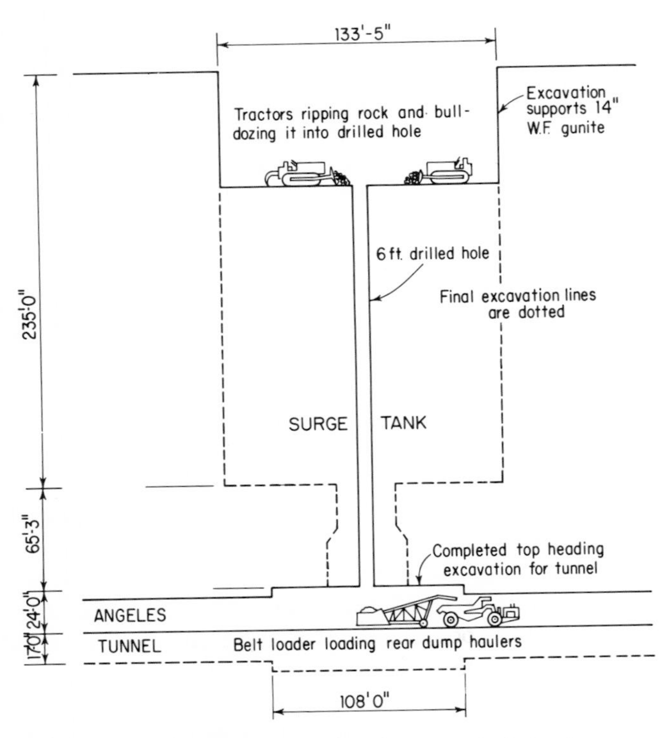

Drawing 12 Method of excavating the surge tank for the Angeles Tunnel.

small crawler muckers can be used. When shafts are of such small diameter that there is insufficient area to use mucking machines, the muck from the shaft enlargement operations must be pushed down the pilot shaft by hand, or in some instances, high-pressure water can be used to wash the muck down the hole. If there is not sufficient space at the bottom of the shaft to operate a belt loader or when the rock size is not suitable for its use, other means of loading out the shot rock at the bottom must be planned. One method is to allow the muck to fall onto the tunnel floor where it can be loaded out with front-end loaders. Or if the flow of traffic through the tunnel must be maintained, the pilot shaft can be used as a muck pocket. The haul units can then be loaded from this muck pocket by means of gates installed at its intersection with the tunnel.

Some shafts must be constructed through a top layer of such incompetent material that pilot-shaft raising through this material is too hazardous an operation to undertake. In these cases the full diameter of the shaft must be sunk from the surface until material is encountered of such a nature that pilot shafts can be excavated.

Special Equipment Needed for Pilot-shaft-enlargement Method. When using the pilot-shaft-enlargement method of shaft construction, certain special equipment is required. To begin with, pilot-shaft-raising equipment is necessary. If required, drills for drilling out the shaft enlargement must be provided. Special mucking equipment is needed, including the crawler type of bulldozers (if the shaft is of sufficient diameter to warrant their use) or high-pressure water if desired. Provision must also be made for muck loading and hauling equipment at the bottom of the shaft. Hoisting service must be furnished to the shaft enlargement operations by either a hoist or a crane. A man elevator is essential to that same operation. Finally, utility services such as compressed air, water, and electricity plus ventilation fans and piping must be supplied to the shaft enlargement operations.

The Long-hole Method of Shaft Construction

In the long-hole method of shaft construction a small pilot shaft is raised the full length of the main shaft. At approximately 100-ft intervals this pilot shaft is enlarged to the full shaft diameter. Then, from one enlarged section to the next, holes are drilled on the main shaft's perimeter and in the center so that the remaining rock sections can be shot and removed. In progressive sections from the bottom, these holes are loaded with explosives and the rock is shot down the raise. One of the most critical problems in this method of shaft construction is keeping the shaft perimeter holes on line from one enlarged section to another.

This method was used for the excavation of the spillway shafts for Hungry Horse and Monticello dams. It has not been used recently, probably because less-expensive shaft-construction methods have been developed.

SHAFT FACILITIES FOR SERVICING TUNNEL DRIVING

Some tunnels may be excavated more economically by driving portions of the tunnel from shafts. These shafts may be included in the contract documents as pay items or may be constructed by the contractor with their cost spread to tunnel excavation. In tunnels where there is a long distance to be driven between two headings, construction time can be decreased and travel time reduced by furnishing additional access to the tunnel by a shaft located midway between the two headings. Tunnel headings can then be driven in each direction from this shaft, which reduces individual heading lengths. When surface elevations permit, the best method of providing additional tunnel access is with an adit. When the topography is such that an adit must be driven a long distance, a shaft sunk down to the tunnel line may be preferable. These shafts must be sized and equipped to service the tunnel heading operations. Shafts are also used to service tunnel driving operations when it is impossible to use the tunnel portals for construction purposes.

When shafts are required to service tunnel driving operations and plans call for permanent shafts in suitable locations, these permanent shafts may be altered by the contractor for construction use. Upon completion of tunnel construction, the shaft must then be changed back to serve its original purpose. Sometimes the design engineers will design the permanent shafts in such a way that they may be used for both tunnel construction and permanent use. The subsequent conversion of one to the other is made with a minimum of changes.

Shafts used for servicing tunnel driving are sunk from the surface by the same methods as those described above under Shaft Sinking. When the shaft excavation exceeds 100 ft, the headframe and hoist required for tunneling service are often erected to aid in the sinking operations. If they are not available, however, a sinking headframe and hoist are used.

Shaft equipment necessary to handle servicing of the tunnel driving operations varies with the depth of the shaft and the size of the tunnel. On shallow shafts, in order to save the capital and operating expense of erecting and operating headframes, contractors are currently handling the muck removal and servicing of tunnel driving with large portable cranes. Either these cranes lift the loaded muck cars or the muck car bodies from the bottom of the shaft, or the muck cars are dumped into a muck skip located in a pocket at the bottom of the shaft and this skip is hoisted to the surface.

On deeper shafts, headframes, complete with hoist and muck bins, are used. The shaft size must be sufficient to provide space for two main compartments, an emergency access ladder, and utility services for each tunnel heading. One of the main compartments is for a counterbalanced muck skip, equipped with an automatic trip which dumps the buckets into the muck bins. The other compartment is for an elevator that lowers and raises the men, tunnel equipment, and materials required for construction of the tunnel.

The utility services needed at each tunnel heading are the ventilation pipes, compressed air piping, water pipes, and electric cables. The shaft is excavated deeper than the tunnel invert, to provide a muck pocket and space for skip travel and loading. Muck cars from the tunnel heading are dumped into the muck pocket. By using gates, this muck is fed by gravity into the muck skip. The skip is then hoisted to the top of the shaft and engages guides in the headframe which cause the skip to dump the muck into the muck bins. From these bins the muck can be hauled away by trucks. The hoist must have drum capacity for the total length of hoisting cable required and furnish a rope speed sufficient to dispose of tunnel muck as fast as it is excavated. Two drum hoists are used, one drum for the muck skip, and one drum for the elevator. Headframes used are of two types; one type has the hoist mounted on top of the headframe, while the other type has the hoist mounted to one side of it. In the latter case, the headframe must be braced in this direction to resist the side stresses. The other facilities on the surface surrounding the shaft are similar to those used at the tunnel portal location.

Photograph 18 is a photograph of the headframe and muck bin that was installed over a 300-ft shaft for the Eucumbene-Tumut Tunnel for the Snowy Mountains Hydroelectric Authority in Australia. This shaft serviced two 21-ft-diameter tunnel headings. The length of tunnel driven from this shaft was 4 miles in one direction and 5 miles in the other direction. After tunnel construction was complete, the shaft was converted to its permanent use, which was a water intake for the tunnel from the stream flowing by the shaft. Because of the heavy stress, the headframe was of substantial construction. Muck was hoisted from a muck pocket in the bottom of the shaft by a 12 cu yd counterbalanced muck skip which dumped automatically into the muck bins. Muck was hauled away from the bins and disposed of by trucks. Weights of steel in the headframe and bin were:

Headframe	253,000 lb
Muck bin	132,000 lb
Rail used in the bin for reinforcing	105,000 lb
Total	490,000 lb

Photo 18 Head frame, muck bins, hoist house, shops and office and junction shaft for the Eucumbene-Tumut Tunnel, Australia.

The hoist for this shaft was a two-drum hoist with 60-in. grooved drums, air-activated automatic safety brakes, block friction clutches, and cable-payout indicator. The hoist was driven by a 300-hp 380-volt 3-phase 50-cycle motor which produced a line speed of 50 to 300 ft per min. The line pull on the $1\frac{3}{8}$-in.-diameter cable was approximately 32,000 lb. The capacity of the shaft was sufficient so its use did not restrict tunnel mucking operations, and a daily progress of 80 ft per day was often made in each tunnel heading.

At the bottom of the shaft, a muck bin was excavated below the tunnel grade. Cars were unloaded into this bin by a rotary car dumper. The muck skip extended past the muck bin, and the muck skip was loaded by hydraulically operated gates which controlled the flow of the material from the bin to the skip.

REFERENCES

1. George E. Kemnitz, Felix and Sisson, Inc., Tulsa, Oklahoma, Big-hole Drilling Methods Are Used for Mine Shafts, reprint from *Oil and Gas Journal,* Hughes Tool Company, Industrial Products Division, January 9, 1967.
2. Shaft-sinking in South Africa, *Engineering and Mining Journal,* Volume 161, No. 6, June, 1960.

Chapter

5 Shields, Boring Machines, and Excavating Tunnels under Air Pressure

INTRODUCTION

The preceding chapters described the methods, equipment, and procedures used in excavating tunnels by the conventional drill, shoot, and muck method. This method of tunnel excavation has been so improved upon in the last few years that the chance of further development is slight. Any further reduction in excavation cost or increase in production is dependent upon the increased use and greater improvement of alternative methods. When these alternative excavation methods are used, the change in methods and equipment occurs only at the tunnel heading, while the tunnel servicing and haulage equipment remains similar to that used in the conventional method. This chapter will, therefore, be limited to descriptions of the work performed at the tunnel heading. However, a knowledge of the conventional excavation method is essential to follow the discussion.

The alternative tunnel excavation methods covered in this chapter are those using tunnel shields and tunnel-boring machines and the excavation of tunnels under air pressure. The special physical conditions that dictate the use of these alternative methods will also be covered. Equipment improvements, such as better bits for tunnel-boring machines, may extend the conditions under which these methods are applicable.

SHIELDS

Purpose

Shields are used in tunnel excavation for one or more of the following reasons: to support the sides of a tunnel until the tunnel supports are erected; to provide breastboard support for the tunnel face if this is required; to provide a cutting edge in soft ground, which forces material into the breastboard openings as the shield is jacked forward; to protect the men who are doing the tunnel excavation; to protect the men who are erecting the supports; and to provide space so that men can erect the tunnel supports within the tail of the shield. Shields are always used in tunnels through mud and sand and wherever hydrostatic conditions require that excavation be performed under air pressure. Depending on the material encountered, shields may be used in tunnels driven through gravel. Finally, shields are used to assist tunnel driving in incompetent material where excavation is performed by either the conventional method or by a tunnel-boring machine.

The principle of operation of a tunnel shield is that as the tunnel excavation advances, the cutting edge of the shield is kept pressed against the excavation face by hydraulic jacks which thrust against the tunnel supports. As the shield is jacked forward, tunnel supports are erected in the tail of the shield. This forward motion of the shield causes it to slide past previously erected supports and the surrounding ground pressure is transferred from the shield to these supports.

Description

Shields are heavy steel tubes formed to the shape of the excavation line of the tunnel and outfitted with hydraulic jacks which propel the shield forward by thrusting against the previously placed tunnel supports. Skin thickness varies between 1 and 5 in., depending on the diameter of the tunnel and the pressures to be resisted. Shields may be circular for circular tunnels, open-bottom horseshoe-shaped for horseshoe tunnels, or open-bottom half-circle shaped for driving the top heading on large tunnels. Shields used in tunnels where air pressure is required to prevent water inflow are of circular shape as this shape has more resistance to pressure. The length of the shield should be sufficient to provide protection for the men excavating the face and allow space for support erection within the tail of the shield. However, the longer a shield, the more skin friction there will be and the greater the required propulsion force will be. A shield should be long enough so it will not have a tendency to change its direction rapidly when it is pushed forward, but short enough so it can be guided to line and grade. Shields used in various sized tunnels have varied in size from a 4-ft 10-in. diameter circular shield, 10 ft 5½ in. long, used in a Philadelphia tunnel[1] to a 22-ft-high, 47-ft-wide semicircular shield, 24½ ft long, used for the top heading of the Caldecott Tunnel in Berkeley.[2] A 45-ft-diameter horseshoe-shaped shield is now being designed for the Straight Creek Tunnel in Colorado.

Shields are propelled by jacks which force the shield forward as they thrust against the tunnel supports. For this reason shields can only be used in tunnels which have tunnel supports capable of withstanding this thrust or have other provisions designed to take this thrust. Hydraulic jacks are generally used except on some small-diameter tunnels where screw jacks are used. The number of jacks required varies with the shield size and type of ground encountered and whether an open face or bulkheaded shield is used. For example, on the 31-ft 8-in. Detroit-Windsor vehicular tunnel, driven under 22 psi of air pressure in stiff, gray clay, with all excavation removed from the face with clay spades, thirty 250-ton jacks were used to propel the shield forward.[3] The amount of propulsion force required varies between 5 and 9 kips per sq ft of the shield's skin surface.

Shields may have an open face with a cutting edge, partial breastboards supported by hydraulic jacks, or a complete breastboard bulkhead with openings that muck can be squeezed through as the shield advances. When shields have breastboard bulkheads, cutting edges are used to prevent soil displacement by guiding the ground into the breastboard openings, which should be large enough so men can crawl through them to the face when changed ground conditions make this necessary.

Being able to guide the shield to line and grade is very critical. The shorter the shield, the easier it is to guide. Some shields have flexible tails to make them easier to guide. In some instances, articulated shields have been used with the front end guided by jacks reacting against the rear section of the shield. Shields may also be guided by shoes, fins, skids placed ahead of the excavation upon which the shield rides, or by controlled excavation at the face. The movement of large-diameter shields in free-air tunnels is controlled by first driving side drifts, then erecting rails or roller tracks in these side drifts; the shield then travels on wheels or rollers which bear on these rails or roller tracks. Since shields always tend to rotate, circular shields are preferred when they can be used so that this rotation will not affect the tunnel shape.

In incompetent ground with a free-standing face, additional protection for the men excavating the face can be provided with a forepoling shield. The forepoling shield consists of individual plates located around the circumference of the shield that can be jacked forward by hydraulic jacks as the material is being excavated.

Shields often contain hydraulically operated erector arm assemblies for ease in placing supports or liner plates. They may also contain conveyor belts for transporting material from the face to the rear. Since each shield is tailor-made for ecah individual tunnel and since tunnel materials and methods of excavation vary greatly, there are wide differences in shield construction.

For preliminary estimating purposes, the weight of a shield can be estimated by the following formula developed by Richardson and Mayo:

Weight in tons = 15(diameter − 10)

Shields in Mud Tunnels

The simplest way to construct tunnels in mud is to use circular shields. The shield is constructed with breastboards to retain the mud; slots are built into the breastboard to allow the passage of mud as the shield is jacked forward. The upper part of the cutting edge is extended approximately 1 ft farther than the lower edge to retard intrusions from above. As the mud is forced through the breastboard slots, it is mucked into cars and transported out of the tunnel. Lining used to support the tunnel until the permanent lining is installed often consists of liner plates erected in the tail of the shield. Excavation progress depends on the speed of mud removal from the face and the time required for erection of the liner plates. In tunnels under 15 ft in diameter with small crews, an average progress of 20 ft per day is often maintained. The greatest construction problem is keeping the shield on line and grade.

Shields in Sand Tunnels

In sand tunnels where the face is stable without the use of breastboards, progress in excess of 100 ft per day in tunnels 12 ft in diameter has been accomplished.[4] Under these conditions, shields can be open-bottomed, horseshoe-shaped, and open-faced. Construction linings are often steel sets with solid lagging. Progress depends on the facility of holding the shield to line and grade and the capacity of the mucker.

Shields in Tunnels Where the Heading Is Excavated under Air Pressure

Circular shields are used and are described when air-pressure tunnels are discussed in the last of this chapter.

Shields in Gravel Tunnels

Excellent progress has been made with open-faced shields in dry gravel. Such shields were used in Berkeley and Oakland, California, for driving subway tunnels for the Bay Area Rapid Transit System. The material encountered was comparatively dry and consisted of silt, sand, gravels, and some rock. The permanent lining in these tunnels is heavy steel liner plate. Progress, which ranged from 15 to 30 ft per day, was restricted by the time required to erect the liner plate, the capacity of the mucking machine, the time required for installing tie bars necessary to prevent deflection of the liner plates until the space left by the shield's skin between the liner plate and the excavation was backfilled, and the time required to place this pea gravel backfilling. (This space must be backfilled with pea gravel and then grouted to prevent deformation of the liner plate and to prevent surrounding-ground movement.) A typical layout for this operation is shown in Drawing 2.

The major differences in construction methods used by various contractors on these projects were in mucking and muck haul equipment. One contractor used an Eimco 916, 5½ cu yd low-profile front-end loader for both mucking and muck hauling. Another used an Eimco 24 B rocker shovel to muck into rail cars.

Shields Used with Tunnel-boring Machines

When tunnel-boring machines are used in rock so incompetent that it will not remain stable until supports can be erected, shields are used in conjunction with the boring machine. In this case the purpose of the shield is to maintain the sides of the tunnel until the supports can be erected, while providing both space for support erection and protection for the men erecting the supports.

Shields Used with Conventional Tunnel-driving Methods

In incompetent rock that requires some drilling and shooting but will not remain stable until supports can be erected, shields may be used to aid the tunnel-driving operation. These shields may or may not furnish breastboard support depending on the type of material encountered. In the past, the use of shields in this type of tunneling has been after other methods have failed. Because of their many advantages, contractors will undoubtedly use shields to a much greater extent in the future.

Crew Size

When driving a tunnel with a shield, compared with excavating without one, there are savings in the manpower required for scaling, preventing run-ins, and support placing. However, the crew size is increased by the men required for shield operation.

Progress for Shield-driven Tunnels

The major advantage in using shields in certain soft-ground tunnels is the accelerated progress obtained, since there is no delay caused by run-ins and since supports are easier to place. However, it is impractical to excavate some soft-ground tunnels with a shield. Progress depends upon the type of ground encountered, the type of mucker used, and the size of crew employed. Progress in soft-ground tunnels is much harder to estimate than progress in hard-rock tunnels. One of the best ways to check the progress estimate is to consult past records of soft-ground tunnels driven under similar ground conditions and circumstances.

TUNNEL-BORING MACHINES

Description

A tunnel-boring machine is a large, electrically powered drill. The cutting action of the tunnel-boring machine is performed by a circular cutting head containing bits. With the application of pressure and either a rotating or oscillating motion, these bits excavate the tunnel face. The machine is equipped with electric motors which furnish power for rotating the cutter head and furnish hydraulic pressure to the jacks. These jacks absorb the torque effect created in the machine, maintain pressure on the tunnel face, and move the machine forward by gripping the sides of the tunnel; if the tunnel is supported, they then can also thrust against these supports. As the bits cut into the tunnel face, rim buckets mounted on the cutter wheel pick up the cuttings and discharge them radially to the center and onto a conveyor. This conveyor discharges the muck into cars, into hopper bins, or onto another conveyor. Muck removal from the tunnel is then done by cars, conveyor, or pumping. If hopper bins are used for car loading, they can be incorporated in a trailer unit that moves forward with the boring machine. These bins, designed to hold the capacity of one trainload of cars, are equipped with doors for fast loading of the trains. The machine should contain spray nozzles positioned on the front of the cutterhead to provide a water-detergent-mist mixture for dust control at the face and to dampen the cuttings and prevent dust at the conveyor discharge points. If a glass-enclosed air-conditioned operator's cab is furnished, it increases the operator's efficiency.

In ground conditions where the stability of the ground requires their use, shields are used with tunnel-boring machines to maintain the sides of the tunnel until supports can be erected. To aid in the handling of these supports, cranes and support handling systems are provided. In order to minimize support-erection time, erector-arm assemblies are provided so that the supports can be placed in position by mechanical means.

Three different classes of bits are used on tunnel-boring machines. In the first class are roller cutter bits of the type developed for big-hole vertical-boring machines. These cutters are generally conical in shape and cutting results from the crushing and pulverizing action of numerous hard teeth or carbon inserts as the bits roll across the rock face under tremendous pressure. Photograph 3 shows this type of bit on a Jarva boring machine. The second class of bits is the disc type of cutter, designed to split the rock instead of grinding it away. The cutters resemble glass cutters for they have a hard knife-edged rim, backed up by a husky shank that houses Timken tapered roller bearings. The Robbins machine shown in Photograph 19 is usually equipped with

Photo 19 Robbins tunnel-boring machine for tunnel in Pakistan. (James S. Robbins and Associates)

Photo 20 Calweld oscillating boring machine. (Calweld, Division of Smith Industries, International, Inc.)

this type of bit. In the third class are simple, solid cutter tooth bits which cut away the surface; Photograph 20 shows this type of bit on a Calweld boring machine.

Surveying control of tunnel-boring machines is now accomplished by the use of laser-beam targets that reflect line and grade.

The resistance to machine rotation that must be developed along the excavated areas of the tunnel at times may not be sufficient to keep the machine from rotating. For this reason, deadman controls should be provided, so that if the machine starts to rotate, it can be instantly stopped and the side thrust adjusted.

A tunnel-boring machine is designed for a particular tunnel and for a particular rock condition. Therefore, there are many variations in design. Some machines have been designed with an airtight bulkhead back of the face with an air lock for the muck conveyor. This allows excavation to be performed under compressed air while the operator is in free air. Other machines have rock drills mounted near their face so that if hard rock is encountered, it can be drilled and shot. Still other machines have airtight enclosures in their front with exhaust ventilation to take care of all dust.

Application

Tunnel-boring machines are used in some tunnels because the specifications make such use mandatory, for example, by limiting the amount of shooting that will be permitted in the tunnel. The other reason for using tunnel-boring machines is when conditions indicate that boring will be the most economical tunnel excavation method.

The tunnel-boring machine works on the principle of machining a hole to exact size instead of roughing it out by the brute force of explosives. Some of the advantages of this technique are obvious: The noise and earth shocks of blasting are eliminated; the surrounding rock is left in an undisturbed state; electrically driven machinery produces no fumes or noxious gases that must be cleared away; overbreak can be minimized; and since mucking can be carried on continuously under the right rock conditions, progress can exceed that made by any other method. Therefore, in choosing the method of construction of a tunnel in comparatively soft, consistent rock, where the tunnel is long enough to amortize the equipment and when time is available for equipment mobilization, the contractor should give consideration to the use of a tunnel-boring machine, for its use will increase production and permit a savings in overbreak excavation and overbreak concrete.

In determining whether a tunnel-boring machine should be used on any particular tunnel, past records should be consulted. These indicate that the tunnel-boring machine has been successful in rock with a Mohs' scale of less than 4.5. This is a comparatively soft rock such as limestone, sandstone, mudstone, or shale, in which progress has been good and bit expense not excessive.

Mohs' scale rates rocks and minerals for resistance to abrasion and lists 10 minerals, arranged in order of increased hardness:[5]

1. Talc
2. Gypsum
3. Calcite
4. Fluorite
5. Apatite
6. Feldspar
7. Quartz
8. Topaz
9. Corundum
10. Diamond

Common rocks encountered in construction have Mohs' ratings approximately as follows:

Shale........Generally less than 3
Sandstone....Between 3 and 7, depending on cementing agency
Limestone....3
Marble......3
Slate........4–5
Granite......6–7
Schist.......6–7
Gneiss.......6–7
Quartzite....7

Another condition influencing the application of a tunnel-boring machine is the consistency of the rock. Hard intrusions, faulted formations, crushed ground, squeezing ground, and caving ground have reduced production with these machines. A roof fall occurring in front of the machine often has to be removed by hand, which retards progress.

Tunnel-boring machine manufacturers use the compressive strength of the rock as a measure of whether their machines can economically excavate proposed tunnels. Among different manufacturers, the limit of the adaptability of these machines varies from the ability to excavate rock of 30,000 lb per sq in. to 70,000 lb per sq in. compressive strength. Since hard-rock boring machines do not vary appreciably in design, a better gauge of the machines' capabilities is obviously needed. Efforts are now being made to develop a set standard that will take into account criteria concerning the rock's hardness, its compressive strength, and its degree of stratification. Until these criteria have been considered and applied, the suitability of these machines for various rock formations is largely a matter of the individual's opinion.

A study comparing the use of tunnel-boring machines with the conventional excavation method of drill, shoot, and muck was made on two adjacent tunnels in New Mexico by Newcomb B. Bennett, III.[6] These tunnels were excavated in shale, but layers of sandstone and siltstone were encountered. The paper lists the advantages of the tunneling machine used on one of the tunnels and concludes that these advantages outweighed the disadvantages.

As tunneling machines are improved and new bits developed, this equipment will be used in harder and harder rock. In the future, one of the main opportunities to increase production and lower the cost of tunnel excavation will be provided by the improvement and wider application of these machines.

Estimated Progress

Unless the owner has purchased a tunnel-boring machine and makes it available to the low bidder, a machine mobilization time of 9 months to a year must be allowed for machine design, construction, and delivery to the job. This time is necessary since each machine is designed to fit a certain-diameter tunnel in a particular rock formation. Boring machines can only be reused, without rebuilding, for a tunnel of the same diameter and same rock condition for which it was designed.

The first few months of operation of the tunnel-boring machine will be a breaking-in period with slow production. This breaking-in period is necessary because almost every machine manufactured is of different size and characteristics than any other machine and must be adjusted to each job's particular conditions. After the machine is broken in, penetration rates will vary depending on the rock strength and condition, the flow of water encountered, and the amount and degree of faulted, crushed, or caving grounds.

Progress in soft consistent rock will be good. Hard intrusions delay progress owing to reduction in bit life. Roof falls in front of the machine slow progress, as they often require removal by hand methods. Overbreak is reduced since the machine cuts to a straight, smooth line, and depending on the specification requirements, this line may be moved in close to the "A" line.

In soft consistent rock, the machine often excavates more muck than can be continuously taken away from the machine. On some jobs, in an effort to overcome this, conveyor belts have been used to carry the material to the surface. On other jobs, efforts have been made to grind the muck and pump it to the surface; increased attention in the future is sure to be given to this type of muck disposal.

Progress in soft rock is very good when the machine is operating, but history on past jobs shows that the downtime is often 50 percent of the available time. Downtime is the result of roof falls, plugging of buckets and conveyors, mechanical and hydraulic repairs, changing bits, delays due to insufficient muck disposal facilities, and delays chargeable to track and fan installation.

The boring-machine manufacturer will quote penetration rates per hour. The engineers should allow for downtime and then weigh the production rates furnished by the machine manufacturer with average production rates on previous jobs made under similar conditions with similar equipment. Some jobs have had very good production records. For instance, records made driving the 10-ft-diameter Blanco Tunnel with a Robbins mole in consistent rock by Boyles Brothers Drilling Company were:[7]

156 lin ft for an 8-hr shift
419 lin ft in a 24-hr day
1,905 lin ft in a 6-day week
6,849 lin ft in a 26-day month

Tunnel-crew Size

The men required to operate and maintain the tunnel-boring machine replace the men in the conventional tunneling method that are required to drill, shoot, and muck at the tunnel heading and the men required to maintain the equipment necessary for these operations. To compare crew sizes for two different methods, the heading crew plus the powderman and the Conway and drill mechanics required by conventional tunneling methods should be checked against the crew required to operate and maintain the tunnel-boring machine. On muck handling, the hauling from the tunnel-boring machine will be a more balanced operation than the hauling from a mucker, so for the same yardage per day, hauling from a tunnel-boring machine will be a more efficient operation.

Specifically, the men required at the heading to operate and maintain a tunnel-boring machine are:

Foreman	Operator
Mechanics	Electrician
Oiler	Muck-hopper operator
Surveyors	General laborers

If supports are required, a support crew

This listing does not take into account the tunnel bullgang which lays track and erects ventilation, air, and water pipes or the electricians necessary to extend the power distribution system.

Heading Supply Cost

Heading supplies required when a boring machine is used include rubber clothing, small tools, and safety supplies for the men. Bits are required for the machine and the cost varies from 50 cents to $3 a cu yd of excavation, depending on the hardness of the rock. Other heading supply cost is for power, grease, oil, electrical supplies, mechanical parts, electrical parts, and hydraulic parts.

Tunnel-driving Equipment

In comparing the equipment required for excavating a tunnel with a boring machine with that required by the conventional tunnel-driving method, the boring machine replaces and eliminates the capital cost of the drill jumbo and drills, powder handling and storage, muck-car loading facilities, mucker, a portion of the compressed-air requirements, and the facilities and equipment requisite to the maintenance of this eliminated equipment. Additional expenses inherent in use of the boring machine are the cost of the tunnel machine, a greater power load, and facilities for maintenance of the machine. The remaining equipment necessary for tunnel excavation, such as ventilation, muck haulage, and outside facilities, are required in either case, but occasionally the amount of this equipment will vary.

Tunnels Driven with Tunnel-boring Machines

The following is a partial listing of jobs that have been successfully performed by tunnel-boring machines:

Year	Location	Bore diameter	Rock type	Type of boring machine
1954	Diversion tunnels, Oahe Dam, Pierre, South Dakota	25 ft 9 in.	Soft shale	Robbins
1959	Power tunnels, Oahe Dam	29 ft 6 in.	Soft shale	Robbins
1961	Saskatchewan Dam tunnels, Canada	25 ft 8 in.	Shale	Robbins
1962	Power tunnels, Mangla Dam, West Pakistan	36 ft 8 in.	Sandstone and shale	Robbins
1963	Toronto sewer tunnels, Canada	10 ft 9 in.	Limestone, sandstone and shale	Robbins
1963	Great Lake Power Development, Tasmania	16 ft 1 in.	Mudstone	Robbins
1963	Chicago sewer tunnel, Illinois	26 ft 0 in.	Silty clay and rock*	Calweld
1964	Blue Ridge Project, Arizona	6 ft 8 in.	Sandstone	Hughes
1964	Navajo Tunnel 1, Farmington, New Mexico	20 ft 0 in.	Sandstone and shale	Hughes
1964	Azotea Tunnel, New Mexico	13 ft 0 in.	Sandstone and shale	Robbins
1965	Sewer tunnel, St. Louis, Mo.	6–7 ft	Limestone	Jarva
1965	Blanco Tunnel	13 ft 0 in.	Sandstone and shale	Robbins
1967	Oso Tunnel, Colorado	10 ft 0 in.	Shale	Robbins

* Where rock was encountered, it required blasting.

TUNNELS CONSTRUCTED UNDER AIR PRESSURE

Tunnels are driven with air pressure in the tunnel heading to prevent the inflow of water, sand, or incompetent material into the tunnel. Air of sufficient pressure is maintained in the tunnel to balance the water pressure in the surrounding ground. This balance of pressure restrains the inflow of water and muck.[8]

Classification

Air-pressure tunnel construction falls into three classifications.

1. ***Tunnels Driven with a Tunnel-boring Machine with Only the Cutter and Front Part of the Machine under Air Pressure.*** With this technique, a bulkhead is built into the machine directly behind the cutterhead, with air locks in the bulkhead for the removal of excavated material and for passage of men to the face for bit replacement or other access. The boring-machine operators and other personnel are located behind this bulkhead, where they work in normal air pressure. The adaptation of the tunnel-boring machine to permit the cutter to work under air pressure is relatively new, but its use should become more widespread.

2. Tunnels Driven with an Air Pressure of Less Than 14 PSI. Tunnel projects of this type are safe and have quite a simple setup and operation. They may be driven with or without shields. To hold the pressure, low-pressure compressor plants and pressure bulkheads with air locks are required. Decompression time is 6 min. Working time per shift is often 6 hr but depends on local regulations.

3. Tunnels with an Air Pressure of Greater Than 14 PSI. These tunnels are driven with specialized bulkheaded shields. Operations are complex; shift times are greatly reduced, and the shift length depends on the air pressure used. Pressure bulkheads complete with air locks, emergency air locks, and decompression chambers are required. Extreme caution should be used to prevent "blows" (the instant release of air pressure through the tunnel face).

Special Equipment Required

Low-pressure Air Compressors and Lines. The air pressure required to balance 1 ft of water is 0.43 psi. Depending on the type of soil encountered, the amount of air required to keep the tunnel dry will vary from less to more than this figure. Air always escapes through a tunnel at a rate dependent on the porosity of the soil and the size and number of air locks used.

A rule of thumb used to compute the amount of air required is to estimate the loss of air through the air locks and to this add 20 cfm of air for each square foot of face area. The minimum amount under any condition should equal 30 cfm per man.

Higher-pressure Air for the Air Tools. Air tools operate best on 100-lb differential pressure. To secure good operation in an air-pressure tunnel with 15 lb per sq in. air pressure, the air tools should receive air at 115-lb pressure.

Shield. The type of shield used in air-pressure tunnels varies with the surrounding water pressure which, as previously stated, determines the amount of air pressure. In tunnels driven with under 14-lb air pressure, shields are similar to those used in tunnels without air pressure. In tunnels driven with over 14-lb air pressure, shields are of much heavier construction with breastboard bulkheads across the tunnel face. Muck is either hand-excavated or forced (by moving the shield forward) through openings in the bulkheads. These openings should be of sufficient size that men can pass through them to the face when conditions call for it.

The majority of shields used for tunneling under air pressure are of a circular design. This shape permits rotation of the shields to occur without changing the shape of the tunnel, incorporates more resistance to semifluid pressure than other shapes, and furnishes a minimum tunnel perimeter per cross-sectional area. Air-pressure shields are constructed with man platforms at the face and support erection arms in the tail and are outfitted with sufficient jacks to propel the shield forward. The shield must be of suitable strength so it can resist the surrounding ground pressure. Shields often have a cutting edge which assists in controlling the rate of displacement of the soil by forcing it into the bulkhead openings. How the progress of the shield is controlled has been discussed in the first part of this chapter.

To retain the air pressure of the tunnel, an air-pressure bulkhead is located at the start of the air-pressure tunnel section. This bulkhead must be designed to have strength sufficient to withstand the air pressure used. The air-pressure bulkhead also contains the material air locks, the man air lock, and the emergency air lock. The material air lock should be sized to handle the heading equipment and of sufficient length to handle one train of cars. Man locks are normally 6 ft in diameter and long enough to handle one crew. Benches are installed along each side of the lock. The emergency lock, located in the roof of the tunnel, should be large enough for one crew.

Heavy steel liner plates, cast-iron liner plates, or precast concrete blocks are used to support the tunnel. If a permanent concrete lining is to be installed at a later date, then light steel liner plates are used. It is necessary to caulk the liner plates to prevent air leaks.

Adequate protection from fires must be provided, since the oxygen present under pressure readily supports combustion. Often a separate fire line is installed. The danger of combustion requires that smoking not be permitted in a compressed air tunnel.

Labor

The labor force is composed of men in good health who do not smoke or drink to excess. They are required at all times to wear a badge which states that they are compressed-air workers; if found unconscious, they are not to be taken to a hospital but to be rushed at once to the medical lock; the badge gives the address of the lock. Air pressure determines the hours of work and the wages paid per shift. Hours of work and pay per shift in California, 1967, were as follows:[9]

Pressure, lb	Hours of work	Wages per shift
1 through 14	6	$44.94
Over 14 through 18	6	48.05
Over 18 through 22	4	47.99
Over 18 through 22	6	71.33
Over 22 through 26	4	52.88
Over 26 through 32	4	55.64
Over 32 through 38	3	58.74
Over 38 through 44	2	60.24

Decompression time varies from 3 min for under 12-lb air pressure to 329 min for 6 hr of work under 50-lb air pressure.[10]

If tunnel work is to be done under air pressure, the wage rates and the compressed-air safety orders from the appropriate agencies having jurisdiction over the area should be obtained.

Blows

A "blow" is the rapid escape of air from an air-pressure heading caused by opening a direct channel of escape to the surface. A blow generally starts with a small leak, which rapidly enlarges and causes a recognizable hissing noise. Blows can be prevented by throwing any material such as boards, tools, and bags into the leak. Men working under air pressure should always be on guard for blows in order to stop them, or if it is necessary, the men can enter the air lock. The foreman should always know the number of men in the heading so that he can check them off if it becomes necessary to enter the air lock.

REFERENCES

1. *Engineering News-Record,* November 13, 1930, Volume 105, page 771.
2. Shield Is Far Faster Than Jumbo, *Engineering News-Record,* April, 1964.
3. *Engineering News-Record:* October 17, 1929, Volume 103, page 600; July 17, 1930, Volume 105, page 110; October 30, 1930, Volume 105, page 703.
4. New Shields Speed Tunneling through Sand, *Engineering News-Record,* April 4, 1967, page 46.
5. *New Development in Tunneling Machines,* a reprint from March and April, 1966, volumes of *Construction Methods and Equipment,* McGraw-Hill Publications, New York.
6. Newcomb B. Bennett, III, U.S. Bureau of Reclamation, Mole versus Conventional: A Comparison of Two Tunnel Driving Techniques, Highway Research Record No. 185, published by Highway Research Board.
7. New Tunneling Records, *Western Construction,* September, 1967, page 107.
8. For a more complete description of tunnels driven under air pressure, refer to Harold W. Richardson and Robert S. Mayo, *Practical Tunnel Driving,* copyright 1941 by the McGraw-Hill Book Company, New York.
9. Labor Agreements, Northern and Central California Chapter of the Associated General Contractors of America, Inc.
10. Compressed Air Safety Orders, State of California, 1966.

ADDITIONAL READING

Harold W. Richardson and Robert S. Mayo, *Practical Tunnel Driving,* copyright 1941 by the McGraw-Hill Book Company, New York.

Károly Széchy, *The Art of Tunnelling,* Akadémiai Kiadó, Budapest, 1967.

Chapter 6 Large-diameter Tunnels and Underground Powerhouses

INTRODUCTION

In the preceding chapters the underground excavation methods discussed were for tunnels excavated by a full-face operation. Unless a tunnel-boring machine is used, large-diameter tunnels are excavated by different methods than those previously described.

Large-diameter tunnels excavated in unsupported ground, or in material stable enough to maintain position until supports are installed, are excavated by a top- and bottom-heading operation. This type of operation is used to permit the bottom heading to be removed by operations similar to those used for open-cut excavation, which result in reduced cost and increased progress. When the material to be excavated is so unstable that run-ins would result, it is necessary to excavate along the sides and roof of large-diameter tunnels by the use of multiple drifts, shields, or breastboard jumbos. After supports for the sides and roof have been installed in these tunnels, the remainder of the excavation can be performed by simpler methods.

Underground powerhouses have such a large cross-sectional area that, for practical reasons, these areas are divided into multiple faces for excavation. This allows excavation to be carried on in many areas at one time, which enables continuous drilling and mucking operations and an efficient and continuous use of drilling and excavation crews. This division into multiple faces also allows a choice of excavation methods at different levels of excavation. Thus, each level is excavated in the most efficient manner possible.

This chapter discusses the procedures used in the construction of large-diameter tunnels and underground powerhouse chambers.

LARGE-DIAMETER TUNNELS

Excavation by Tunnel-boring Machines

If the proposed tunnel has a circular shape, passes through soft consistent rock, and has a length sufficient to amortize the equipment, consideration should be given to excavation by a tunnel-boring machine, as discussed in Chap. 5. If a tunnel-boring machine is used, the large volume of excavation per lineal foot of tunnel makes fast disposal of the muck one of the most critical problems. Conveyor belts should be installed to transport muck from the cutting head to loading points back from the face. In some instances it may be advisable to run conveyor belts the full length of the tunnel.

Full-face Top-heading Excavation

If the tunnel passes through unsupported rock or rock that will be self-supporting until supports can be installed, a full-face top heading can be used. In large-diameter tunnels, the area available in the top heading allows sufficient space for the operation and passing of large rubber-tired and crawler types of equipment. The capacity of this equipment makes it preferable to rail-mounted equipment for excavation purposes, unless the muck-haulage distance becomes excessive. In long tunnels as the haulage distance increases, it becomes important to construct adits along the tunnel line to reduce haulage distances and thus allow more economical use of rubber-tired equipment.

When top headings are driven with rubber-tired haulage units, this equipment provides flexibility and speed in transporting men between two headings, which makes alternate heading operations practical over long distances. In some tunnels, alternate headings are used for all the top-heading excavation.

When rubber-tired equipment is used, the drill jumbos are often manufactured in pairs so that each jumbo covers one-half the face. These jumbos are mounted on second-hand, off-highway diesel-powered trucks. The advantage in using two jumbos is that upon completion of the drilling cycle, they can be parked in tandem back from the face and still leave passing space around them. If one jumbo is made wide enough to cover the full face of the top heading, it must be removed from the tunnel during the mucking cycle, or have collapsible side wings that can be lowered when the jumbo is not in use to provide passing space, or be of the gantry type with collapsible center platforms to allow the passage of other equipment through its center.

For loading the muck into haulage units, front-end loaders, with side-dump buckets are commonly used. To increase loading capacity, a crawler-mounted overshot loader can be used to load the rear of the truck while at the same time the truck is loaded from the side by a standard front-end loader. In the past, electrically driven shovels were used for muck loading in tunnels over 28 ft in diameter. Since the development of the overshot and front-end loaders, the expense of purchasing, converting, and operating these large shovels makes their use noncompetitive. The haulage units most commonly used are separate rubber-tired tractor units pulling an Athey type of rear-dump trailer.

If the tunnel is equipped with rail-mounted equipment, two muckers are often worked side by side to increase production and to provide cleanup coverage across the width of the tunnel. The cleanup width of rail-mounted muckers is tabulated with their dimensions in Table 4, pages 52 and 53.

Except in the above instances, excavation of the top heading is performed by standard tunneling methods, as discussed in Chap. 2.

Multiple-drift Excavation

When large tunnels are constructed in unstable ground, it is often impossible to hold the face if a full top heading is excavated. One method of solving this problem is to use multiple drifts. Side drifts are driven along each side of the tunnel and supported as required. At the same time or after the side drifts are driven, a top or crown drift in the center and at the top of the tunnel is driven and supported. Then the side and crown drifts are connected along the crown of the tunnel and arch supports are installed. It is possible to recover and reuse the drift supports if their excavation is scheduled to lead the full crown operations. The length of unsupported excavation made in the crown, between the side drifts and the crown drift, is limited to the distance between tunnel ribs.

After the multiple drifts are excavated and connected and the arch sets are placed, the majority of the tunnel excavation remains in the center of the tunnel. With the tunnel roof and walls completely supported, this central excavation can be performed by any method. As an example, at the Waldo approach tunnel, constructed by the Atkinson Company in Marin County, California, this center was taken out by the use of self-propelled scrapers.

When timber sets were used in the past, the side drifts were driven along the spring line of the tunnel in order to reduce the required span of the supports. Driving the side drifts at this elevation presents the problem of transferring stress from the wall plates in the drift to the mud sill of the main tunnel. It is present tunneling practice to use steel sets, which have a greater span than wood, so the side drifts are often driven at an elevation that allows their invert elevation to be the same as the bottom of the main tunnel. When the drifts are then connected, the arch steel sets completely support the tunnel's roof and walls and are supported by a mud sill at the bottom of the excavation. In some instances, design engineers have anticipated the use of multiple drifts and have designed concrete sidewall supports that can be poured in side drifts, which resist side thrust and support the arch steel. After the sidewalls are poured and the top drifts are completed, the drifts are connected and arch rib sets installed, supported on the concrete sidewalls. The center excavation can then be removed. This procedure was used in the Caldecott Tunnel in the Berkeley Hills and the Hazelview Tunnel in the Siskiyous. However, the contractors who drove these tunnels did not make full use of this design and used construction methods which resulted in slow and expensive construction. Side drifts and crown drifts of large tunnels are driven with either rubber-tired or rail-mounted tunnel equipment, depending on availability of equipment and the length of tunnel.

Shield Excavation of the Top Heading

When the ground conditions are such that a top heading cannot be constructed with standard tunneling methods, a heavy top-heading shield, equipped with breastboards, is sometimes used. Shields have been used in tunnels that have been excavated with and without side drifts. When the excavation plan requires side drifts, these drifts are sometimes driven at spring line and the shield then rides on tracks placed in the side drifts. To date, the use of shields in top headings of large tunnels has been a last resort measure. However, because of the good and safe progress obtained by these shields, their use should be considered more frequently when the initial excavation plan is selected.

Breastboard Jumbo Excavation of the Top Heading

Large breastboard jumbos have been used to drive top headings in large tunnels through material that is hard to hold. When it has been possible to compare the progress made by using a breastboard jumbo with that made by the use of a shield, the shield has been found to be more advantageous. When a shield is used, tunnel excavation and tunnel support erection can be performed at the same time, but if a breastboard jumbo is used, excavation must be shut down while supports are erected.

Bottom-heading Excavation

There are many excavation methods for taking out the bottom heading of large tunnels. The choice of a method is dependent upon the amount of drilling and shooting necessary to break the rock.

When the material requires extensive drilling and shooting, the method in most common use is horizontal or breast drilling of the bottom bench from a drill jumbo. The holes are then loaded and shot, and the broken material is loaded into trucks and hauled away. This cycle operation of drill, shoot, and muck results in low production but allows overbreak to be held to a minimum, an important consideration if the tunnel is to be concrete lined. This bottom-heading excavation method is similar to that used in the top heading, except that the top-heading excavated area furnishes relief for the bottom-heading holes.

A bottom-heading excavation method that gives a lower excavation cost but a higher concreting cost, because of the large amount of overbreak, is the downdrill method. Downdrilling is done from the floor of the top heading. To control the depth of holes, a drill jumbo is often used, consisting of structural members spanning the diameter of the tunnel, on which drifter drills are supported. This jumbo rides on a longitudinal track set at a constant elevation. A sufficient number of drills are mounted on the jumbo to drill a round, while the previous round is being excavated. At Sir Adam Beck Tunnel, drilling far ahead of the shooting and mucking was tried, but this was abandoned because a number of holes were lost on each shot by adjacent unloaded holes' being closed as they acted to relieve rock pressure caused by the explosion. The practice now generally followed is to drill only enough holes to keep the mucking operation going at a steady rate. With this method of excavation, mucking and hauling can be performed with any type of equipment, but shovels or front-end loaders and large rubber-tired hauling units give the most flexibility. The main advantage of this down hole drilling and shooting method compared with the horizontal drilling method is that mucking and hauling can be a continuous operation. The disadvantage of this method is that, because the holes are drilled vertically, in order to prevent tights, they must be drilled and shot below grade, which results in a large percentage of overbreak.

When the tunnel has a flat invert and is driven in soft material, the most economical method of bottom-heading excavation is ripping and then using scrapers to load out and haul away the material. This method does not present any problem when the tunnel is unsupported or when complete arch supports are in place, as in the case of the tunnel that is excavated by a multiple-drift operation. On the other hand, when a top heading is used and rests on wall plates, the transfer of the load from the wall plates in the top heading to the mud sills in the bottom of the tunnel does present a definite problem. This problem is discussed later in this chapter, under the heading Tunnel Supports.

If the tunnel is being driven through soft material, the bottom heading can be removed by light shooting, ripping, bulldozing to a pile, and loading the muck into trucks by a front-end loader. This method works best when supports are not required in the bottom part of the tunnel. In circular tunnels, this method works best on a retreat operation. After light shooting, the material is ripped and shoved up the slope into a pile at the bottom of the top heading. This leaves a finished grade in the rear of the excavation, with the excavation's being performed from this grade, up a slope, to the top of the bottom heading. From the pile at the top of the bottom heading, the muck is loaded into haul trucks which travel out of the tunnel on the floor of the top heading. Excavation is started at the farthest point in the tunnel and retreats to the exit. This method does not necessitate truck travel on the finished grade, so cleanup for concrete placing can be held to a minimum. Invert concreting can then be done by the advance method, which also eliminates any travel on the finished grade.

Four methods of bottom-heading excavation have been described. Since conditions and the shape of bottom headings vary, many other methods may also be used. Furthermore, equipment is developing so rapidly that additional new methods may be applicable at any time.

Tunnel Supports

In incompetent ground, the arch action developed in the tunnel crown to support the roof load decreases as the tunnel diameter increases, with a corresponding increase in the requirements for tunnel supports. This is why heavy supports and excavation by multiple drifts, shields, or breastboard jumbos may be required in large-diameter tunnels, when small-diameter tunnels driven in the same material would only require a minimum of support.

One of the major problems in supported tunnels excavated by top- and bottom-heading methods is the transferring of the load from the top-heading wall plates supporting the tunnel ribs to the bottom-heading mud sills while the bottom heading is excavated. This can be readily done if short sections of the bottom heading are removed by horizontal drilling, shooting, and mucking, a procedure similar to top-heading excavation. In soft ground when scrapers or bulldozers are used for excavating the bottom heading, the area being excavated is of considerable extent, which complicates the transfer of the wall-plate load. This load has been transferred, in certain instances, by drilling holes from the top heading to the elevation of the final invert grade and installing column supports in these holes prior to the bottom-heading excavation. In other cases, prior to bottom-heading excavation, holes are excavated from the wall plate to final grade by backhoes or other equipment and wall-plate supports are installed in these holes.

In the Angeles Tunnel, which is a large, circular, supported tunnel in soft rock, a tunnel-rib support for the top heading was developed that made it unnecessary to place steel supports in the bottom half of the tunnel. This resulted in a large savings in steel and a less-difficult excavation of the bottom heading. The support was accomplished by cutting a shelf in each side of the tunnel at spring line, concreting-in pairs of I beams to serve as wall plates in the shelf, and then supporting the arch ribs for the top heading on these wall plates. Immediately after excavation of the bottom heading, the bottom half of the tunnel was covered with gunite. The gunite protected the rock in the bottom heading and helped to support the wall plates. The use of gunite also helped to eliminate much of the cleanup ordinarily required for concrete placing. This procedure was extremely successful. It saved the owner money by eliminating one-half the steel supports.

Tunnel Ventilation

When excavation of the top heading is performed with trucks and front-end loaders, the large amount of diesel power necessary for this operation may make it necessary to install two large ventilation lines in order to provide adequate ventilation in the tunnel.

When the top heading is holed through, the natural ventilation through the top heading is generally adequate for the bottom-heading operation. In cases where this natural ventilation is not sufficient, it can be supplemented by erecting a barrier wall at one end of the tunnel containing ventilation fans exhausting to the outside. Access can be provided by installing doors that open and close automatically when passage is desired for men or equipment.

Concreting Problems Unique to Large-diameter Tunnels

Placing concrete lining in large-diameter tunnels presents unique problems not encountered in smaller tunnels. In planning the concreting methods, the following points should be considered.

1. The shape of the bottom of circular tunnels prevents passage of trucks, and if trucks are used, then truck passage platforms should be constructed at intervals along the tunnel line. This restriction on truck passing reduces the volume of concrete that can be hauled into the tunnel by trucks. On short tunnels, the truck travel time in the tunnel is of such short duration that the construction of passing areas is not a critical item. On long tunnels that have been excavated by rubber-tired equipment, truck transportation of concrete becomes so complicated that, in some instances, it is more economical to switch over to rail-mounted equipment for concreting. Since each train carries a large volume of concrete, only a few trains are required and switching of trains is only necessary at a few points in the tunnel. When a circular tunnel is estimated, comparative studies are often necessary to determine the best method of concrete transportation. Horseshoe-shaped large tunnels do not have this problem of truck passage since their bottoms are wide enough for trucks to pass at any location.

2. In large-diameter tunnels, a long length of concrete forms is necessary in proportion to the lineal feet of arch poured per day, owing to the long side slopes taken by the fresh concrete, which are a function of the height of the arch pour. Because of the exposure of the fresh concrete in these long side slopes, some specifications call for bulkhead pours. Each set of specifications should be checked carefully concerning this point.

3. Because of the large circumference of the tunnel, the concrete in the arch pour has a long flow distance around the perimeter if the pour is made with one slick line. For this reason multiple slick lines are used. Because of the large volume of concrete to be placed per lineal foot of tunnel, it is necessary to use multiple placers to maintain a reasonable progress. If multiple placers are used, concrete mixing and hauling equipment must have a capacity sufficient to supply these placers.

4. If a full-circle pour with invert forms is made, flow of the concrete under the invert forms is a major problem because of the long, nearly horizontal distance the concrete must travel. If the full-circle method is used, the forms should be designed so that the invert forms

can be lifted as soon as possible so that any concrete defects can be corrected.

UNDERGROUND POWERHOUSES

Application

At some locations, if powerhouses were constructed on the surface, it would be necessary to have long runs of surface penstocks to develop sufficient hydraulic head to generate the power desired. At these locations if the powerhouses were constructed underground, the hydraulic head could be developed with near-vertical shafts and the tail water could be conveyed from the powerhouse in tailrace tunnels. When the cost of the long penstock runs needed for the surface location exceeds the added cost of excavation for the underground location, the underground location is the most economical solution.

Powerhouses are also located underground for security purposes or to locate them out of sight for esthetic reasons. Whatever the reasons, the use of underground powerhouses is becoming widespread, and their construction a more common problem.

Description

Underground powerhouse excavation consists in excavating inclined penstock shafts; excavating other shafts that may be required for permanent powerhouse access, for air-venting purposes, or to bring the power cables to the surface; excavating underground chambers required to house the generators and transformers and to provide an area for water surging after it passes through the draft tubes; and excavating tunnels that are required for permanent access to the various chambers and tailrace tunnels used to convey water from the powerhouse. Illustrating the different parts of an underground powerhouse, Drawing 13 shows the general layout of the T. 2 Powerhouse in Australia.

Construction Access

For ease in excavating an underground powerhouse, proper access is very important. It is desirable to provide access to both the top and bottom elevations of each chamber to be excavated. It is also desirable to provide access to a point near the bottom of the inclined penstocks. Access to the top of the underground chambers permits the excavation of a top heading along the chamber to be one of the first operations. It is important to complete this top excavation to the full arch width as soon as possible so that roof supports can be installed if required and

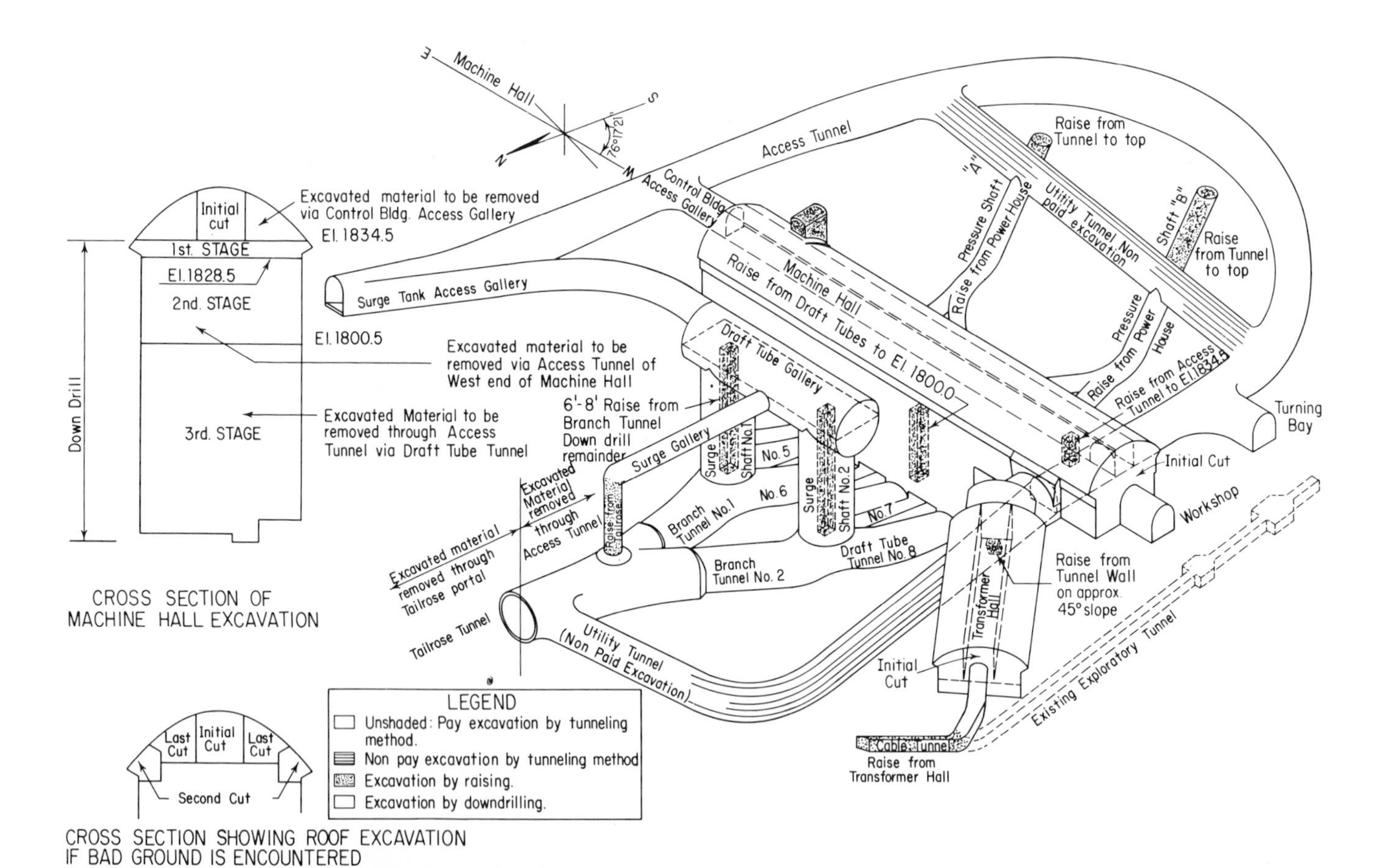

Drawing 13 Method of excavating T. 2 Powerhouse, Snowy Mountain project, Australia.

a working floor can be furnished for the removal of the remaining excavation.

The advantage of having access to the lowest point in the powerhouse is that none of the excavated material need then be moved by the hoisting method, a slow and expensive manner of handling muck. So, after the top is excavated, the bottom access is completed, and after the muck shafts are raised, the remaining excavation can be removed by bulldozing down the raises and loading into haul trucks. As soon as access to the bottom of the powerhouse is available, drainage can be installed and the whole powerhouse can be dewatered at all times.

Another advantage of top and bottom access is that many areas can be excavated at one time, which allows continuous drilling and mucking operations. This is the most economical use of manpower and equipment. Access to the penstock shafts permits them to be excavated by raising methods, which are more economical than those for sinking shafts from the surface. To provide early access to the powerhouse area and to enable the contractor to observe the type of rock that will be encountered, some owners have the access tunnels excavated as separate contracts before the main contract is advertised. If an underground powerhouse has short tailrace tunnels, these tunnels can be excavated in time to furnish access to the bottom of the powerhouse.

A large underground powerhouse, which is also one of the largest in generating capacity, is now being constructed at Churchill Falls, Labrador, Canada.[1] It will contain 11 generating units, each with a capacity of 475,000 kw. Three million cubic yards of underground excavation is required for its construction. The main chamber will be 1,000 by 76 by 150 ft. Two other chambers are used, the transformer chamber and the tailrace collector chamber. The powerhouse will operate under a 1,000-ft head and eleven 1,200-lin-ft penstocks must be constructed. Two tailrace tunnels, 1 mile long and 60 by 45 ft in size, are required. The engineers (a joint venture of Acres and Bechtel) did an excellent job of providing access to various excavation areas. They also let a preliminary excavation contract which will furnish access for the main powerhouse contractor. This preliminary work permits inspection of rock conditions to be made by contractors interested in bidding on the main contract. The preliminary contract was for excavating an access tunnel, the top half of one tailrace tunnel, and a vertical shaft. A review of this powerhouse layout would be of value to engineers planning this type of construction.

Excavating Equipment

Rubber-tired equipment is preferred for underground powerhouse excavation since this equipment can negotiate steeper grades and permits a more flexible operation than rail-mounted equipment. In underground powerhouse excavation, the distances from excavation to muck disposal areas are usually short, which also suits the use of this equipment. Steep grades are encountered since there are great differences in the elevation of the underground chambers and the access tunnels are laid out steeply to shorten their length. Flexibility of operation is important because many faces are available for excavation at one time. If the excavating equipment can be readily moved from face to face, the drilling and mucking crews and equipment can be worked on a continuous basis instead of in cycles as required in tunnel construction.

Haulage can be performed by any type of diesel-powered dump truck. Since it is possible to secure short turning radius in large-capacity units with separate tractor-trailer units, they are more popular than the standard dump truck.

Horizontal drilling can be performed by drills mounted on truck jumbos. Downdrilling can be accomplished by any wet drill, from jackhammer size to that of drills on air track mountings.

Crawler type of overshot loaders, front-end loaders, or diesel shovels can be employed for muck loading. Because of the many diesel motors which may be working in the powerhouse area, the amount of ventilation required may be more than in tunnel construction. Because of the short distance the air must be transported, ventilation problems can be solved simply by adding more vent lines and fans.

After the top headings are holed through and the shafts are constructed, circulation of air may be possible without vent pipe. This is accomplished by exhaust fans placed in air barriers at the shaft openings. If this is done, small localized ventilating systems are often required to prevent dead-air pockets.

Top-heading Excavation

Excavation of the top of each chamber down to spring line should be one of the first operations. This is important since if the ground needs supporting, the supports can be installed and the remainder of the excavation can then be performed under a supported roof. This top excavation will also furnish a working floor for removal of the remainder of the excavation.

In strong, solid rock, these top cuts can be made the full width of the chamber in one operation.

In other rock types, the ability of the rock to withstand the roof stresses caused by the wide roof span is of crucial importance when planning the excavation method. In the underground powerhouses excavated to date, records indicate that even in very competent rock, the roof has been supported with rock bolts. In powerhouses constructed in ground with weaker rock structure, the top cuts were constructed with multiple drifts, steel arch supports were used, and before the remainder of the excavation was completed, concrete arch beams were poured. The steel sets and the concrete in the arch can be supported by haunches excavated in the sides of the powerhouse at the spring line. Pouring the arch before the remainder of the excavation is completed not only provides safe working conditions, but allows less-expensive arch concrete because the height of the form shoring is shortened and simplified. The amount and extent of arch support required for construction purposes are two of the most difficult problems to solve in estimating underground powerhouses.

Main Chamber Excavation

While tops of the various chambers are being driven, access can be completed to the bottoms of the chambers and raises constructed to intersect the top cuts. Then the bulk of the excavation can be removed by downdrilling, shooting, and bulldozing the material into the raises. At the bottom of the raises, the muck can be loaded into trucks for haulage to the disposal areas.

The rock side walls of the powerhouse can be preserved by either predrilling or presplitting. In some cases, presplitting has been combined with long-hole drilling. These procedures, when properly executed, will result in smooth vertical walls.

Shaft Excavation

As discussed in Chap. 4, the cheapest method of excavating the shafts is to raise them from the bottom. This can be done by using Alimak raise climbers. Another method used on vertical shafts is to drill a hole down the center of the shaft and then lower or raise a work cage from the bottom by a cable put through this hole. For a further discussion of shaft construction, refer to Chap. 4.

If the construction time is short, shafts may have to be both raised from the bottom and sunk from the top.

Examples of Powerhouse Excavation

Drawing 13 illustrates the method proposed and carried out on an underground powerhouse excavation by a joint venture with Kaiser Engineers as the sponsor for the Snowy Mountains Hydroelectric Authority. The tailrace tunnel was approximately 6 miles long and access for driving this tunnel was from the outlet portal. Time did not permit the use of this tunnel for access to the powerhouse. Two lengths of tunnel,

Photo 21 Gates being installed for loading excavated material into trucks where the access tunnel was constructed intersecting the pressure shafts. T. 2 Powerhouse, Australia.

as coded on the drawing, were nonpay tunnels driven for access by the contractor to expedite excavation and reduce the cost. One nonpay tunnel allowed raises to be started in the pressure shafts and allowed direct loading from the bottom of the shafts to trucks. The shafts were equipped with gates to retain the muck and allow truck loading of the muck as shown by Photograph 21. The other nonpay tunnel connected with the tailrace tunnel, which in turn was excavated into the powerhouse. This tunnel permitted access to the bottom of the surge gallery shafts as well as into the bottom of the powerhouse through the draft tubes. The powerhouse was excavated in accordance with the plan shown in the drawing, consisting in top-heading excavation, access to the bottom of the excavated areas, raises, and downdrilling. This excavation plan did not require the hoisting of any muck. One truck drill jumbo had access to seven different faces which it could drill out in rotation. Photographs 22 through 25 show the different stages in the excavation of the powerhouse. Because of the nature of the rock and the large opening required for the powerhouse, after the top heading and part of the remaining excavation were removed, the arch was sup-

Photo 22 Excavation of the top heading. T. 2 Powerhouse, Australia.

Photo 23 Concreting the arch of the T. 2 Powerhouse, Australia.

Photo 24 Downdrilling operation in the powerhouse chamber. T. 2 Powerhouse, Australia.

ported with concrete for protection during the remainder of the work. Owing to space restrictions in the powerhouse, shops and storage were located in the access tunnel, as shown in Photograph 26.

The method used for excavating the powerhouse at Portage Mountain Dam in British Columbia is shown by Drawing 14.[2] The main chamber of this powerhouse is 66.5 ft wide and 890 ft long. The distance from the top of the arch to the bottom of the drainage gallery is 152.5 ft. Excavation of the main chamber was done in seven stages:

1. Excavation of the arch section for its entire length from center and side headings. Temporary support and the primary main support for the arch were furnished by rock bolts.
2. Presplitting the side walls and drilling, shooting, and mucking a center slot approximately 34 ft deep and 22 ft wide.
3. Drilling and shooting the side sections along the central slot. The shot material furnished a work platform for arch concrete placement. Preshooting reduced the hazard of damage to the arch concrete during blasting as the chamber was deepened.

Photo 25 Breaking through from the underground powerhouse to the draft tubes. T. 2 Powerhouse, Australia.

Photo 26 Storage and shop areas located in the access tunnel for the T. 2 Powerhouse, Australia.

4. Placement of a subhaunch leveling section of concrete at each arch abutment.

5. Placing the arch concrete and pumping contact grout between the arch concrete and the rock surface. The arch concrete assumes some of the rock load with time, but the rock bolts continue as the main source of rock support.

6. Removal of side section material to the first bench.

7. Excavation of the remainder of the powerhouse chamber in benches. (Concrete was delivered to the powerhouse chamber from the ground surface through a pipe placed in a drilled hole. This pipe had an 8-in. diameter and was 400 ft long.)

Other Excavation Methods

The excavation methods described above are for underground powerhouses with comparatively short access tunnels, where access can be provided to both the top and bottom of the powerhouse. In a few

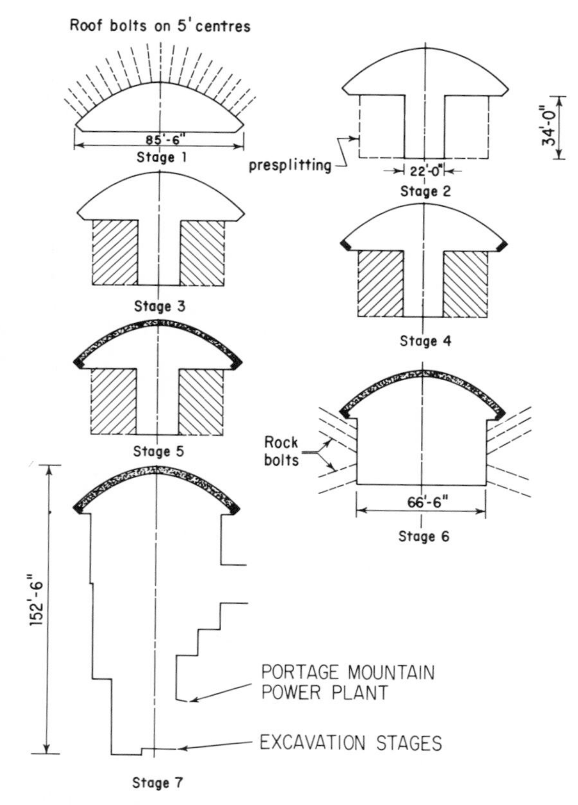

Drawing 14 Portage Mountain Power Plant, excavation stages.

cases, underground powerhouses are located at the bottom of deep shafts with the only other access through a long tailrace tunnel. Excavation of these powerhouses is often delayed until the tailrace tunnel is completed. Rail service is then provided to the powerhouse area. Excavation plans must be modified to provide for rail haulage.

Another special case occurs when access to the powerhouse is only possible at one point. The ingenuity of the estimator is then challenged to find the best method of performing the operation. Ramps have been used inside the powerhouse, but these ramps interfere with the excavation. Records to date indicate that when powerhouses are laid out with only one means of access, the contractors have not sufficiently allowed for the expense of this type of excavation and have consequently lost money on the contract.

Powerhouse Concrete

After the excavation is completed, concrete can be transported into the powerhouse by diesel-powered rubber-tired agitators through the access tunnel. A trestle is often erected the length of the powerhouse, slightly above the generator floor elevation. Concrete is placed by a crane operating from this trestle. Powerhouse concrete has a high form ratio and involves many small pours; thus, placing rates are slow with a resultant high cost per cubic yard.

Special points to remember when estimating the concrete are:

1. When pouring the arch roof concrete, the forms must be supported with shoring from the floor of the excavation or by a truss spanning between the walls. Form support may be one of the largest expenses in this operation.
2. Area is restricted and both form storage and the storage of embedded articles present problems.
3. If the scroll case is unlined and requires inside forms, the forms when stripped can only be removed from the scroll cases through the wicket gate area.
4. Draft tube forms can only be removed from the draft tubes by way of the tailrace tunnel or the stay ring area.

Penstock-shaft Concrete

The penstock shafts normally are lined with steel penstocks backed with concrete and then grouted through grout connections in the steel liner. Placement and welding of these steel liners present a definite rigging problem, as shown by Photograph 27. Concrete placement is often done by the prepack method. This method calls for placement of concrete aggregate around the penstocks. This aggregate is then consoli-

Photo 27 Start of installation of the steel liners in the pressure shafts. T. 2 Powerhouse, Australia.

dated by pumping in grout and an intrusion agent through previously placed pipes. Prepack concrete is a specialty item and should be supervised by an expert in this field.

REFERENCES

1. Labrador Turns on with Power Spectacular at Churchill Falls, *Engineering News-Record,* March 14, 1968, page 34.
2. *Field and Office Manual,* 1967 edition, page 86, published by Engineering News-Record.

Chapter 7 Estimating Procedure

INTRODUCTION

The preceding chapters have discussed the construction methods and equipment used in underground construction. A working knowledge of both subjects is required in estimating.

This chapter discusses estimating procedure and includes the description of a format suitable for estimating a tunnel, briefly describes how to classify the geological formations that could occur along the tunnel line, describes the types of tunnel supports and their application, and describes each step in estimate preparation.

In Chap. 8 a contractor's estimate is presented for a fictitious hard-rock tunnel located in the Sierra Nevada. Both this chapter and Chap. 8 will be more clearly understood if frequent reference is made from one to the other. This cross referencing will correlate the estimating description with the estimate computations.

TYPE OF ESTIMATE

Estimates may be prepared either by the longhand method, or by the computer method. The longhand method requires that the estimator write down all explanations and computations and that all calculations be performed on a calculator. By the computer method, scheduled rates of production, crew sizes, wage rates, and other basic factors are fed into a computer which then computes the cost and turns out a typed tabulated estimate.

Both of these methods have advantages and disadvantages. The primary advantage of a computer estimate is that the computer does not make any arithmetical mistakes and tabulates the information in such a manner that details can be readily obtained. The main advantage of the longhand method of estimating is that the estimator, in spending more time on all the details and calculations, has more opportunity to change and refine his assumptions and judgment factors.

The estimator who uses a computer must thoroughly understand the procedure used in a longhand estimate. He must furthermore compile all basic information in detail before programming the computer, so that the computer run is a purely mechanical operation. Any change in assumptions or facts after the start of the computer run requires that the estimate be run through the computer again.

The longhand method of estimating is used in the example shown in this book, for it illustrates tunnel estimating procedure most completely. The bulk of the time spent preparing a tunnel estimate is required for selecting equipment and estimating progress and crew size. All of these things must be determined before either a longhand or computer estimate is made. As shown in the example estimate in Chap. 8, the actual computations that can be performed by a computer are so few and simple that many estimators consider the expense of a computer run to be unjustified.

ESTIMATE FORMS

There are many methods of setting up a tunnel estimate and advantages may be presented for any method. Some estimators only estimate direct labor and job supplies, such as powder and exploders, for the individual bid items. They then place all maintenance labor, service labor, supervisorial labor, equipment, plant, and repair parts in a general account. These are then prorated to the bid items.

This method is not recommended, for the larger the amount of expense that is prorated, the less accurate is the cost of the individual items. Since an estimate is a collection of individual items of cost, the more accurate the estimated cost of each item, the more accurate will be the complete estimate.

An estimating format should be designed to provide ease in estimating and to act as a guide for cost accounting. If cost accounts follow the estimate, or the estimate follows the cost accounting method, then it is easier for the job supervision to compare the actual cost with the estimated cost and exercise closer job control. Keeping estimates and cost reports on the same form furnishes job records of the cost of individual items that can be directly compared with similar items in future tunnel estimates.

The estimate format that we recommend has the following advantages:

1. It follows good accounting procedure in classifying expenses, capital accounts, and overhead.
2. It places expense that can be reduced with good job control in the direct cost division and furnishes unit cost of individual items, which can readily be compared with actual job costs.
3. If cost accounting follows the estimate form, good cost records will be available for bidding on future work.
4. It makes all details of the estimate readily available to compare with estimates prepared by joint venture partners.
5. It allows the estimate to be prepared in a logical progression of steps and provides an arithmetical check on most of the estimated cost.

This recommended form of estimate is divided into the following classes of cost:

1. *Direct cost.* This is the cost of direct labor (including payroll burdens), supplies, repair parts, permanent materials, and subcontracts relating to bid item work. Labor charged to direct cost should include all labor, including maintenance labor, except indirect labor and labor required to install the outside plant and equipment. The underground plant and equipment are installed by the regular tunnel crew and therefore are chargeable to direct cost. Also included in direct cost is the cost of tunnel supervision, with the exception of the tunnel superintendent. Direct cost is the part of the total cost that can vary with good supervision and job control and is the part most difficult to estimate. Thus, good job records are invaluable in furnishing a guide to bid work. Summary sheets showing a tabulation of direct cost for "Sierra Tunnel" are included in Chap. 8, Exhibit 9.

2. *Net cost to the job of plant and equipment.* The cost of plant and equipment covers the move-in and invoice costs of the plant and

the equipment necessary to do the work, plus the cost of installing the outside plant and equipment. A form showing a tabulation of this cost for Sierra Tunnel is shown in Chap. 8, Exhibit 10. Rules cannot be formulated to work in all cases when making a distinction between plant and equipment. Therefore, since each estimator's distinction between the two classifications will differ, the two are added together and the sum is used to compare estimates at a prebid estimators' meeting. Most contractors use the following definitions when making the distinction between plant and equipment: *Plant cost* is the cost of facilities necessary to construct the project which do not have a salvage value at the end of the job, and it includes work performed on equipment which will not increase its salvage value. An example of this second classification of plant cost is the move-in and erection cost of equipment. *Equipment cost* is defined as the cost of machinery and facilities necessary to construct the project that will have a salvage value at the completion of the project. When estimating the net cost of plant and equipment chargeable to the job, the salvage value should be deducted from the total cost. The deducted salvage value should be the net salvage value, after allowance has been made for the cost of moving out, cleanup, and storing and selling the equipment.

If equipment is rented for the project, the rental cost of the bare, nonmaintained, nonoperated equipment should be included as a separate item in the plant and equipment cost. If this cost is placed in the direct cost division it will distort the unit direct cost items when recorded cost is used to estimate future work.

The net cost of plant and equipment is determined at the start of the work when methods and equipment are decided upon. After the method of construction is determined, this cost will not vary to any great degree from the original estimate during the construction of the project since it is not dependent on job control.

3. *Indirect cost.* This includes all cost not charged to the other divisions of cost. It includes project supervision, job engineering but not surveying, office payroll and expense, insurance, property taxes, special taxes, and bond premiums. Indirect cost should not include sales tax since this tax should be added to the cost of plant and equipment, permanent materials, and supplies. The amount of indirect cost is dependent upon the efficiency of the engineering and office staff, the complexity of cost records required, and the number of reports that must be submitted.

4. *Camp cost.* If the tunnel is in an isolated area, it may be necessary to install camp facilities and operate them for the life of the contract. If a prefabricated camp is planned and a caterer used, quotations for these costs can be secured before bid submission. Thus, this cost of the operation can be well determined before bid submission. The

major cost variable here will then be the number of men who will use the camp.

5. *Escalation.* Most estimates are made by using wage rates in force at the time of bid submission. The escalation item covers the cost of anticipated wage increase occurring during the life of the project. This cost is dependent upon future wage rates and fringe benefits that will be negotiated by the union, plus any anticipated increases in workmen's compensation insurance and payroll taxes. If it is anticipated that during the contract period there will be a rise in material and supply price, escalation on these items should also be computed.

An example of these divisions of cost for a tunnel estimate is shown by Exhibit 13, Chap. 8. Camp cost is not shown in this estimate since a camp was not needed for this proposed tunnel.

After the estimate is completed, the estimator should evaluate the following expenses and should recommend to his principals that proper consideration should be given these costs when job markup is determined:

1. *Interest expense.* This expense is the interest on the contractor's capital required to finance the work. To determine the capital and interest expense properly, it is necessary for the estimator to prepare a cash forecast for the job.

2. *Contingencies.* On work where there is an exposure that is indeterminate and cannot be estimated, the maximum cost to the contractor for this exposure should be determined and explained to the principals. The principals can then determine to what extent the job will be subject to any contingencies and can determine markup accordingly.

STEPS IN PREPARATION OF THE ESTIMATE

The steps taken in estimating a tunnel are interrelated, so judgment factors used in one step may affect decisions made in another step. This makes it impossible to prepare the estimate in the exact order presented below and requires a continual review of all preceding steps as each additional step is completed. In following these steps in estimating, the engineer should always keep in mind the fact that the controlling and largest item in the cost of tunnel construction is labor, and the fact that labor cost varies with the construction progress, construction methods, and type of equipment. So that comparisons can be readily made with the estimating procedure described in this chapter and with the contractor's tunnel estimate presented in Chap. 8, the following estimating steps have been numbered and these same numbers are used for estimating computations in Chap. 8:

I. Study of plans and specifications
II. Job inspection

III. Geological review
IV. Quantity takeoffs
V. Request for quotations on permanent materials and subcontracts
VI. Job wage rates
VII. Excavation method
VIII. Selection of equipment
IX. Estimated progress and preparation of a construction schedule
X. Cost of outside development
XI. Estimating the cost of tunnel excavation labor
XII. Estimating the cost of tunnel excavation supplies
XIII. Estimating the cost of concrete lining labor
XIV. Estimating the cost of concrete lining supplies
XV. Estimating the direct cost of other bid items
XVI. Direct cost tabulations
XVII. Estimating the cost of plant and equipment
XVIII. Estimating the cost of indirect expense
XIX. Estimating camp cost
XX. Escalation
XXI. Tabulation of the total estimated cost
XXII. Information for the principals

I. STUDY OF PLANS AND SPECIFICATIONS

The planning and preparation of a tunnel estimate is similar to estimating any other type of construction in that the first task is to become thoroughly familiar with the plans and specifications in order to grasp the overall job picture and to understand the specific conditions and work requirements stipulated by the owner. When the plans and specifications are reviewed, consideration should be given to the fact that they are the owner's and that they are written for the benefit of the owner and will be interpreted and enforced by the owner's representative.

Specifications and bid advertising announcements should be checked for any requirements regarding prequalification of the contractor. Prequalification is required by some governmental agencies and private owners. If required, fulfillment of this requirement should be expedited. Prequalification requirements vary from proof of financial responsibility to the listing of job experience in similar types of work. Contractors' licensing requirements should also be reviewed; this point is not mentioned in the specifications but is covered by local laws. When receiving joint venture bids, some states classify bids as nonresponsive if they are not presented in numbered bid forms checked out to the joint venture, and will rule out bid forms checked out to individual members of the joint venture.

The general and special clauses of the specifications should be carefully examined. Special attention should be paid here to determine whether they furnish any relief to the contractor in contract price, and whether extension of contract time is provided in the event of unforeseen underground conditions, acts of God, strikes, war, weather, etc. Contract completion dates and liquidated-damage provisions should be understood, and the bond and insurance provisions should be reviewed.

Payment provisions and bid items should be reviewed to determine whether provisions have been made for reimbursements to the contractor for mobilization, whether the owner will withhold a percentage from each progress payment until job completion (known as *contract retention*), when and how progress payments will be made, and whether payment is on a unit price or lump sum basis. Payment on a lineal foot basis is the same as on a lump sum basis, since the length of the tunnel is always very well defined before bidding. On a lineal foot basis of payment, the amount of steel supports, the excavation delay for supported ground, the amount of lagging and blocking, and the amount of contact grouting constitute some of the risks passed on to the contractor, and the contractor should recognize this when he determines the markup.

The plans and specifications should be examined closely for any requirements that may change the standard method of underground construction or any limitations restricting the amount of work that can be done from any portal or area. Specific points to review are limitations on blasting; how close the steel sets have to be placed to the face; the maximum size of aggregates in the concrete; any restrictions on the placing of concrete; the types of concrete forms required; the curing time, i.e., the length of time before tunnel forms can be stripped; and the type of invert cleanup required. Restrictions on any of the above will reflect in the contractor's cost and should be reflected in the estimate.

The plans and specifications should be examined to determine if there are any special costs connected with its construction. These costs may result from the location of the job or special construction considerations. Typical examples of these special cost items are the following:

A diversion tunnel may be located with its portals below the streambed elevation. To keep the portals dry, it may be necessary to construct cofferdams, or at other types of locations, unexcavated plugs may be left adjacent to the streambed. Transportation to and from the tunnel portal will be complicated because of the presence of these cofferdams or plugs. If the plug method is used, the plug must be removed upon job completion. In diversion tunnels that are to contain a permanent concrete plug, special excavation of its anchorages is required. Diversion-tunnel construction may require the use of high-pressure consolidation grouting at the tunnel portals and at the permanent-plug location. Occasionally diversion tunnels must be holed through into a body of water. Extra work and extra costs occur in this operation, such as excavating a bottom pocket in the tunnel to receive the rock when the final round is shot.

A tunnel may be located in such a remote area that special off-site cost is required for labor recruiting, purchasing, and expediting. At remote locations larger stocks of spare parts, materials, and supplies are needed. Initial transportation from hiring hall to jobsite may be required for job personnel as well as daily transportation. Travel-time payments to and from the job might be a requirement. Labor turnover will increase. There will be added material handling and hauling cost. It may be desirable to provide helicopter or airplane service to the job area, including landing and servicing facilities at the jobsite. A tunnel may be located in an area where heavy snowfalls will occur. Then equipment must be winterized and snow removal may be necessary. The weather may be so extreme that there will be a loss in job efficiency.

If a tunnel is located in a state or national park or a national forest, there will be added cost of waste disposal, as preservation of trees and stream pollution are rigidly controlled in these areas.

Work in military installations may cause additional costs owing to security requirements. Such costs may be for security clearance, special transportation of men because of private-car restrictions, and additional travel-time payments.

When tunnels are located in populated areas, there are many additional cost items. Blasting may be restricted to daylight hours, and restrictions may be applied to the amount of powder that can be exploded at one time. Tunnel muck must usually be hauled a long distance to the disposal area, and this haulage may be restricted to specified hours. Portal or shaft construction will present special problems because of the congested area and because utilities may have to be moved or altered. The space available for a contractor's work area may be limited. Noise must be suppressed, which will increase the cost of compressor installations. Ground settlement will be a problem and expenditures may be necessary for foundation underpinning and street repair. The tunnel may be located in a filled area where piling, foundations, and even sunken ships may be encountered. Employee parking will be a critical and often an added cost.

If the work is located in a foreign country, many special costs will be incurred. Passports, shots, health clearance, and air transportation are required for each American employee. Turnover of American personnel is quite high on foreign work. Premium wage rates are paid for overseas duty. Board and lodging are usually supplied without cost to the single American employees. The American employees are reimbursed for any local income taxes which exceed the United States rates. The local labor must be trained to use American equipment and American methods. Job logistics are a problem, and if large inventories of supplies, materials, and spare parts are not maintained, air freight will be spent for emergency orders. Local operators are hard on equipment and hard on tires. Maintenance cost of equipment will greatly increase because local personnel will operate the equipment and because local mechanics will be inefficient. Local equipment operators will not be the equivalent of their American counterparts in production rates. Job inspection will be less standardized. Local corporate taxes will reduce profits. Import duties may apply to the importation of equipment, materials, supplies, and commissary items. Camp cost, including mess hall and commissary cost, will be high. It may be desirable to provide a purchasing and expediting office either in the United States or in a European country. Travel expenses to and from the site by the contractor's American executives, engineers, and consultants will be incurred. It may be necessary to hire local lawyers and engineers to help in job negotiations. Finally, at job completion the sale of the plant and equipment may present considerable difficulties. Construction equipment has been shipped back to the United States by American contractors from other countries upon job completion.

Before bidding, the contractor should bring to the owner's attention any discrepancy between the plans and specifications, mistakes in the specifications, or any instance where the owner's intention needs clarification. Verbal clarification of the plans and specifications by the owner or the owner's representative does not hold the owner to these opinions or interpretations; this clarification must be obtained in writing. In all cases the specifications place the primary responsibility of their interpretation on the contractor, so it is important that they be thoroughly understood by the estimator.

One method of becoming familiar with the plans and specifications is to prepare an abstract of them similar to Exhibit 2, Chap. 8. This abstract is also useful to have on the job inspection trip and to furnish to management to use for quick job review purposes.

II. JOB INSPECTION

The job inspection should be made after the plans and specifications have been studied so that the inspection team will have a concept of the job and some grasp of the problems resulting from specification requirements. On this inspection trip, attention should be paid to the points involving special problems as well as the overall job review.

Particular points that should be considered during the job inspection are:

1. The surrounding area should be examined for towns and other places having capacity to house the construction force. This is necessary before a decision can be made concerning camp requirements.

2. Access to the job should be investigated to ascertain what difficulties will be encountered when bringing in equipment, supplies, and materials and to determine whether access roads need to be constructed or improved. Weather conditions should be checked to determine their influence on job access and construction progress.

3. The availability of power and water should be examined so that the cost of the facilities to the job can be estimated.

4. The portals and adit locations should be examined with reference to the amount and kind of opencut excavation that will be required, and any other work that may be necessary to construct a proper plant setup at each location.

5. If the owner has provided areas for spoil disposal, these areas should be examined to determine the needs for clearing and drainage. If the owner has not provided such areas, the estimator must make complete provision for the cost of spoil disposal.

6. If natural aggregates are to be used, the aggregate pit should be examined and the length of haul to the portal location should be determined. If manufactured aggregates are to be used, the quarry site should be examined and the haul distance determined.

7. The rock along the tunnel line and any existing excavation cuts should be examined. Drill-hole cores and records should be examined. Geological reports should be studied, including any published by the owner, national government, or state. This geological information will furnish the basis for choosing the tunnel-driving methods, drilling rates, and powder factor. It will further indicate how the rock will break, the type of supports that will be required, the amount of overbreak, whether squeezing or running ground will be encountered, the presence of bad faults, and the anticipated water inflow into the tunnel. To assist in this geological study, the use of a structural geologist is recommended.

8. Labor rates, crafts employed, and availability and suitability of labor vary from area to area. Therefore, labor should be investigated and the local labor agreements secured. These agreements will cover, for the specific area, craft classifications, the existing wage rates, any future wage rates that have been negotiated, hours of work, overtime

rates, fringe benefits, subsistence rates and areas where paid, travel time, and hiring rules.

III. GEOLOGICAL REVIEW

The controlling factor in planning and estimating tunnel excavation is the estimated daily progress that can be maintained. One of the large indeterminates that control daily progress is the nature of the material to be excavated. Therefore, all data concerning this material should be obtained. No matter how difficult the ground, if the estimator assumes the proper progress, the job should make money. In many instances the design engineers will include geological information in the contract drawings, and in other cases, supplementary geological reports are published. All this information should be secured and studied. If the engineers have exploratory drilling done along the tunnel line, cores and hole records should be examined. Structural geologists are often retained by the contractor to submit their findings on the tunnel line and to report on the aggregate deposits. The estimator should inspect the proposed tunnel line and form his own opinion of the structural characteristics of the material.

In tunnel construction, the nature of the material to be excavated affects all construction operations, including drilling speed, mucking speed, amount of supports, overbreak, and water handling. The best progress in tunnel excavation is obtained in a dry, soft rock that has a fast drilling rate, requires no support, and produces a well-broken muck pile or in rock that is suitable for the use of a tunnel-boring machine. The worst progress is made in wet, running ground that requires breastboarding, spiling, and solid lagging between sets or in ground that requires liner plates. In between these two types are many gradations of material, and to properly evaluate progress, an estimator must rely on a geologist, experience, and past history in similar material. A tunnel often passes through many different classes of materials so the characteristics and extent of each class of material should be investigated.

Rigorous geological classification of tunnel material may be made in many ways and such classification is outside the scope of this book. The following general classifications can be understood by laymen and may help the inexperienced engineer to determine the physical characteristics of the tunnel material.

Area Classifications

Tunnels driven in the same general area often encounter the same general types of problems with regard to the material in which they are driven. Experienced estimators know the problems that are encountered in specific areas and use this knowledge when they prepare an estimate. If the history of past tunnels driven in the areas under consideration is not known, it can be formed in the articles published in trade magazines. This history is useful in evaluating the proposed construction.

As an example, the state of California can be divided into areas where tunnels tend to follow certain patterns:

In the granite areas in the Sierra Nevada, the rock will be competent and will present no problems. The best rock is near the Kings River area. Rock decreases in desirability both to the north and south of this point.

On top of the Sierra Nevada, water-bearing gravel beds may be encountered.

In the lower reaches of the Sierra, unless serpentine is encountered, there will be no tunneling problem.

In the Redding-Pit River area, volcanics may be encountered. These may require supports and result in the presence of running and squeezing ground. Tunnels in this area may be subject to large inflows of water.

In the Coast Ranges all tunnels have problems. Supports are necessary; earthquake faults may occur along the tunnel line; squeezing and running ground may be encountered; gas may be present; water may cause problems from high temperature, high pressure, or large inflows. The past history of tunnels driven in the Coast Ranges is that few contractors have made money except by relief from the owners.

In southern California, tunnel driving varies so much that no general rules can be formulated.

In the Owens Valley, many tunnels have passed through volcanic pumice and similar material.

The above general classifications for the state of California include almost all conditions that would be encountered in any area.

Geological Classification

Rocks are classified geologically into the following three divisions:

1. ***Igneous Rocks.*** Igneous rocks are cooled from molten masses and are generally hard crystalline mixtures of feldspar, quartz, and ferromagnesian minerals. Rhyolite, granite, monzonite, felsite, diorite, andesite, gabbro, and basalt are examples. Their classification is difficult, and the layman may best refer to them as granitic, basalt, or traprock or by local names. Igneous rocks are best drilled by percussion drills because of their abrasive properties and resistance to penetration.

2. *Sedimentary Rocks.* Sedimentary rocks were deposited by waters or gravity and include limestones, dolomites, shales, sandstones, conglomerates, gypsum, salt, potash, and others. Most sediments can best be drilled by rotary or rotary-percussion methods.

3. *Metamorphic Rocks.* These are igneous or sedimentary rocks that have been altered by heat or pressure or both. Metamorphic rocks include crystalline limestones, marble, slate, shales, gneiss, quartzite, serpentine, and the iron ores—magnetite and hematite. These rocks are generally drilled with percussion drills.

Hardness Classification

This type of classification determines whether a tunnel-boring machine can be used successfully. If conventional tunnel-driving methods are used, such a classification will help in determining drilling speeds and the amount of explosives required per cubic yard of rock.

The rock's hardness is determined by Mohs' scale.[1] In this scale, the higher the number, the harder the rock. Tunnel-boring-machine experience to date indicates that progress and cost have not been satisfactory in rock with a Mohs' scale rating exceeding 4.5, although future developments in these machines may make them suitable for harder rock. With conventional tunnel-driving methods, the harder the rocks, the slower the drilling speed, and the greater the amount of powder required to break the rock. Below are listed some different types of rock with their corresponding Mohs' scale rating.

Shale. . . . . generally less than 3
Sandstone. . . . . between 3 and 7, depending on cementing action
Limestone. 3
Marble. 3
Slate. 4–5
Granite. 6–7
Schist. 6–7
Gneiss. 6–7
Basalt. 8–9

Particle Size and Stratification

Tunnel material can be classified further according to its ability to be self-supporting and when it requires supports, according to whether the supports should be nominal, light, or heavy. Rock size and stratification influences the overbreak. The more blocky the rock is, the greater the amount of overbreak will be. Incompetent rock will also result in a large amount of overbreak because it tends to run in and spall off from the sides and arch of the tunnel. Rock that requires constant scaling also produces a large amount of overbreak. When a mole is considered, it performs best in consistent rock without stratification. Blocky rock and fine material may cause roof falls which must be removed manually and thus will delay the operation of a tunnel-boring machine. One of the easiest ways to determine whether a tunnel-boring machine will be satisfactory, whether supports will be required, and what the amount of overbreak will be is to segregate the material into the following divisions:

1. *Intact rocks* contain neither joints nor hairline cracks. Breakage occurs across sound rock and is not influenced by joints and fracture patterns. This material should not require supports. Rock breakage should follow the drill-hole pattern. If the rock has a hardness of less than 4.5 on Mohs' scale, a tunnel-boring machine should make excellent progress at low cost.

2. *Massive, moderately jointed rocks* contain joints and hairline cracks, but the blocks between joints are locally grown together or are intimately interlocked. This material does not require supports. If Mohs' hardness is less than 4.5, a tunnel-boring machine should produce excellent results.

3. *Stratified rock* consists of individual strata with little or no resistance to parting along the boundaries between the strata. Slope of this stratification should be determined. If the tunnel is driven in this strata and the tunnel only occasionally passes through the boundaries between the strata, supports may only be required in these areas. If the tunnel is driven through thin, stratified rock beds with joints and fractures so spaced as to destroy the bridging action, continuous supports may be necessary. If thin, weak strata follow along the roof of the tunnel line, continuous supports may be required. Tunnel-boring machines may or may not be suitable.

4. *Moderately blocky or seamy rock* is rock with joints and fractures so spaced that individual rocks are larger than 2 ft across. The rock consists of chemically intact rock fragments that are entirely separated from each other and imperfectly interlocked. In most cases this rock requires supports. Tunnel-boring machines are not recommended in this type of material.

5. *Very blocky and seamy rock* occurs with intervening blocks less than 2 ft across and consists of chemically intact rock fragments entirely separated from each other and imperfectly interlocked. This type of ground needs support. Tunnel-boring machines are not recommended.

6. *Completely crushed or unconsolidated rock* ranges from sand to pebble-size particles that are chemically intact and are very loosely consolidated. This type of rock requires heavy supports, continuous lagging, or use of liner plate. Shields are recommended.

7. *Mud* is fine clay, loam, or disintegrated rock particles saturated with water. Mud requires breastboarding, spiling, continuous lagging,

or liner plates. The use of a shield and, at times, the use of air pressure on the headings are advantageous or essential.

8. *Fault zones* involve only a few inches or, in some active earthquake zones, may last thousands of feet. Often fault zones contain finely ground material in a saturated condition which produces a running effect. Support can vary from none on small fault zones to breastboarding, spiling, sets, and continuous lagging on others. Each fault zone should be investigated.

9. *Squeezing ground* occurs when fine material continues to build up pressure on the periphery of the tunnel. This may require that the contractor use spreaders between sets, it may necessitate trimming and new lagging, or it may even cause the invert of the tunnel to rise. Squeezing ground can occur in both dry and wet tunnels.

Tunnel Supports

Before the estimator can estimate the number and type of tunnel supports necessary, it is important that he know the types available and how and where they are used. Where supports are required, their spacing and size are, with few exceptions, left to the decision of the contractor. Exceptions occur when the specifications call for a maximum spacing of sets or when in certain soft-ground tunnels, the specifications require permanent cast-iron, steel, or concrete tunnel-lining sections to be placed as the tunnel is excavated. (Since the decisions concerning support size and type involve the safety of both the workmen and the tunnel, design engineers leave the responsibility of making these determinations largely to the contractor.) In the past, the most commonly used supports were wood sets, but because of the ease in placing steel supports, wooden supports are now seldom used. The supports used now are roof bolts, steel sets, gunite, temporary liner plate, permanent liner plate made from steel or iron castings, permanent precast concrete blocks, and shotcrete. In water tunnels where steel sets or temporary liner plate is used for support during construction, a permanent concrete lining is installed to provide permanent support, to protect the construction supports from corrosion from hydraulic action, and to improve the hydraulics past these supports.

1. ***Roof, or Rock, Bolts.*** Roof, or rock, bolts are round bars having an expansion shield on one end and threads, a washer, and a bolt on the other. Holes are bored in the side and arch of the tunnel, and the rock bolts are installed in these holes with the expansion shield in the bottom. The bolt is then stressed to expand the shield so its anchorage will develop the full strength of the bolt. The most commonly used rock bolts are from 6 to 12 ft long. Thier purpose is to pin the rock at the surface back to rock that can take this load because

of arch action. Rock bolts are used when nominal or light supports are required or when rock must be pinned back to prevent its slabbing off the arch.

Rock bolts are used with large plate washers. When spalling of the rock is a problem, wire mesh may be stretched between, and anchored by, the bolts to provide protection from rockfalls. If the rock bolt's washer does not provide sufficient area to anchor the surface, steel channels or other structural members may be placed against the rock and anchored by the rock bolts.

When rock bolts are used for tunnel supports in unlined tunnels, they are protected by grouting them in place. Complete grouting of the hole is very difficult to accomplish because of the air that becomes trapped in the hole. To solve this problem of entrapped air, the majority of rock bolts used under these circumstances have a circular hole down the center of the bolt. Grout is then forced through this bolt hole, and the grout fills the hole from the back to the front.

2. *Steel Sets.* Steel sets are made from H sections. They are bent to the shape of the tunnel and fabricated in two or more sections with end butt plates, which are bolted together when the set is erected. On tunnels that are driven full force, the bottom of the set is equipped with a footplate and rests on mudsills. Compression members, called *collar braces* or *struts,* and tension members, called *tie rods,* are installed between sets to hold the sets in a vertical position. (Collar braces or struts are timber or steel-pipe members; tie rods are made from steel rounds.) In ground that develops considerable side pressure, compression struts made from H sections are installed across the bottom of the tunnel to prevent the sets from moving inward. If the stress is not too great, the legs of the set may be held in position by rock-bolting back into the tunnel sides.

Steel channel lagging is used when it is difficult to get underground at the portal, when specifications do not allow wood lagging, or when pay items are set up in the specifications for steel lagging. The majority of the lagging installed is wood. Lagging is used to span between sets. Timber blocking is used to transfer the inward force from the tunnel surface to the sets, lagging, or collar braces. Steel sets are used for nominal, light, medium, or heavy supports. Spacing ranges from side-by-side to 8-ft spacing. Sizes range from 14-in. built-up sections to rolled 4-in. H sections.

In tunnels driven with a top and bottom heading requiring supports, the top-heading supports rest on longitudinal structural members, such as double I beams, placed at the bottom of the top-heading excavation. These longitudinal members are called *wall plates.* One of the major problems of excavating the bottom heading involves the transfer of the support of the sets from the wall plate to the mudsill. One solution to this problem has been to drill or excavate holes from the bottom of the top heading to the bottom of the bottom heading. Supports for the wall plates are then placed in these holes before the bottom heading is excavated. Another solution is to take out the bottom heading in short rounds so that the wall plate is not overstressed when it spans the excavated area prior to being supported. In many instances the wall plate is tied back with rock bolts to help maintain its position. In some circular tunnels and in the arch sections of powerhouse chambers, the wall plates are set in a shelf excavated in the side of the tunnel at spring line and are then concreted in position. The bottom heading is then excavated, and this excavation is stabilized by guniting the tunnel from the wall plate around the bottom half circle to the other wall plate.

On headings driven by multiple drifts, temporary drift supports are used, and as the arch excavation is widened out, sets are installed supporting the entire tunnel arch. In some cases these sets rest on permanent concrete side supports poured in the side drifts.

3. ***Gunite.*** Gunite is used to support some shale tunnels. The gunite not only supports the shale but prevents the shale from disintegrating after becoming wet. In some shale tunnels supported by steel sets, the dampness of the tunnel caused the shale to disintegrate so badly that the supports had to be removed, the sides and bottom cleaned up, and the supports replaced. If these tunnels had been supported with gunite, these operations would not have been necessary.

4. ***Liner Plates.*** Liner plates are used in unstable or running ground and transmit the vertical load horizontally to the surrounding ground. With the liner plate in place, the principal load acts vertically downward on the ring of liner plates, which causes the top of the ring to deflect toward the bottom and the sides to bulge outward. The resistance of the ground at the sides absorbs the vertical load.

Three different types of steel liner plates are used:

a. Pressed-steel liner plates are manufactured from one piece of plate steel. The press forms it to the shape of the tunnel and forms continuous square-edge side flanges. Bolt holes are provided in these flanges so that the liner plate can be bolted to similar members with butt connections to form a complete tunnel lining. Plates come in full-plate and half-plate sizes. Common dimensions for a full plate are 16 by 37¹¹⁄₁₆ in.; for a half plate, 16 by 18²⁷⁄₃₂ in. Thickness varies from ⅛ to ⅜ in. depending on the load on the tunnel.[2]

b. Pressed-steel liner plates supported by steel ribs are used for extremely heavy loads. The steel ribs are of H or I sections bent to shape and placed inside the liner plates. Spacing of the ribs is a maximum of one per liner plate. The ribs should be firmly wedged to the liner plate and connected to each other by rods.

c. Prefabricated liner plate is made from heavy plates and Ts or channels and is used in tunnels under high pressure. The dimensions of each plate of this type are generally larger than those of pressed-steel liner plate.

When liner plates are used in conjunction with a shield, they may incorporate longitudinal stiffeners to take the thrust of the shield's jacks. When used for permanent lining, liner plate sections are made from precast concrete, steel, or cast iron, and are made to great accuracy so that a watertight tunnel can be secured with proper caulking.

Some tunnels, notably subway tunnels, that are excavated with a shield or boring machine, are designed to have the permanent lining erected at the time of excavation, which makes temporary supports unnecessary. This permanent lining consists of precast concrete sections, iron castings, or fabricated steel sections that bolt together in a manner similar to that of liner plate. This type of construction reduces the worry of ground subsidence, an important consideration since subways are generally constructed in areas where subsidence would be hazardous to buildings.

5. *Shotcrete.* Shotcrete is a proposed method of supporting tunnels by which concrete is applied directly behind the tunnel face. The concrete either supports the tunnel fully or allows a greater spacing of the steel sets. This requires that the concrete take a quick and strong early set. The term *shotcrete* refers to the technique of application as much as to the structural material. The material is a dry-mix, carefully graded, coarse aggregate concrete. It is applied by spraying, the required water for hydration being added at the spray nozzle. Quick-setting additives are included in the mix when required to impart early strength to the shotcrete and to accelerate resistance to the effects of blasting. When properly applied, shotcrete not only provides structural support to the recently excavated surfaces, but by adhesion, induces the material adjacent to them to assume a large portion of the loading which would otherwise necessarily be carried by some alternative method of rock support. In other words, shotcrete helps the rock to support itself. Before this method can come into common use, quick-setting additives must be developed further, and the equipment for the application of shotcrete must be improved to increase its capacity. Present equipment has an average capacity of only about 10 cu yd per hr.

Wet Tunnels

Tunnels may be considered from yet another point of view; they may be classified according to whether they will be dry or wet. Dry tunnels occur where the water inflow to the tunnel does not result in any tunnel-driving difficulty and can be handled with the normal size of drainage lines and pumps.

Wet tunnels are those in which the water inflow presents special problems, such as:

1. When the water saturates fine, unconsolidated material and so causes it to flow into the tunnel and produce what is called *running ground.* This type of tunnel must be driven with breastboarding and complete lagging, and, in some cases, compressed air must be used at the heading.

2. When the temperature of the water causes discomfort to the crews driving the tunnel. Excessively high water temperatures are sometimes encountered in volcanic zones. Tunnel driving in this case requires the installation of refrigeration so that men can be safely transported into the tunnel and can work at the face.

3. When the water is under such extreme pressure that it causes trouble in drilling. This pressure, occurring sometimes when tunnels are driven under a high cover, may necessitate special drill hookups and continuous drilling and grouting ahead of the excavation.

4. When continual infiltration of water results in a large amount of panning and care of water during the concrete operation.

5. When the flow at the face is in such quantity that excavation is practical without drilling and grouting ahead of the excavation. In competent rock, grouting can often be done with cement grout. In other ground conditions, it may be necessary to have a chemical-grouting subcontractor grout off the inflow of water.

6. When inflow into the tunnel is such that extra drainage lines and pumps must be installed.

Water in a tunnel is one of the most indeterminate factors affecting tunnel driving. Special attention should be given to folded and faulted areas and volcanic areas, either of which may result in large water inflows and, in the presence of fault gouge or volcanic ash, in running ground.

Tunnels with Special Structural Problems

If the proposed tunnel will encounter any of the following conditions, the difficulties they will involve should be taken into consideration when planning progress and equipment:

1. *Serpentine,* which because of the nature of its formation, has many slick shear planes and usually requires heavy support.

2. *Volcanic formation,* which may have large inflows of water and if volcanic ash is present, may therefore have considerable running ground.

3. *Weak sedimentary rocks* that are extremely folded and faulted

may result in the tunnel's encountering water pockets, gouge zones, squeezing ground, natural gas, and extremely incompetent rock.

4. *Earthquake fault zones* where ground movement may have produced a layer of gouge, where water may be present in large quantities, and where if both are present, there will be running ground.

5. *Artesian water,* which may be of such volume that grouting is necessary and may, with the presence of fine material, produce running ground.

IV. QUANTITY TAKEOFFS

In any discussion of quantity takeoffs it is necessary to define properly three terms: takeoff quantities, bid quantities, and final pay quantities. Each of these quantities may differ from the others for any item of work.

1. Takeoff quantities are quantities taken off the bidding plans and specifications by the estimator and represent to the contractor the most accurate estimated quantities of work to be performed.

2. Bid quantities are quantities printed on the bid comparison sheets. These quantities are furnished by the owner's engineer and used for comparison of bids. The bid quantities multiplied by the unit bid prices will add up to the total bid submitted by each contractor.

3. Final pay quantities are quantities of materials measured during the construction progress. Final pay quantities multiplied by the unit bid prices will add up to the total payment to the contractor.

Accurate quantity takeoffs are required for the preparation of an estimate for the following reasons:

1. Quantity takeoffs are needed to check the bid quantities. If takeoff quantities vary greatly from the bid quantities, this will influence greatly the spreading of the cost of the plant, equipment, indirect labor, escalation, and markup to the bid quantities to arrive at the unit bid prices. On any item where the final pay quantities will be less than the bid quantities, the spread of cost to this item must be held to a minimum or the contractor will not be properly reimbursed for his cost. This is explained in greater detail in Chap. 9.

2. A quantity takeoff is required to determine the lineal feet of tunnel supported with each different type of support and with each different spacing of supports. For an example of this, refer to Chap. 8, Exhibit 3, which is a summary of the quantity takeoffs for Sierra Tunnel. When the supported lengths of tunnel have been determined, the total number and weights of the supports should be computed. This takeoff of lineal feet of supported tunnel and number of supports influences the direct cost of tunnel excavation since a supported tunnel is

more costly to drive than an unsupported tunnel and the closer the spacing of supports, the greater the cost.

3. A quantity takeoff is necessary to determine the amount of overbreak. Overbreak is the volume of excavation removed and concrete placed in a tunnel, outside the pay line. The cost of overbreak excavation and overbreak concrete are not paid for separately, so this cost must be included with the pay quantities. These overbreak quantities must also be considered when the capacity of the construction equipment is determined.

4. Quantity takeoffs are necessary in order to determine the square feet of forms and the form ratio for concrete work other than tunnel lining. On these other concrete items, the largest portion of the construction cost is the cost of the forms for retaining the concrete. The next largest portion of cost is the placing cost, which increases in direct proportion to the increase in form ratio of the concrete. (Form ratio is the square feet of forms per cubic yard of concrete.) The thinner and more complicated a concrete section, the greater the form ratio, and because of its small volume and complexity, the greater the concrete-placing cost. In order to determine the form ratio, the square feet of form contact and the total cubic yards of concrete must be taken off the drawings. For pricing purposes, the forms should be taken off in such a manner that the following information will be available:

a. Square feet of form contact where panel forms can be used:
   Wall forms
   Soffit forms
   Special forms

b. Number of times panel forms may be reused:
   Wall forms
   Soffit forms
   Special forms

c. Square feet of panel forms required:
   Wall forms
   Soffit forms
   Special forms such as curved forms

d. Square feet of built-in-place forms

e. Total square feet of form contact

f. Cubic yards of concrete

g. Form ratio, which is the total square feet of form contact divided by the takeoff quantity of concrete

5. Takeoff quantities are used when the total cost of one operation is divided by the quantity of work to arrive at a unit cost for bidding purposes. This will give a more accurate unit cost than if bid quantities

are used, since the more accurate the quantities are that are used as the divisor, the more accurate the unit is. In this respect the takeoff quantities are considered the more accurate of the two by the contractor.

A summary sheet of quantity takeoffs, as shown in Exhibit 3, Chap. 8, should be prepared. The quantity takeoff calculations should be taken to the estimators' meeting so that if there are any differences in takeoffs among the estimators, they will be available for comparison.

V. REQUEST FOR QUOTATIONS ON PERMANENT MATERIALS AND SUBCONTRACTS

In preparing an estimate, little time or effort should be spent on estimating the cost of permanent materials or subcontracts. These costs are put in the estimate, using past prices as a guide. If the work is to be bid by a joint venture, the sponsoring partner often sends out these prices to be plugged into each partner's estimate, so that at the estimators' meeting, there will not be any time wasted in comparison of costs on these items. An example of the plugged-in prices used is given in Exhibit 4, Chap. 8. Quotations on these items are received from suppliers and subcontractors shortly before the time for bid submission. At this time adjustments are made in the estimate and bid for the difference between these quotation prices and the prices used in the estimate. The procedure used in making these adjustments is described in Chap. 9 and illustrated by Exhibit 18.

The estimator should advertise for prices on permanent materials and subcontracts as soon as possible after securing the bidding documents so that suppliers and subcontractors are informed that the prime contractor is interested in securing their quotations.

Permanent materials for tunnel construction vary depending on the amount of related construction, but include tunnel supports, timber, rock bolts, cement, and concrete admixtures.

The work to be subcontracted depends on the particular prime contractor. The estimator may complete an estimate of the proposed subcontract work with which to check the subcontractor's price. If the subcontractor's price is lower than this estimated price, the work is usually subcontracted. Subcontracting a part of the tunnel excavation is seldom done since the work is so interrelated that a subcontractor performing one operation and failing to meet his scheduled progress causes a delay in the total operation. There is an advantage in subcontracting specialty items that are isolated from the remainder of the work since it allows the contractor to concentrate his efforts on tunnel excavation and concreting. Another advantage of subcontracting work is that it fixes the cost of the work before bid submission.

Work often subcontracted is roadwork, drilling and grouting, furnishing concrete aggregates, and placing reinforcing steel.

VI. JOB WAGE RATES

Tunnel estimates are often prepared by several engineers functioning as a team. In order that all individuals use the same wage rates, these wage-rate computations are usually one of the first tabulations prepared for any estimate.

To prepare this tabulation it is necessary to determine the cost to the contractor of each different labor classification that will be used inside and outside the tunnel. The elements of this labor cost are:

1. Hourly wage rate
2. Percentage of overtime worked, due to:
   a. Change at the heading
   b. Travel time inside the tunnel
   c. Allowance for working through lunch hour
   d. Overtime if over 40-hr week is planned
3. Fringe benefits, such as health and welfare, pension, and apprentice training
4. Workmen's compensation, public liability, and property damage insurance
5. State and federal taxes for social security and unemployment insurance
6. Subsistence, if the job is within a subsistence zone
7. Travel pay, if employees get travel from home to jobsite

For an example of this type of labor determination, refer to Exhibit 5, Chap. 8.

VII. EXCAVATION METHOD

After studying the plans and specifications, inspecting the jobsite, and reviewing the physical characteristics of the tunnel material, the first major decision the estimator must make is the selection of the method of construction.

A tunnel-boring machine should be considered if the tunnel meets the following conditions:

1. Its location should be in soft, consistent rock that has a hardness of 4.5 or less on Mohs' scale. This hardness requirement is based on boring machines' performances up to the time of writing this book. This requirement may change with further development of the machine's cutting action.

2. The tunnel should be long enough to justify the write-off on the first cost of the boring machine. The construction time allowed in the specifications should be sufficient to allow for the purchase and manufacture of the boring machine. This purchase and manufacturing time will vary between 9 months and 1 year.

3. The tunnel must have a round shape, or there must be an alternate bid schedule allowing bids on a circular tunnel.

4. Suitability of the machine for the proposed tunnel will decrease if the rock along the tunnel line contains hard intrusions, if roof falls will occur frequently, or if squeezing or running ground is anticipated.

The tunnel-boring machine should be given first consideration when the estimator is choosing construction methods. This priority is due to the fact that under proper ground conditions, greater progress will be obtained and a smaller crew can be used with a boring machine than if excavation is performed in the conventional manner. Also, since the machine can bore to the neat line of the tunnel, overbreak excavation and overbreak concrete will be at a minimum. Another advantage of using the boring machine compared with conventional tunneling methods, is that it will cause less disturbance to the surrounding material, which reduces the amount of supports required. Because of its ability to bore the tunnel without disturbance to the surrounding material, the use of a tunnel-boring machine is sometimes required by the specifications.

If it is decided to use a tunnel-boring machine, it can be used without a shield in an unsupported tunnel. However, if supports are necessary, a shield should be provided so that the supports can be erected inside the shield and excavation can progress without delay.

Tunnels in which boring machines cannot be used are driven in the conventional manner. The primary decisions influencing method in these tunnels concern whether or not a shield should be used or the tunnel should be driven under air pressure. If the tunnel passes through loose or fine material which will readily run into the tunnel, a shield is necessary. If this material is under pressure from water, then air pressure may be necessary.

No general discussion can be given on powerhouse construction since each individual powerhouse presents its own special problems and the decision concerning the method used must be based upon the access that can be provided.

Determining Number and Locations of Headings

The next step in determining the excavation method is to determine the number of headings that will have to be worked to meet the owner's time schedule.

To date, in tunnels driven with boring machines, one machine has had the capacity to complete the work in time. The machines have started at the outlet portals and progressed to the inlets. On contracts having a number of short power tunnels through dam abutments, one machine has completed the tunnel work required on each contract. On future work the tunnel might be of such a length, or the contract time so short, that more machines will be required. Therefore, anticipated progress should be checked against available time to determine the number of machines required.

Since the preliminary scheduling to determine the number of headings required must be developed before the actual estimated progress is computed, it is accurate enough at this time to use a production of 40 to 90 ft per day in soft, consistent rock for a tunnel-boring machine. Concreting time similar to that used for the conventional tunneling method should be allowed. Approximately 9 months to 1 year must be allowed for the manufacture and delivery of the tunnel-boring machine. The above production figure should only be used for the purpose of this study and should not influence the estimator when he determines his estimated progress in the detailed portion of the estimate.

When driving tunnels by the conventional tunnel-driving method, a preliminary schedule should be developed so that the number of headings required to complete the job within the contract time can be determined. In conventional tunnel driving, the number and location of headings greatly influences cost. Therefore, an approximate cost analysis should be prepared to determine the economical number of headings and their locations. (This type of a study for Sierra Tunnel is shown by Exhibit 6, Chap. 8.) For Sierra Tunnel, this study indicated that the least construction cost would be incurred if the tunnel were driven with a double heading setup at a construction adit.

To facilitate explanation of the method of preparing the cost analysis, the following terms are first defined:

1. *Portal* The permanent entrance or outlet to a tunnel. If the contract covers a tunnel that daylights because of a ground depression, there will be four portals, two of them close to each other.

2. *Heading* The face, or end, of the tunnel excavation. This is the point at which excavation is carried on to advance the tunnel.

3. *Adit* A short section of tunnel, driven from the surface and intersecting the tunnel. An adit is often constructed by the contractor for his convenience in order to have additional headings at which to work.

4. *Construction shaft* A vertical shaft excavated from the surface to intersect the tunnel line. This may be a pay item or may be constructed by the contractor for his convenience. Its purpose is to furnish access to two additional tunnel headings.

5. *Single-heading setup* Plant equipment and manpower are located so that one tunnel heading is advanced from one surface location. A single-heading setup is generally located at a tunnel portal.

6. *Double-heading setup* Plant equipment and manpower are located at one surface location so that two tunnel headings can be excavated from the same location. Double headings are located at adits, shafts, or where a tunnel daylights for a short distance, which results in two adjacent portals. Double headings should be used wherever possible because they are more economical than two single headings. Savings can be made in outside facilities, overhead, and service labor where one setup can be used for two headings.

7. *Alternate heading crew* A single drilling crew which works at one heading while a separate mucking crew is mucking out the other heading. When these crews have finished both drilling and mucking, they are switched from one heading to the other. An alternate heading crew is generally used where there is a double-heading setup until such time that rock conditions or travel time between headings makes its use impractical. When alternating crews are planned, the rock should be consistent in both headings so that the drilling and mucking operations can stay in balance. On a single- or double-heading crew, when the drilling crew is drilling, the mucker and mucking crew is idle, and while the mucker is operating, the drilling crew is idle (except for a few men employed in switching cars and barring down or sprinkling the muck pile). An alternating crew is slightly larger than a single-heading crew because there cannot be any duplication of a driller's duties in the mucking cycle. However, the progress in the two headings for the alternating crew is about 50 to 60 percent greater than that of a single-heading crew. Theoretically the alternating crew's progress should be almost twice as great since the transfer time between headings is the only lost time. But, owing to the delays in switching men and equipment and the impossibility of keeping the two headings in a perfect time balance, the production of twice a single-heading progress is seldom obtained. The distances that alternating heading crews can be used economically vary for each particular tunnel but generally fall within a range of from 2,500 to 5,000 lin ft in each heading direction. Excavation cost when using an alternating crew is less than when employing a double-heading crew because of the more efficient use of the men.

The preliminary schedule and cost analysis should tabulate in comparative form the progress and comparative cost of driving the tunnel by every method that the estimator can visualize, so that the final estimate can be prepared for the best solution. Consideration should be given to double headings, alternate headings, adits, and construction shafts. If the best solution requires the construction of either an adit or a shaft and these are not listed in the bid quantities as pay items, then, when the estimate is priced, their cost must be included in plant and equipment.

Normally only a short period of time is available for the preparation of this comparative study, so the following cost and rough production rates are accurate enough to be used in this study. It must be emphasized that they should only be used in this study and actual cost and progress for the particular tunnel should be computed for the remainder of the estimate.

1. In constructing a shaft where tunnel driving is to be performed through the shaft, allow 6 to 9 months before the start of tunnel driving if the shaft servicing is to be accomplished by a movable crane or stiffleg. If shaft servicing is to be done by a headframe and hoist, allow 9 months to 1 year before tunnel driving can start. If the shaft contains a headframe and hoist, the cost of shaft construction should be approximately $1 million.

2. In sinking a shaft, the progress should be from 5 to 10 ft per day, depending on shaft diameter.

3. If a construction adit is considered necessary, the cost of driving the adit varies considerably, depending on ground conditions. If it can be driven at a rate of 40 lin ft per day, cost, including the concrete plug, will be approximately $300 per ft. The cost of other rates of progress varies proportionately. In considering the construction time required to construct the adit, extra time should be allowed for excavating a Y connection from the adit to the tunnel.

4. When a tunnel is excavated in good rock without supports, progress attained will vary from 50 to 70 ft per day.

5. Excavating a tunnel in rock with supports spaced at from 4- to 6-ft centers should produce from 30 to 40 ft of progress per day.

6. Excavating a tunnel in rock requiring closer spacing of supports or breastboarding should result in approximately 10 to 20 ft of progress per day.

7. Excavating a tunnel in squeezing or running ground produces from 5 to 10 ft of progress per day.

8. Excavating a tunnel with a shield in comparatively dry sand should make from 60 to 100 ft of progress per day.

9. When a shield is used in incompetent rock, progress should be between 10 and 30 ft per day.

10. In excavating a large tunnel, the tunnel is excavated down to spring line, or slightly below spring line with a top heading, with standard tunneling procedure and progress. The bottom section is taken out later by faster and cheaper methods.

11. In raising a pilot shaft, the progress should be between 10 and 20 ft per day.

12. In downdrilling a shaft, when muck is removed through the pilot raise, progress should be from 5 to 15 ft per day, depending on the shaft's diameter.

13. In excavating an underground powerhouse, production should be approximately 2½ to 3 cu yd per manshift.

14. For cleaning the invert to rock before concrete placing, production should be approximately 250 to 500 ft per day.

15. For preparing the invert for concrete where tunnel muck can be graded and specifications do not require cleanup to rock, allow a progress of approximately 500 to 900 ft per day.

16. When invert concrete is poured, the estimator can expect approximately 500 to 900 ft of progress per day, depending upon the tunnel diameter.

17. If the arch pour is a continuous one, approximately 300 ft of progress can be attained per day. The limits of any concrete pour are set by the capacities of the concrete plant and the concrete-placing equipment. Concrete placement has seldom exceeded 2,400 cu yd per day. If the tunnel is reinforced, production will be lessened to a degree that is dependent on the extent of reinforcement required.

18. If curbs are used and not poured during excavation, the curb pour should progress at from 300 to 500 ft per day.

The foregoing figures are based on an operation involving three shifts a day. These figures are provided for the sole purpose of preparing a study to determine the number and location of headings and should be changed when the detailed estimate schedule is prepared. This detailed schedule should take into account the structural characteristics of the tunnel material, the size of the tunnel, the method of construction, and the amount and type of equipment.

VIII. SELECTION OF EQUIPMENT

The next estimating step is to choose the type and the amount of equipment and plant required and to estimate their cost.

In selecting the equipment for a tunnel, two objectives should be kept in mind: The contractor wants to accomplish the work with the least construction cost and to complete the work in the shortest possible time. These two objectives are interrelated since approximately 80 percent of the construction cost of tunnels is labor, supplies, equipment operation, and equipment write-off; these are a direct function of construction time. In other types of construction these factors are a much smaller proportion of the total cost, which results in a much lower cost-time relationship. For example, in industrial construction these factors run from 10 to 20 percent of the total cost. As a result, the scheduled construction time of industrial construction is controlled by other economic factors.

When equipment is selected for tunnel construction, the more money that is spent for tunnel equipment, the less will be the amount of money spent for tunnel excavating labor. Tunnel equipment is a fixed sum, so the equipment write-off per lineal foot of tunnel will decrease as the length of the tunnel increases. Excavation labor per lineal foot of tunnel is independent of tunnel length and varies only with the type of equipment provided. Taking these two facts into account, the longer the tunnel is, the greater is the amount that can be spent for equipment in order to save labor. Similarly, the shorter the tunnel is, the more can be spent for excavating labor in order to reduce the equipment cost.

The plant and equipment required for different methods of tunnel construction have been described in previous chapters. The type and amount of equipment selected should meet the following criteria:

1. The type of equipment selected should fit the most economical method of driving the tunnel. In some cases it may be necessary to estimate the cost of using two different types of equipment in order to find the type that will give the lowest construction cost.
2. The equipment should be suitable for the type of ground to be encountered. Whether a shield, mole, or a particular type of conventional tunneling equipment is used is determined by ground conditions.
3. The equipment should be balanced against the volume of work to be done. The larger the volume of work, the more equipment can be justified.
4. There must be enough units of equipment of sufficient capacity to complete the work on schedule.
5. The equipment should be in proper balance with itself. That is, equipment should be provided in such amounts that the drilling cycle balances the mucking cycle, the diesel equipment balances the ventilation system, and the compressed-air consumption balances the compressed-air production.
6. The equipment should fit the cross section of tunnel to be constructed. To check this equipment clearance, drawings should be made showing the excavated cross section of tunnel, steel sets, vent pipe, water, compressed air, drainage pipes, and track (see Drawing 3, Chap. 2). On this cross section, sketches

should be made showing the clearance required for operating and passing the drilling, excavating, hauling, and concreting equipment. This drawing should illustrate the maximum size of equipment that can be used in the tunnel and show whether it will be necessary to enlarge the tunnel at intervals for car passers or passing trucks. If a main-line jumbo is used, the swing clearance it requires because of overhanging the wheel trucks should be checked.

7. The equipment should comply with local laws and good safety practices.
8. When a tunnel is excavated in hard rock with the conventional method of tunnel driving, the more drills used, the faster the tunnel is driven. Thus, equipment should be selected to utilize as many drills as can be economically worked at the face. There are so many different types and capacities of drills for hard-rock tunneling that no other general rules for equipment selection can be formulated. For further information on drills, Chap. 2 should be reviewed.
9. When a tunnel is excavated in incompetent rock by the conventional method of tunnel excavation, very few drill holes are required and drilling rates are fast. Therefore, the number of drills and men required to drill out a round should be held to a minimum. A large percentage of the miners' time is required for setting supports. The amount of labor required for this operation instead of the number of drills at the face may control crew size. The amount and capacity of mucking and haulage equipment should be controlled by the estimated daily progress (explained in the next step of estimating).
10. In concrete-lined tunnels where the combined pay and nonpay concrete is less than 9 cu yd per lin ft of tunnel, where the invert concrete is one-fourth the total, and the poured invert can support traffic in 16 hr.
    a. Provide for arch forms sufficient for pouring 300 lin ft of arch per day.
    b. Provide for an invert bridge 600 ft long.
    c. Estimate the average concrete production per day as three-fourths the amount of concrete per lineal foot of tunnel times 300. For a tunnel 9 cu yd per lin ft, concrete production will average approximately 2,000 cu yd per day, which is maximum average pour with one concrete setup. Size the mixing plant, concrete transporting equipment, and placing equipment for 120 percent of average production. For the tunnel requiring 9 cu yd per lin ft, the size of equipment should be

capable of producing, transporting, and placing 2,400 cu yd of concrete per day.

11. In a concrete-lined tunnel where the combined pay and nonpay concrete is over 9 cu yd per lin ft, where the invert concrete is one-fourth of the total, and when the invert concrete can support a load in 16 hr:
    a. Provide enough arch forms for an average production of 2,000 cu yd per day.
    b. Provide an invert bridge, the length of which is twice the arch-pour length.
    c. Provide mixing plant and concrete transporting equipment and placing equipment with a capacity of 2,400 cu yd of concrete per day.
12. If progress as computed in item 11 is not adequate for a large tunnel, an alternative method of handling concreting operations allows increased progress. For this method, facilities should be provided so that two concrete trains can be loaded and unloaded at the same time. Likewise, two concrete placers, each with a capacity of 100 cu yd per hr, should be used. The length of forms and the invert bridge and the capacities of the concrete-mixing and transporting equipment as computed in item 11 should be doubled.
13. An invert bridge is not required for a concrete-lined tunnel poured by the full-circle method. For this type of tunnel, when the combined pay and nonpay concrete is less than 6⅔ cu yd per lin ft of tunnel:
    a. Provide sufficient arch forms to pour 300 lin ft of arch per day.
    b. Compute the average daily production as 300 times the concrete yardage per lineal foot.
    c. Provide mixing, transporting, and placing equipment for 120 percent of the average daily capacity.
14. For concrete-lined tunnels poured by the full-circle method, having over 6⅔ cu yd of concrete per lin ft, size the plant as shown in items 11 and 12 and then adjust in the same manner as for item 13 above for full-circle pours.

IX. ESTIMATED PROGRESS AND PREPARATION OF A CONSTRUCTION SCHEDULE

Because estimated progress and the selection of equipment are so interrelated, after progress is determined, a review and an adjustment of the equipment are generally necessary.

Excavation Progress with Conventional Driving Method

The lineal feet of tunnel that can be excavated at each heading per day is the measure of the excavation progress. This progress is determined by the length of each round and the number of rounds that can be excavated in one day. In a supported tunnel, the round length is limited to the distance between the sets. In an unsupported tunnel, the length of a round is determined by the type of cut used and the diameter of the tunnel. When a burn cut is used, it is theoretically possible to use any length round. In practice, production has seldom increased if rounds over 10 ft long have been used. When a V or diamond cut is used, the round length is limited to a distance of not more than two-thirds the diameter of the tunnel. If longer rounds are attempted, a large amount of drilled but unbroken rock will be left at the end of the round.

To determine the length of the rounds, it is first necessary to estimate how much of the tunnel is supported and the spacing of the supports. This spacing of supports depends upon the rock conditions and is estimated after reviewing the geological information available. To estimate the time required to excavate a round, separate round calculations should be made for each anticipated length of round and for each type of material that the tunnel passes through. When it is anticipated that the tunnel will encounter ground that is running or squeezing, requires breastboarding, or includes large flows or high-pressure water, then round calculations cannot be estimated accurately and only judgment on the lineal feet accomplished per day can be used.

When round calculations are made, the time required to drill, shoot, and muck out each round depends on lineal feet of drilling, drilling speed, number of drills, time required to load the holes with powder, shooting and ventilating time, mucking time, time required to place supports, and miscellaneous delay time. Exhibit 7, Chap. 8, illustrates the amount of time required to excavate one round and the number of rounds and the lineal feet excavated per day for various round lengths and different types of rock.

The lineal feet of drilling required is found by multiplying the average length of holes drilled times the number of holes. The average length of holes is assumed to be 1 ft longer than the length of round pulled.

The number of holes required per round is dependent upon the diameter of the tunnel and how the rock will break, or in other words, its hardness. A measure of how the rock breaks is the pounds of explosives required per cubic yard of excavation. The type of cut used also has an effect on the number of holes required. A rule of thumb for determining the number of holes needed is: In a 12- to 14-ft tunnel driven through granite, one hole is required for every 5 sq ft of face. In tunnels with smaller diameters, the square feet per hole decreases, while in tunnels with larger diameters, the square feet per hole increases. As the rock decreases in hardness, the number of holes required also decreases. One of the best methods for estimating the number of holes required is to research past records of tunnels of similar size and in similar rock to find out how many holes were drilled.

Drill penetration ranges from 40 to 120 lin ft per hr. An average penetration of 60 lin ft per hr can be expected in granite. As the rock gets softer, penetration rate increases to 100 lin ft per hr in sandstones and shales. In rocks that are harder than granite, the penetration rate decreases rapidly.

The time required for loading the holes is dependent upon the number of holes and the crew size for loading the holes. When loading holes with powder, one miner will generally load a hole in 4 min.

Mucking time is determined by the size of the mucking machines used and the time required to switch cars. A rule for determining mucking time is: One mucker will load a haul unit in 3 min, and at the end of the mucking cycle, 15 min will be used in final cleanup.

After completion of the round calculations, the number of heading days for a single, for alternating, and for double-heading crews should be tabulated for estimating purposes. The working days at each location should be tabulated and shown on a construction schedule. In computing this time, delay time for portaling-in the tunnel, changing equipment, making Y connections, etc., should be allowed. An example of the work involved for portaling-in is shown by Photograph 28 which was taken during the portaling-in operations for the access tunnel to the T. 2 Powerhouse in Australia. Photograph 29 shows the completed portal and the office, shops, and dump area at the portal location.

For examples of a typical construction schedule, refer to those prepared for the Sierra Tunnel as shown by Exhibit 8*A*, Chap. 2 (shown in bar chart form), or Exhibit 8*B* (in critical path form). The bar chart was prepared to show an allowance for some delay time. The critical path schedule was prepared according to the standard procedure of not allowing any delay time for the critical path. The delay time accounts for the difference in completion time between the two schedules. By examination of the schedule, it can be seen that under a crash program, the construction could have been completed earlier if more transportation equipment had been provided so that fan-line removal, resetting of steel, and cleanup could all have been done concurrently on one leg, while excavation or concreting was on the other leg. Further

Photo 28 Portaling-in for the access tunnel to the T. 2 Powerhouse, Australia.

Photo 29 Portal of access tunnel, ventilation pipes, office, shops, and dump area. Access tunnel portal for T. 2 Powerhouse, Australia.

time savings would have resulted if the concrete-mixing and transportation equipment capacities had been increased so that invert concrete could be placed on one leg while arch concrete was placed on the other. These savings in time could have amounted to 99 days but would have necessitated a large expenditure in plant and equipment.

Concrete Progress

The cost of the concrete lining in a tunnel is one of the most neglected items in tunnel estimating. For this reason, on many tunnel construction jobs the contractor has made money on tunnel driving, but has lost it on tunnel concrete because the estimated cost of concrete was too low. As mentioned in Chap. 3, we recommend that progress be estimated separately on each of the following concrete operations so that a suitable time allowance for each will be included:

1. Removal of fan line. Progress here is determined by:
   a. Length of joints.
   b. Diameter of the pipe.
   c. How many joints can be carried on one transporting unit.
   d. Number of cranes used to unhook, uncouple, and lower.
   e. Number of haulage units used.
2. Reset steel sets, retimber, and remove tights. In a tunnel perfectly driven in ground that is not squeezing, there would be no work to be done under this item. However, since there is no perfect job, progress is determined by:
   a. Amount of supported ground. Ordinarily, the majority of this work involves resetting steel and retimbering.
   b. Whether or not squeezing ground is encountered. This is a large factor in resetting of steel sets and retimbering.
   c. Amount of heavy ground. The heavier the ground, the more retimbering will have to be done.
   d. Nature of the ground. In a tunnel driven through blocky rock there will be more tights than in one that is driven through rock that breaks fine.
3. Tunnel cleanup. The biggest progress factor in this item is the cleanup requirements set forth in the specifications. Other factors are the nature of the materials the tunnel is driven through and the amount of water in the tunnel. Cleanup production figures vary from 500 lin ft under some specifications to 1,500 lin ft under others.
4. Panning and care of water. The amount of time spent on this item is directly proportional to the amount of water in the tunnel.
5. Arch and invert concrete. Past records indicate that certain

assumptions can be made concerning the placing rates for arch and invert concrete:

a. When concrete is hauled by rail-mounted agitators into a tunnel with one setup for loading the agitators and one setup for unloading, maximum production rates are limited to approximately 100 cu yd per hr. If 80 percent efficiency is used, this results in an average production rate of approximately 2,000 cu yd per day.

b. Records on various tunnels indicate that very seldom is an average of 300 lin ft of arch pour per day exceeded.

c. The cubic yards per lineal foot of concrete in the invert pour is approximately one-fourth of the total in the tunnel.

d. The concrete in the invert can support traffic 16 hr after it is placed.

With these assumptions, arch and invert concrete placing can be balanced in the following manner:

a. Find the lineal feet of arch that can be placed with an average production of 2,000 cu yd of concrete per day. This amount of concrete placed per day should include overbreak concrete.

b. If this lineal footage of arch exceeds 300 lin ft per day, limit average production to the 300 lin ft figure.

c. Multiply the lineal feet of arch by 3 to find lineal feet of invert that can be placed per day.

In very large tunnels, it is possible to double the maximum placing rate of 100 cu yd of concrete per hr and thus double the progress. When this is planned, allowances should be made in the plant and equipment cost for a greater mixing-plant capacity, facilities for two concrete trains that can be loaded and unloaded simultaneously, increased number of trains, measures taken for the fast routing of trains, and increased concrete-placing capacity.

6. Low-pressure grouting. Progress is a function of the quantity of grout required per lineal foot of tunnel. The two factors that determine this quantity are the type of material the tunnel passes through and whether or not the arch of the tunnel has been completely filled with concrete.
7. Final cleanup. This is removal of the track and any other cleanup required. If all other concrete operations have been performed correctly, this should be of short duration.
8. Time required to assemble equipment and start each operation, as well as time required to move operations between headings.

The times required for the above operation should be tabulated to use in concrete estimating and should be shown on the construction schedule so that the overall construction time can be determined.

X. COST OF OUTSIDE DEVELOPMENT

Since the locations that will be used to excavate the tunnel have been determined, the cost of the outside work required to develop these portals or adits can now be estimated. This may involve access roads and the development of a power source and water supply. Other cost items are site development, development of waste disposal areas, erection of outside buildings, facilities and trackage, and the opencut excavation required to develop the portals. If any of the above items of work is included in the bid schedule as a bid item, then its cost is a direct cost item. For those not listed in the bid schedule, their cost should be charged to plant and equipment.

XI. ESTIMATING THE COST OF TUNNEL EXCAVATION LABOR

The noise generated in the restricted area of the tunnel face makes it difficult to continue to instruct men on new duties. For this reason, crew operations should be set up so that they are repetitious and each man has the same duties in each cycle.

Excavation labor cost is the number of crew days multiplied by the labor cost of the crew per day. Excavation crew days were determined in the previous step of estimating production. Cost per crew day is computed by multiplying the number of men in each labor classification by the cost per shift. Labor cost per manshift has previously been determined under Step VI, so the only remaining step in determining excavation labor is to set the crew size.

Crew size is determined by the number of drills required and the desired progress per day. Daily progress times the cubic yards of pay and nonpay excavation gives the cubic yards of excavated material to be handled per day. This yardage determines the capacity of the mucking machine and number of haulage units required. Local labor laws and union regulations should be checked since these sometimes provide a minimum limit of manpower in crafts such as drillers, brakemen, and electricians. In determining the crew size for tunnel estimates, it is a general practice not to charge equipment operators and equipment mechanics as so many hours of equipment operated, but rather to list them with the other labor. On the other hand, if rock bolts are used, they are generally installed by extra men and the labor cost is placed directly against the rock bolt item so that these miners are not included in the regular excavation crew.

Crew size is worked out on a daily basis rather than on a shift basis, since some crafts are required for only one shift per day. As a rule of thumb, the total crew per day should equal 8 to 12 times the number of drills. The larger the tunnel is, the smaller is the number of men required per drill. Among different estimators, most variations in tunnel crew size will not be due to the number of drillers or drills but will vary with each estimator's opinion of the men required to keep the drillers working, such as mechanics, electricians, carpenters, and track laborers. Setting the number of these men is not a matter of estimating but rather a matter of reviewing how many men were used on similar work in the past.

In determining crew size, it is necessary to allow one miner per drill, plus a nipper on the jumbo. The bull-gang crew is only used on the daylight shift. This crew's function is to lay track; keep up track; maintain ditches; extend air, water, drainage, and vent lines; and do all the housekeeping in the tunnel. The number of locomotives necessary is determined by how many are required at the face for switching cars and how many for hauling trains. The number of mechanics is proportional to the equipment, drills to be maintained, and bits to be sharpened. There should be two electricians on the daylight shift to extend power lines and one on other shifts for maintenance.

The cost per day for an excavation crew is determined by multiplying the number of men in each craft by the shift rate and then totaling the result to arrive at the crew cost per day. From this tabulation an average cost per man-day can be determined and this cost can be used to determine the cost of different-sized excavation crews. The accuracy of this method is within the degree of accuracy of any estimate. When the total excavation labor is determined, it is arbitrarily split between tunnel excavation, steel sets, and timbering. To the tunnel excavation labor, found by multiplying the heading days required by cost of crews, must be added an allowance for Saturday and Sunday maintenance work.

When takeoff quantities differ from bid quantities, the most accurate unit cost figure is found by dividing the total cost of excavation by takeoff quantities. For bid comparison a unit bid price, based on this unit cost, is used for multiplication by bid quantities. This method gives the most accurate unit cost figure and does not penalize the contractor in total bid comparisons with other contractors.

XII. ESTIMATING THE COST OF TUNNEL EXCAVATION SUPPLIES

Supplies cover the invoice cost of materials necessary to do the excavation, such as caps and powder for excavation. Included in this classification are the fuel, oil, and repair parts necessary to operate equipment; the rubber clothing and tools required by the construction personnel; the cost of electrical power and materials to keep the equipment in operation and the electrical system functioning; heating, water, and any other utility component. In summary, supply cost includes the cost of all materials not charged to plant and equipment, permanent materials, or indirect expense.

Excavation supplies vary with the type of material in which the tunnel is excavated; the type, amount, and length of operation time of equipment; number of men employed; and length of time of employment.

1. Supplies that vary with tunnel material are:
   a. Powder and exploders. The cost is determined by the number of holes per round, the number of rounds required, the pounds of powder required per cubic yard of excavation to break the material properly, and the type of powder used. One of the best methods of checking the pounds of powder per cubic yard is to research the history of tunnels of the same size in similar rock. As the diameter of a tunnel increases, the pounds of powder per cubic yard decrease. Also, as a rock decreases in hardness, the pounds of powder per cubic yard decrease. If ammonium nitrate prills can be used, their cost is approximately one-fourth that of powder. Their use depends on local laws and the amount of water in the tunnel. This type of explosive is difficult to use if water is flowing out of the drill holes since they will not propagate in this situation. Often ammonium nitrate prills are used for all holes but the lifters where water inflow requires that regular powder be used. Whether it is powder or prills, all powder has to be stamped "permissible" by a recognized powder company. Whether ammonium nitrate prills or powder is used, exploders will be required. In some soft-rock tunnels, the exploder cost is greater than the powder cost.
   b. Steel and bit cost. This cost varies with the type of rock. Carbide-insert bits are now used throughout the industry, since the speed of drilling and life of this type of bit has made steel bits obsolete. Bit life per carbide-insert bits will vary from 10 to 1,000 lin ft per bit, depending on the abrasiveness of the rock being drilled. Steel cost is based on drilling 1,000 lin ft of holes with one piece of steel.
   c. Timber. This cost varies with the amount of supports required and the amount of timber included in the pay quantities.

2. Equipment supplies which vary with the type, amount, and length of time the equipment is operated. This type of supplies includes electric power, fuel, oil, grease, and repair parts.
3. Supplies dependent on the number of men employed and length of their employment include:
   a. Rubber boots and protective clothing for each man.
   b. Small tools.
   c. Miscellaneous supplies, which vary according to the particular tunnel.

Allowance should be made in the supply cost for an inventory loss. If this allowance is not made in the estimate of supplies, it should be carried as a separate item of cost.

XIII. ESTIMATING THE COST OF CONCRETE LINING LABOR

Concreting crews and the cost per crew day should be set up in the same manner as excavation labor, in the eight concrete operations described previously.

Concrete crews vary with each type of setup and can only be described in general terms. For example, the arch concrete-placing crew consists of personnel for the following operations:

Aggregate handling
Concrete mixing and concrete loading
Concrete hauling
Concrete dumping and transferring of concrete to the placing equipment
Operating concrete-placing equipment
Moving pipe
Control of slick line
Operating vibrators
Moving forms
Curing and patching
Repairing and maintaining equipment (mechanics)
Moving power lines and maintaining equipment (electricians)
Operating compressors
Warehousing
Surveying

For more detail on the concrete crews, see the typical tunnel estimate in Chap. 8.

XIV. ESTIMATING THE COST OF CONCRETE LINING SUPPLIES

Concrete supplies should include the following:

1. Concrete aggregates, including the aggregates in the overbreak concrete.
2. Cement waste and other nonpay cement. Cement in overbreak concrete is often paid for by the owner.
3. Form lumber. This is dependent upon the amount of bulkhead forms and the square feet of forms required for structural concrete.
4. Form hardware and form oil. This is dependent on the total square feet of form contact area.
5. Power. Cost is determined by the horsepower of the electrical equipment operated, lighting requirements, and period of time it is used.
6. Fuel, lubricants, grease, and repair parts. This cost is controlled by type of equipment, number of units, and hours of operation.
7. Rubber, protective clothing, small tools, and miscellaneous supplies. The cost of these items is based on the number of men employed and the length of their employment.

XV. ESTIMATING THE DIRECT COST OF OTHER BID ITEMS

The direct cost of excavation and concrete will be the major part of the direct cost for any tunnel job. Cost of the labor for installing structural steel sets and for installing timber supports will have been separated from the excavation labor when the direct excavation labor cost was estimated. This labor must now be placed against the appropriate bid items. Direct cost must now be estimated for the remaining items.

XVI. DIRECT COST TABULATIONS

The direct cost for all the bid items should now be posted to a direct cost spread sheet (Exhibit 9), which has separate columns for labor, supplies, permanent materials, and subcontracts.

XVII. ESTIMATING THE COST OF PLANT AND EQUIPMENT

This equipment tabulation should be started when the equipment is first selected. As the direct cost is estimated and special equipment and plant requirements are found necessary for proper execution of the work, these units should be added to the plant and equipment sheets. Now this tabulation of the amount and cost of the plant and equipment should be completed.

Information supplied by salesmen and quotations put out by manufacturers are invaluable for pricing equipment. Estimating quotations on equipment are generally 10 percent higher than the prices paid at the time of purchase, and the estimator may wish to adjust his own estimate accordingly. When the first cost of the plant and equipment is estimated, the amount of salvage for each item of equipment should also be estimated. The total salvage revenue, less the cost of dismantling, move-out, and sales, is subtracted from the first cost of plant and equipment to arrive at the net cost of plant and equipment to the job.

If allowances are not made in the salvage value for the cost of dismantling the equipment, moving it out, and general job cleanup, then a separate item containing this cost should be added to the estimate.

Both the number of years that the equipment will be in service and the number of hours it will work should be considered when setting the salvage value. Maximum equipment life is often set at 5 years or 10,000 hr of service. Salvage can be estimated for this predicted maximum life. As an aid in determining salvage value, various publications are available that set forth the values of secondhand construction equipment. One of these is the *Green Guide*, published by Equipment Guide Book Company in Palo Alto, California.

If part of the equipment used is rented, this rental of bare equipment that is nonoperated and not maintained should be included in plant and equipment cost so that the direct cost records in the estimate will not be distorted. The cost of rental should be kept as a separate division in the plant and equipment steps of estimate preparations so it will not cause confusion when the salvage value of purchased equipment is computed.

For an example of the method of tabulating the amount, cost, and salvage value of plant and equipment, refer to Exhibit 10, Chap. 8, which was prepared for the Sierra Tunnel estimate.

XVIII. ESTIMATING THE COST OF INDIRECT EXPENSE

The majority of the items in indirect cost vary with the length of the construction period, the efficiency of the overhead personnel, and the number of reports that are required to be submitted to the owner and to the contractor's main office. The items that are based on other factors are office equipment, engineering equipment, taxes, insurance, and the bond premium. The bond and builder's risk insurance premiums cannot be computed until the approximate value of the contract has been determined.

The distribution of the items that compose indirect cost is as follows:

1. Labor
   a. Supervision. This item includes the salaries and payroll burden of the project manager and as many tunnel superintendents as there are locations of work. Other supervisory labor, including walkers, mechanical superintendents, and shift superintendents, is charged to direct cost.
   b. Engineering. The wages, salaries, and payroll burdens of the job engineer and any office engineers are charged to this item. Surveyors are included in the tunnel crew and charged to direct cost.
   c. Office force. This includes wages, salaries, and payroll burdens for accounting, purchasing, and other clerical labor. It does not include the warehousemen, who are included in the tunnel crew and charged to direct cost.
2. Other Cost
   a. Transportation of supervisory personnel. The cost of operation and maintenance of automobiles and pickups required on the project is covered here.
   b. Office and engineering supplies. Included here are office rent if applicable; heat, light, and power for the office; postage; stationary; purchasing and accounting forms; engineering supplies; and any other similar miscellaneous expense.
   c. Telephone and telegraph. This item covers telephone and telegraph charges. Most estimates do not provide enough money for this service.
   d. Entertainment and expense accounts. The cost of entertaining the client and other visitors should be included in this item. This cost also covers any expense connected with any traveling by supervisory personnel.
   e. Licenses and fees. The cost of licenses and fees required to do the work is covered here.
   f. Blue prints, photostats, and photographs. The cost of making prints and photostats and taking job pictures is covered here.
   g. Office equipment. The cost of office equipment may be placed either here or under plant and equipment. It is the net cost to the job of the office equipment provided. The

net cost is first price less salvage, or the rental cost of the equipment.

h. Engineering equipment. This is another item which may be carried either in indirect cost or in plant and equipment. It is the net cost to the job for engineering equipment.

i. First aid and safety engineering. This is to cover the cost of first aid and safety personnel and supplies. On some jobs the industrial compensation insurance company provides first aid services, and as a result, it is not a separate item of expense to the contractor but is included in the workmen's compensation rates. The specification requirements determine if it is possible for the safety engineer to have other duties so that only part of his time is charged to this item.

j. Outside consultants. Funds are provided here for hiring outside legal or engineering help to assist on the job or to help present claims.

k. Legal cost. The cost of any legal help supplied by the home office or employed on the jobsite are provided for here.

l. Audit cost. The cost of yearly audits, performed by outside auditing firms, is covered here.

m. Moving personnel in and out. The cost of moving key personnel to and from the jobsite is provided for here.

n. Sign cost. This is intended to cover the cost for signs erected for the owner and also the cost for the contractor's signs. For example, the Army Engineers always require the contractor to erect a sign designating that it is an Army Engineers' job.

o. Miscellaneous cost. Any item of cost not defined above.

3. Insurance. Funds are here provided for insuring the plant and equipment, for builder's risk and vehicle insurance, individual bonding, and any special insurance required. An example of a special insurance occurs when construction is carried on near railroad tracks. In this case, the railroad often requires bonds or insurance to be furnished by the contractor.
4. Taxes. Here funds are provided for the county and city property taxes on the contractor's plant and equipment. Some states also have a business tax and other special taxes. Sales tax should not be included here, but should be added to the cost of plant and equipment, materials, and supplies.
5. Bond Premium. In the majority of jobs, the contractor is required to post bonds to guarantee the successful completion of the job. Typical bond premium rates are as follows:

Contract price	Bond Premium	
	Towner group of bonding companies	Non-Towner group of bonding companies
First... $ 100,000	$10.00/1,000	$7.50/1,000
Next... 2,400,000	6.50/1,000	5.25/1,000
Next... 2,500,000	5.25/1,000	4.50/1,000
Next... 2,500,000	5.00/1,000	4.00/1,000
Over... 7,500,000	4.70/1,000	4.00/1,000

The foregoing bond premiums are based on a contract period of under 24 months. If the contract covers a longer period of time, a charge by the bonding companies of 1 percent per month of the total premium is added to the above rates. Bond premiums are computed on the total contract volume and not on the amount of the bond.

XIX. ESTIMATING CAMP COST

Construction camps are of two different uses and types:

Married-quarters Camp

These are provided to house key married personnel that the contractor may wish to have live near the project. These quarters may be necessary to secure competent supervision. Camp size varies from one unit for the project superintendent to enough units to house the family of every key man. House trailers are often used, and cost should be included for site grading, water supply facilities, sewage disposal system, and an electrical distribution system.

Single-status Camp

This type of camp is not used as much as formerly owing to the men's preferences for driving long distances rather than living in single-status camps. Contractors always lose money on their operation, so these camps should only be used in very remote locations. Facilities consist of sleeping quarters, washrooms, and mess hall, and sometimes a clubhouse is provided. Local laws should be checked for the number of men that are allowed to occupy one room and the square feet of room area required for each man. Locked storage for personal articles and clothes is almost a necessity.

It is now possible to secure quotations before bidding on prefabricated single-status camps completely erected, including mess hall, clubhouse, grading, sewage disposal, water supply, heating, and electrical distribution. The contractor must furnish the graded camp location. The advantage in using this type of camp is that it has good salvage value at the end of the project and the cost of construction can be definitely determined before bidding.

Single-status-camp operation is often subcontracted to a caterer who contracts to supply meals and run the camp for a price per man-day. Prices for catering service can be secured before bidding and this determines the operating loss before bid submission. When a caterer is used, the camp operating cost will be the difference between his charges and the per diem charges to the men for staying in the camp. This charge, by union agreement, is limited to the amount each craft receives per day for subsistence.

Whether prefabricated single-status camps are used, other types of camps are built, or a caterer is used, the greatest variation in estimated cost will be in the determination of how many men will stay in the camp. It does not matter how remote the area; some men will drive to work and it is difficult to estimate how many will do so. The number that stay in the camp makes a difference in camp loss since the caterer will quote a different cost per man-day depending on the number of men in residence.

In tabulating the cost of camps, it should be summarized as follows in order to allow estimates to be compared and if the contractor is the successful bidder, to provide the estimated cost in such a form that it can be readily compared with actual cost.

CAMP COST

Capital cost of married-quarters camp	________
Capital cost of single-status camp	________
TOTAL CAPITAL COST OF CAMPS	________
Operation cost of married-quarters camp	________
Revenue from married-quarters camp	________
PROFIT OR (LOSS) FROM OPERATION	________
Operation cost of single-status camp	________
Revenue from single-status camp	________
PROFIT OR (LOSS) FROM OPERATION	________
TOTAL CAMP COST	________

XX. ESCALATION

It is common practice for estimators to compute the estimated construction cost on the basis of wage rates prevailing at the time of bidding. Under this system of estimating, it is then necessary to determine the increased cost of labor and burden that will occur during the construction period and add this to the estimated cost. To compute this increased cost, it is necessary to estimate the percentage increase in wages per year and the time of year these increases will occur. Existing labor contracts should be checked to find if there are any increases in wages already negotiated for future years and the month that any such increases take effect. For the yearly periods that are not covered by existing contracts, it is necessary to estimate the anticipated labor wage increase. The trend of labor increases in the particular area and for the particular crafts involved, with weight given to the increase occurring in the last few years, should be researched and used as the basis for anticipated future increases.

The total labor cost should then be distributed in yearly periods over the estimated life of the contract with the construction schedule used to make a proper distribution. The yearly periods should start and end on the month that the majority of the crafts shall have received their yearly wage increases. This distribution multiplied by the cumulative percentage increase per year, will result in the total labor escalation to be added to the estimated cost. For an example of such a computation, refer to Exhibit 12, Chap. 8.

Escalation on materials and supplies during the life of the contract is a smaller item. The determination of the amount required for these items can be made in a similar manner to that used for labor escalation.

XXI. TABULATION OF THE TOTAL ESTIMATED COST

The tabulation of the total estimated cost should be set forth in such a form that the distribution of this cost can be readily understood by the construction company's principals. A recommended tabulation is shown in Exhibit 13, Chap. 8.

XXII. INFORMATION FOR THE PRINCIPALS

After the estimate of cost is completed, it should be used in estimating the following items which are not a part of the estimate of cost but constitute information that should be furnished to the principals to assist them in determining the proper markup.

Contingency

A contingency is an exposure to some cost that may or may not occur. The cost cannot be fixed and only the maximum exposure can be estimated. Such an exposure should not be included in the estimated cost but should be reported as a separate item to the principals for help in determining markup. If there are *force majeure* and unforeseen-condition clauses in the specifications, the contractor may not be subject to any exposure. If these clauses are not included in the specifications or if there is too much restriction placed on their interpretation, then the contractor may be subject to the following exposure and these items should be reflected in his markup:

1. In tunnel construction there is always a chance of encountering unforeseen conditions. The maximum exposure for any tunnel may be measured by the extent of the geological investigation and the type of formation the tunnel will encounter.

2. Exposure to large flows of water, high-pressure water, or high-temperature water. The extent of the exposure is again determined by the structural geology.

3. War, floods, weather, strikes, earthquakes, etc. The maximum exposure here is beyond estimating ability and if the contractor has the exposure, it should be brought to the principals' attention so that they can make their own determination of how it should affect the markup.

Capital Requirements and Interest Expense

To determine the amount of capital the contractor will have to furnish to finance the construction work, the periods of different capital requirements, the time when the job will be able to return the capital, and the interest cost of this capital, it is necessary for the estimator to prepare a cash forecast for the construction work.

A preliminary cash forecast can be made by totaling the following items and assuming the cash will be required for 50 percent of the contract time.

PRELIMINARY CASH FORECAST

Item	
Plant and equipment outlay necessary to start the work	________
Cost of payment and performance bond	________
One year's insurance	________
Inventory	________
Camp cost	________
Cost of any bid item whose payment is to be deferred for any reason	________
Overhead required to start job before any bid-item money is received	________
Working capital	________
TOTAL OUTLAY	________
Less any plant and equipment prepayment or mobilization payment	________
TOTAL CASH REQUIREMENT	________

A more detailed and more accurate cash forecast requires that the cash revenue received per period be estimated and the cash expenditures for direct cost, plant and equipment, camp, and indirect cost be estimated per period. The period used may be 1 month, ¼ year, or ½ year depending upon the accuracy required and the contract time. This cash forecast cannot be made until the estimate is completed and the construction schedule and different cost elements are available. To arrive at the total revenue, it is necessary for the estimator to assume a markup which, when added to the total estimated cost, will give the

Exhibit 1

FORMAT FOR A CASH FORECAST FOR A JOB UNDER CONSTRUCTION

	Through period of last financial statement	Monthly or quarterly period	Monthly or quarterly period	Monthly or quarterly period
Revenue:				
Bid item revenue..........				
Advances from client.....				
Subtotal..............				
Less retention............				
Total from client.......				
Salvage revenue..........				
Miscellaneous revenue....				
Total revenue..........				
Disbursements:				
Direct construction costs..				
Indirect cost.............				
Plant and equipment and camp construction......				
Camp operation..........				
Inventories..............				
Advances to suppliers.....				
Accounts receivable.......				
Deferred cost				
Total disbursements....				
Payables:				
Accounts payable........				
Accrued payroll charges...				
Accrued other cost........				
Total payables.........				
Cash required..............				
Financing:				
From partners...........				
Bank borrowing..........				
Total.................				

total revenue. The simplest method of determining the period bid-item revenue is to multiply the direct cost by the factor determined by dividing the total direct cost into the estimated total bid price. A more accurate method of determining period revenue would be to assume a method of spreading plant and equipment which may give a higher factor to use in determining revenue on the excavation direct cost items, and less on the concrete direct cost items.

Receipt of revenue will lag from 30 to 45 days after direct cost expense since progress payment requests are submitted near the last of each month and a period of time is required by the owner to check the progress payment estimates and make cash delivery.

A cash forecast which shows capital requirements for each period and the interest cost on this capital is illustrated by Exhibit 14, Chap. 8. This cash forecast was formulated with quarterly periods and sufficient detail to forecast the job before construction started.

If a cash forecast is prepared for a job that is already under construction, additional items such as accounts receivable, accounts payable, prepaid and deferred charges, and miscellaneous revenue must be included in order to tie into the appropriate starting point. These additional items are secured from the financial statements. Engineers should understand how to read a balance sheet and a profit and loss statement and be able to get a starting point for a cash forecast on any job from these statements. A sample form for this type of cash forecast is shown by Exhibit 1.

REFERENCES

1. Ralph Jergens, Assistant Editor, New Developments in Tunneling Machines, a reprint from March and April, 1966, *Construction Methods and Equipment*, copyright 1966 by McGraw-Hill Publications, New York.
2. Commercial Liner Plate for Support of Excavation in Tunnel and Shaft Construction, Commercial Shearing and Stamping Company, 1965, Catalogue 300-C6.

Chapter 8 Example of a Tunnel Estimate

INTRODUCTION

Presented in this chapter is an example of a contractor's estimate of cost for constructing a fictitious hard-rock tunnel by the conventional excavating method of drill, shoot, and muck. If this estimating procedure is thoroughly understood for the conventional tunnel-driving method, then the necessary changes in this procedure can be readily made to accommodate any other driving method or any other type of underground construction. Each step in this procedure has the same number as its description given in Chap. 7; frequent reference to that chapter will help in following the estimate. A knowledge of tunneling terminology and the methods and equipment used in tunnel construction is also necessary; this information is presented in earlier chapters and in the glossary.

In preparing this estimate, labor extensions for each individual tunnel crew were made by using wage rates, working conditions, and fringe benefits in effect during the first half of 1968. This procedure could be changed to eliminate some of the detailed computation. After the total daily crew cost for the first excavation crew and the first concrete crew have been determined, an average cost per manshift could be computed for excavation work and for concrete work. The cost of any additional excavation and concrete crews could then be determined by multiplying the number of men required per day times these average costs per manshift. This change in procedure would not result in decreased estimating accuracy.

The estimate concentrates on underground construction. Therefore, all work except tunnel and shaft work is shown as done by others. "Plugged" material and subcontract prices were used in the estimate as shown in Exhibit 4 in this chapter. These prices are adjusted to actual quotes at the time of bid submission.

I. STUDY OF PLANS AND SPECIFICATIONS

This study was completed and an abstract of the specifications, showing the major contract and specification requirements as well as reduced prints of the job layout and the shaft and tunnel sections, was prepared.

Exhibit 2

ABSTRACT OF SPECIFICATIONS FOR THE CONSTRUCTION OF SIERRA TUNNEL

Scope.................The work includes the excavation and concrete lining of 23,650 ft of 21-ft-finished-diameter horseshoe-shaped tunnel descending on a 0.1 percent grade from the inlet portal. Also included is the excavation, concrete lining, and first-stage concrete in a 24-ft-finished-diameter gate shaft 246 ft high, which is 200 ft from the inlet portal.

Location.............. The site of the work is on the South Fork of the China River, 8 miles northeast of Austin in Arizona County, California.

Agency............... Arizona County Water District, Austin, California.

Engineers............. Tunnel Designers, Inc.

Bid date..............May 1, 1968.

Bid procedure..........Proposal must be submitted on a serially numbered standard proposal form bound into the specifications specifically issued to the prospective bidder.

Other than the bid bond, none of the required documents may be detached from the bound book.

If the proposal is signed by an agent other than an officer of the corporation authorized to sign contracts on its behalf, a power of attorney must be on file with the District prior to the opening of bids or submitted with the proposal.

Bids shall be submitted in a sealed envelope plainly marked as a bid. The cover shall state the name of the project and the date and time for opening of bids.

Data to be submitted with bid.................. Bid bond, 10% of the contract price.

List of subcontractors performing work in excess of ½ of 1% of the contract price.

Fair Employment Practices certification.

Workmen's compensation insurance certification (can be either submitted with bid or executed later by the successful bidder).

Signed copy of each addendum.

Bonds................ Bid bond, 10% of bid amount.

Performance bond, 50% of bid amount.

Labor and materials bond, 50% of bid amount.

Award................ Award will be made within 30 days after opening of bids.

Time of completion..... The contractor shall begin work within 30 days after receipt of notice to proceed and complete all work in 42 months.

Liquidated damages.... $500 a calendar day for each day after 42 months.

Extensions of time...... Contractor shall be entitled to an extension of time for completion of the work for delays due to:

1. An order for changes or a suspension of the work for the convenience and benefit of the District.
2. A suspension of the work due to weather conditions such as earthquake, fire, flood, cloudburst, or other cataclysmic phenomena of nature.
3. Failure of the District or its other contractors to furnish, within contract time requirements, access to the work, right-of-way, working areas, excavation at portals, drawings, materials, water, or power for which the District is responsible under the contract.
4. Survey error by the District.

Extensions of time......5. Changed conditions, i.e.:

a. Subsurface or latent physical conditions at the site of the work differing materially from those represented in this contract; and

b. Unknown physical conditions at the site of the work of an unusual nature differing materially from those ordinarily encountered and generally recognized as inherent in work of the character provided for in this contract.

6. Act of the public enemy, governmental act other than an act of the District, epidemic, freight embargo, strike, or labor dispute.

Payments..............*Progress payments.* Monthly payments in an amount equal to 90% of the value of the work performed shall be made to the contractor for the first 50% of the contract amount; thereafter monthly payments shall be made in full. The amount of money retained on the first 50% of the contract shall be paid upon completion of the work.

Force account payment. Force amount payments for any change shall consist of the actual necessary costs of labor, materials, and equipment and construction equipment used in the portion of work materially affected by the change, plus an allowance on the sum of such costs for superintendence, general expense, and profit determined in accordance with the following schedule:

Sum of actual necessary costs	*Allowance*
Less than $25,000........	16%
$25,000–$100,000........	16% minus 0.08% per $1,000 over $25,000
Over $100,000...........	10%

Changed conditions. If changed conditions are encountered, an equitable adjustment shall be made in the contract revenue.

Lines and grades.......The engineer shall establish centerlines and grades on original ground and cross section of excavation sites prior to excavation and shall provide survey services required for this purpose. The engineer shall also check line and grade in the tunnel.

Wages ....Prevailing wages are contained in the specifications.

Access ....Access roads to the inlet and outlet portals, to the adit, and to the top of the gate shaft have been constructed by a previous contractor.

Work done by others. . . . Other contractors will do the following:

1. Construct access roads to the inlet and outlet portals, adit location, and the top of the surge tank. Roads will be complete by April 1, 1968.
2. Run power distribution and water distribution lines to these locations. Distribution lines will be complete by April 1, 1968.
3. Complete all opencut excavation at the portals, adit, and surge tank location. This work will be complete by April 1, 1968.
4. Construct inlet and outlet structures after tunnel contract is completed.
5. Place second-stage concrete, gates, hoist, ladders, platforms, control house, and air vent pipe that is not embedded for the gate shaft after tunnel contract is completed.

Mobilization payments. . . None mentioned in specifications.

First aid facilities. . . . . . First aid equipment and licensed first aid attendants are required at each portal used in construction.

Safety engineer . . . . The contractor must have a competent and experienced safety engineer.

Insurance. . . . . The contractor shall be responsible for any liability imposed by law for any damage to any person or property resulting from any cause whatsoever during the progress of the work. Therefore, he must carry insurance on this exposure.

Taxes. . . . . The contract price paid for the work shall include full compensation for all taxes which the contractor is required to pay, whether imposed by the federal, state, or local government.

Power and water. . . . . . . Distribution lines supplied by the owner. Contractor to make own arrangements for cost of power and water.

Method of construction. . The contractor may drive the tunnel from either or both portals or may, at his option, construct a 650 lin ft adit to aid in his tunnel driving. The adit is 10,750 ft from the inlet portal. If contractor elects to construct the adit, he must place a 50 lin ft concrete plug in it upon completion of his work. There will be no separate payment for constructing this adit or placing the concrete plug; so the cost of this work must be absorbed by the contractor in bid-item work.

Muck disposal . . . . Adequate space for muck disposal is located at each portal and at the adit, and no special treatment of disposal areas will be required.

Invert cleanup.........Cleanup of the tunnel invert does not have to be carried to bare rock. All soft material must be removed from the invert, but sound tunnel muck can be leveled to grade as foundation for invert concrete.

Concrete pour..........Use of air placers is permitted.

Major quantities........

Item	Quantity
Tunnel excavation	431,000 cu yd
Steel sets	2,290,000 lb
Timber lagging	400 MBM*
Roof bolts	12,000 lin ft
Shaft excavation	5,300 cu yd
Concrete in tunnel lining	111,000 cu yd
Concrete in shaft	1,900 cu yd
Cement	163,000 bbl
Reinforcement in shaft	285,000 lb
Consolidation grouting	10,000 sacks

* MBM is a thousand board feet of measurement.

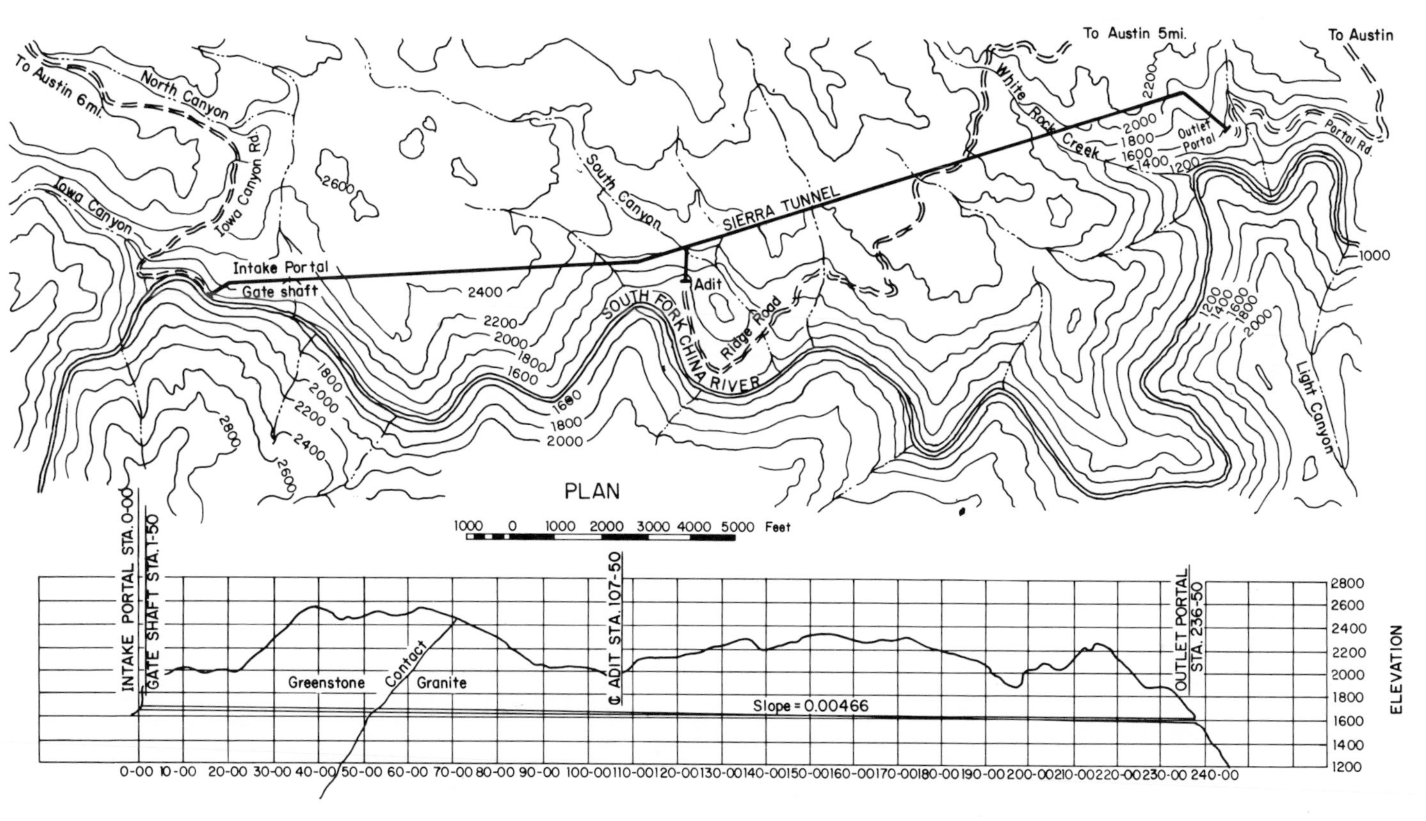

Drawing 15 Sierra Tunnel general arrangement.

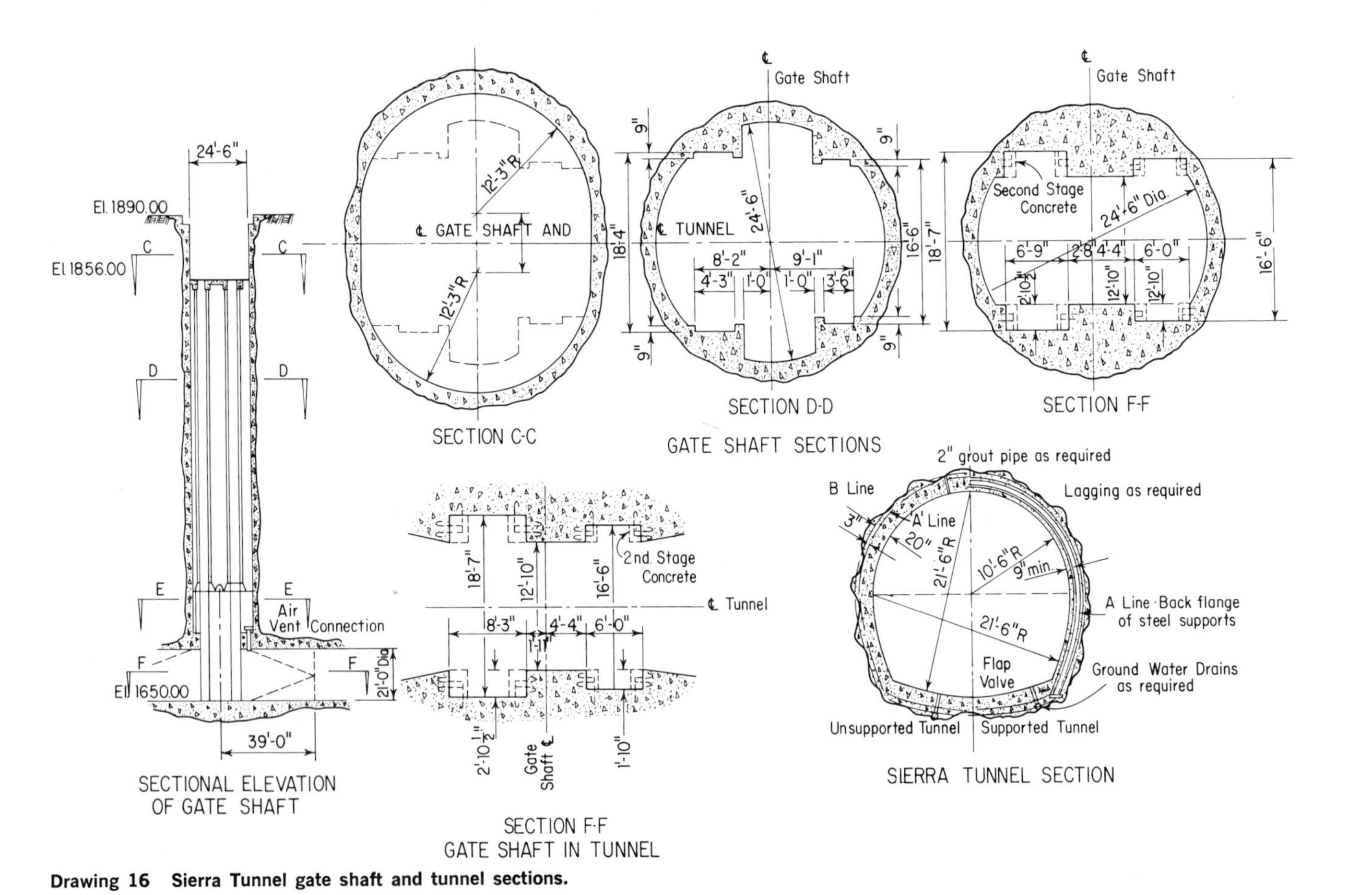

Drawing 16 Sierra Tunnel gate shaft and tunnel sections.

II. JOB INSPECTION

An inspection of the job site was made.

III. GEOLOGICAL REVIEW

A review of the geological report indicates that the first 50 ft of tunnel from each portal must be supported on 4-ft centers.

The gate shaft is in sound granite and will not require supports.

The adit is in sound granite and except for the first 50 ft will not require supports.

The report states that the outlet portal and adjacent 18,500 lin ft of tunnel will be in granitic formation and that the inlet portal and adjacent 5,150 lin ft of tunnel will be in greenstone. About 10 percent of the granite will require supports on 4-ft centers, and the remainder will be unsupported tunnel except at the contact with the greenstone. For 50 ft on each side of the contact, supports on 2-ft centers will be required, and for 20 ft on each side of the contact, breastboarding will be required. Except for the 50 ft near the contact and the 50 ft from the portal, only 30 percent of the greenstone will require supports and these supports will be on 4-ft centers. An additional 30 percent of the tunnel in the greenstone will require roof bolts in the arch.

This information is summarized in table form as follows by rounding out figures to fit support spacing:

	Total, lin ft	Bare rock, lin ft	Roof bolts, lin ft	Supports on 4-ft centers, lin ft	Supports on 2-ft centers, lin ft	No. of sets
Main tunnel:						
Granitic formation	18,500	16,570		1,880	50	495 ea
Greenstone	5,150	2,012	1,520	1,568	50	417 ea
Subtotal	23,650	18,582	1,520	3,448	100	912 ea
Adit	650	600	.....	50	...	12 ea
Shaft	214	214				

The following table shows tunnel lengths of the same round spacing and groups them into the two rock classifications. This kind of summary is helpful in computing the excavation crew days after the round calculations have been completed.

	Toward outlet	Toward inlet	Total
Granite formation:			
Breastboarding	....	20 lin ft	20 lin ft
2-ft rounds	....	30 lin ft	30 lin ft
4-ft rounds supported at portal	50 lin ft	....	50 lin ft
4-ft rounds supported	1,280 lin ft	550 lin ft	1,830 lin ft
10-ft rounds unsupported	11,570 lin ft	5,000 lin ft	16,570 lin ft
Total granite formation	12,900 lin ft	5,600 lin ft	18,500 lin ft
Greenstone formation:			
Breastboarding	....	20 lin ft	20 lin ft
2-ft rounds	....	30 lin ft	30 lin ft
4-ft rounds supported at portal	....	50 lin ft	50 lin ft
4-ft rounds supported	....	1,518 lin ft	1,518 lin ft
10-ft rounds with roof bolts	....	1,520 lin ft	1,520 lin ft
10-ft rounds unsupported	....	2,012 lin ft	2,012 lin ft
Total greenstone formation	....	5,150 lin ft	5,150 lin ft
Grand total	12,900 lin ft	10,750 lin ft	23,650 lin ft
Total number of rounds	1,490	1,413	2,903

IV. SUMMARY OF QUANTITY TAKEOFFS

Exhibit 3

SIERRA TUNNEL ESTIMATE

	Lineal feet	Quantities per lineal foot			Total Quantities		
		Pay, cu yd	Over-break, cu yd	Total, cu yd	Pay, cu yd	Over-break, cu yd	Total, cu yd
Excavation:							
Main tunnel							
Standard section	23,572	18.18	1.85	20.03	428,539	43,608	472,147
Under gate shaft	78	29.52	2.59	32.11	2,303	202	2,505
Total main tunnel	23,650	.....	....	.....	430,842	43,810	474,652
Shaft	......	.....	....	.....	5,299	496	5,795
Adit	......	.....	....	.....	4,472	Not used	4,472
Concrete:							
Main tunnel							
Standard section	23,572	4.63	1.85	6.48	109,138	43,608	152,746
Under gate shaft	78	.....	2.59	2.59	1,315	202	1,517
Total main tunnel	23,650	.....	....	.....	110,453	43,810	154,263
Shaft	......	.....	....	.....	1,894	496	2,390
Adit	......	.....	....	.....	572	28	600

Forms Other than Tunnel and Tunnel Bulkhead:

	Square feet				
	Straight	Curved	Transition	Slipped	Total
Tunnel at Y.	352	. . .	. . . . .	. . . . . .	352
Tunnel under gate shaft	1,513	. . .	3,091	. . . . . .	4,604
Shaft.	1,304	658	145	14,218	16,325
Adit.	176	. . .	. . . . .	. . . . . .	176

Weight of Tunnel Sets:

	lb per set
Main tunnel, 8-in. WF 40 lb.	2,510
Adit, 6-in. WF 20 lb.	810

V. REQUESTS FOR QUOTATIONS

Requests for quotations were sent out for permanent materials, supplies, and the plant and equipment items.

Requests were also made for subcontract prices for furnishing aggregates, for furnishing and installing reinforcing steel, and for drilling and pressure grouting.

A list of "plugged" prices was prepared as shown in Exhibit 4.

Exhibit 4

SIERRA TUNNEL ESTIMATE

Plugged Material and Subcontract Prices Sent Out by Sponsor to Other Partners (Permanent-material Price, FOB Job, Including Sales Tax)

Item No.	Description	Unit	Permanent-material price	Subcontract price
2	Steel sets.	lb	$ 0.12	
3	Timber.	MBM	80.00	
4	Roof bolts.	lin ft	0.40	
9	Tunnel lining.	Ton of aggre.	. . . . . .	$2.10
10	Shaft concrete.	Ton of aggre.	. . . . . .	2.10
11	Cement.	bbl	5.25	
12	Steel reinforcing.	lb	. . . . . .	0.13
13	Embedded anchor bolts.	lb	0.40	
14	Embedded vent pipe.	lb	0.23	
15	Drilling grout holes.	lin ft	. . . . . .	4.00
16	Consolidation grouting.	cu ft	. . . . . .	4.00
17	Cement for grouting.	Sack	. . . . . .	1.25

VI. JOB WAGE RATES

The labor cost to the contractor is composed of direct wages per hour; overtime payments; workmen's compensation insurance; social security and unemployment insurance taxes; fringe benefits which include vacation allowance, health and welfare, apprentice training, subsistence if required by job location; and public liability and property damage insurance.

Amount of overtime payments depends on whether "the job" works 6 days or 5 days a week, whether heading work is carried on continuously, and whether shifts change at the portal or at the face.

In computing the labor rates for the Sierra Tunnel, it was assumed that the work is in a subsistence area; shifts will change at the tunnel face, so travel time will be paid; work will be carried on continuously, so each shift will run an extra 30 min; approximately one-half the crew will be worked through their lunch hour; and the job will work only 5 days a week.

Under these job conditions and assuming an average one-way travel time of 10 min for the entire work, the hours worked and total hours paid per shift for the tunnel crews are tabulated as follows:

	Hr worked	Elapsed hr paid per shift	Equivalent straight time hr paid per shift
Surface crew:			
Standard shift	7 hr	8 hr	8 hr
Work additional ½ hr	0 hr 30 min	0 hr 30 min	0 hr 45 min
Total 7½-hr shift	7 hr 30 min	8 hr 30 min	8 hr 45 min
Decimal equivalent	7.5	8.5	8.75
Underground crew:			
Average travel time, start of shift	....	0 hr 10 min	0 hr 15 min
Standard shift	7 hr 0 min	8 hr 0 min	8 hr 0 min
Extra ½ hr of work	0 hr 30 min	0 hr 30 min	0 hr 45 min
Work ½ crew through lunch period	0 hr 15 min	0 hr 15 min	0 hr 22½ min
Travel time, end of shift	....	0 hr 10 min	0 hr 15 min
Total hours per shift	7 hr 45 min	9 hr 05 min	9 hr 37½ min
Decimal equivalent	7.75	9.08	9.625

Therefore, the surface crew has fringe benefits paid for 8.5 hr and actual pay for 8.75 hr per shift. The underground crew has fringe benefits paid for 9.0 hr and has wages paid for 9.625 hr per shift.

Fringe benefits used in this estimate are tabulated below.

	Laborers	Operating engineers	Teamsters
Health and welfare	$0.30	$0.30	$0.245
Vacation allowance	0.30	0.20	0.35
Pension	0.30	0.35	0.25
Retired employees health and welfare	.....	0.02	0.01
Drugs, dental care, and visual care	.....	.....	0.12
Apprenticeship	.....	0.10	
Total per hour	$0.90	$0.97	$0.975

Subsistence of $9.00 a day has been used in the estimate.

Labor burden has been used as follows:

	Percent
Workmen's compensation insurance	18.15
Social security tax	4.20
Federal unemployment	0.40
State unemployment	3.50
Public liability and property damage insurance	0.16
Total labor burden	26.41

Total cost of hourly workers per shift has been computed in Exhibit 5.

After having determined the labor rates, the sponsoring company's estimator should send out the following information to the other estimators in the joint venture:

1. A description of the estimating format that he desires the other estimators to use
2. Estimate comparison sheets (refer to Exhibit 15, Chap. 9)
3. Labor rates, payroll taxes, workmen's compensation rates, and personal liability and property damage insurance rates
4. Permanent material and subcontract plugged prices (refer to Exhibit 4)
5. Equipment and plant insurance rates
6. Builder's risk insurance rates
7. Bond rates
8. Geological reports

Exhibit 5

SIERRA TUNNEL
Five-day Work-week Labor Cost per Shift

	Basic wage/hr	Total shift 9.625 hr	Taxes and insurance, 26.41%	Fringe benefits 9 hr	Sub-sistence/shift	Total cost/shift
Underground:						
Shifter, shaft	$5.35	$51.49	$13.60	$8.10	$9.00	$82.19
Miner, shaft	4.875	46.92	12.39	8.10	9.00	76.41
Shifter, tunnel	5.10	49.09	12.96	8.10	9.00	79.15
Miner	4.625	44.52	11.76	8.10	9.00	73.38
Chucktender, nipper	4.475	43.07	11.37	8.10	9.00	71.54
Bull gang foreman	4.75	45.72	12.07	8.10	9.00	74.89
Bull gang	4.375	42.11	11.12	8.10	9.00	70.33
Nozzleman	4.625	44.52	11.76	8.10	9.00	73.38
Vibrator men	4.475	43.07	11.37	8.10	9.00	71.54
Concrete crew	4.375	42.11	11.12	8.10	9.00	70.33
Brakeman	4.75	45.72	12.07	8.73	9.00	75.52
Conway operator	5.89	56.69	14.97	8.73	9.00	89.39
Motorman	5.07	48.80	12.89	8.73	9.00	79.42
Heavy-duty mechanic	5.89	56.69	14.97	8.73	9.00	89.39
Chief of party	6.125	58.95	15.57	8.73	9.00	92.25
Instrument man	5.66	54.48	14.39	8.73	9.00	86.60
Head chainman	5.07	48.80	12.89	8.73	9.00	79.42
Rear chainman	4.75	45.72	12.07	8.73	9.00	75.52
Concrete-belt operator	4.94	47.55	12.56	8.73	9.00	77.84
Pumpcrete or Press Weld	5.50	52.94	13.98	8.73	9.00	84.65
Slip-form Jumbo	5.565	53.56	14.15	8.73	9.00	85.44
Front-end loader	6.125	58.95	15.57	8.73	9.00	92.25
Koehring Dumptor	5.165	49.71	13.13	8.78	9.00	80.62

	Basic wage/hr	Total shift 8.75 hr	Taxes and insurance, 26.41%	Fringe benefits 8½ hr	Sub-sistence/shift	Total cost/shift
Surface crew:						
Powderman	$4.475	$39.16	$10.34	$7.65	$9.00	$66.16
Dumpman	4.375	38.28	10.11	7.65	9.00	65.04
Watchman	4.075	35.66	9.42	7.65	9.00	61.73
Compressor operator	5.375	47.03	12.42	8.25	9.00	76.70
Heavy-duty mechanic	5.76	50.40	13.31	8.25	9.00	80.96
Warehouseman	4.505	39.42	10.41	8.28	9.00	67.11
Tractor operator	5.76	50.40	13.31	8.25	9.00	80.96
Crane operator	6.00	52.50	13.87	8.25	9.00	83.62

VII. EXCAVATION METHOD

Inspection of the geological reports indicates that this will be a hard-rock tunnel, so construction will be performed in the conventional manner. From inspection of the plans and specifications, four different methods of tunnel driving are apparent. The long distances involved dictate a rail operation except for a few local situations where rubber-tired equipment is indicated.

Method 1. A construction adit will not be used. The main tunnel will be excavated by driving a single heading up the slope from the outlet portal. At the inlet portal a small crew will drive approximately 200 lin ft of tunnel with rubber-tired equipment. Then the shaft will be excavated by constructing a small raise from the tunnel. Excavation to the full dimension of the shaft will be done by downdrilling and disposing of the shot muck down the raise. When the shaft excavation is complete, the section of the tunnel under the shaft will be enlarged to its full diameter.

Method 2. A construction adit will not be used, but tunnel excavation will be done from both portals with two separate single headings. As soon as the tunnel is driven well past the gate shaft at the inlet end, the shaft will be constructed in the same manner as Method 1 except that muck disposal will be with rail equipment.

Method 3. A construction adit will be driven and the main tunnel will then be driven toward the inlet portal by using a single heading. After completion of the excavation of this leg of the tunnel, excavation will be started on the gate shaft and on the section of tunnel from the adit to the outlet portal. The gate shaft will be constructed in the same manner as described in Method 1 except that muck disposal will be with rail equipment.

Method 4. A construction adit will be driven and the main tunnel excavated by single-heading operations until approximately 1,000 lin ft are excavated in each direction. This will be done with rubber-tired equipment. Then this rubber-tired equipment will be used to drive a short section of tunnel at the inlet end and construct the gate shaft. Rail equipment will be installed in the tunnel, and with alternate-heading operations, double-heading operations, and single-heading operations, will finish driving the tunnel.

Cost Comparison of the Four Proposed Tunneling Methods

To determine which of the proposed construction methods is the most economical, a comparison will be made by using Method 1 as a base. A

Exhibit 6

COMPARISON OF FOUR METHODS OF EXCAVATING SIERRA TUNNEL

		Method 1 single heading from outlet portal	Method 2 single headings from both portals	Method 3 single heading from adit	Method 4 double heading from adit
Geology summary:					
Breastboarding	40 lin ft				
2-ft rounds	60 lin ft				
4-ft rounds	3,448 lin ft				
Remainder	20,102 lin ft				
Total	23,650 lin ft				
Estimated heading production:					
Breastboarding	5 lin ft/day	8 days			
2-ft rounds	15 lin ft/day	4 days			
4-ft rounds	30 lin ft/day	115 days			
Remainder	60 lin ft/day	335 days			
Start-up		10 days			
Total		472 days			
Average daily production		50 lin ft			
Comparative production:					
Lin ft driven					
Single heading		23,650 lin ft	23,650 lin ft	23,650 lin ft	2,150 lin ft
Alternate heading					4,000 lin ft
Double heading					17,500 lin ft
Total		23,650 lin ft	23,650 lin ft	23,650 lin ft	23,650 lin ft
Single-heading crew days at 50 lin ft/day		472 days	472 days	472 days	43 days
Alternate-heading crew days at 80 lin ft/day					50 days
Double-heading days at 100 lin ft/day					175 days
Total crew days		472 days	472 days	472 days	268 days
Concrete days		200 days	200 days	200 days	200 days
Number of headings		1	2	1	2
Calendar months, 20 days/month:					
Start-up and portal-in		3 months	3 months	3 months	3 months
Drive adit				2 months	2 months
Excavation		24 months	12 months	24 months	14 months
Delay before concrete		1 month	1 month	1 month	1 month
Concrete		10 months	10 months	10 months	10 months
Cleanup and move-out		1 month	1 month	1 month	1 month
Contract time		39 months	27 months	41 months	31 months
Overhead cost reduction at $18,000/month			$216,000		$144,000
Overhead cost increase				$36,000	
Excavation man-days:					
Excavation crew size/day:					
Single headings, 10 × drills		100	200	100	100
Alternate headings, + 10%					110
Double headings, 8.5 × drills					170
Concrete average crew days		140	140	140	140
Man-days:					
Excavation, single heading		47,200	47,200	47,200	4,300
Excavation, alt. heading					5,500
Excavation, double heading					29,750
Total		47,200	47,200	47,200	39,550
Concrete man-days		28,000	28,000	28,000	28,000
Total man-days		75,200	75,200	75,200	67,550

	Method 1 single heading from outlet portal	Method 2 single headings from both portals	Method 3 single heading from adit	Method 4 double heading from adit
Labor cost:				
Total labor cost at $80/man-day	$6,016,000	$6,016,000	$6,016,000	$5,404,000
Labor cost reduction	...	...	...	$ 612,000
Supplies:				
Cost reduction based on 25% of labor	...	...	...	$ 153,000
Travel time:				
Estimated travel time, man/day	34 min	20 min	20 min	20 min
Decimal equivalent	0.57 hr	0.33 hr	0.33 hr	0.33 hr
Travel time, hr	42,864 hr	25,067 hr	25,067 hr	22,527 hr
Savings in hours over Method 1	...	17,797 hr	17,797 hr	20,337 hr
Travel payment cost reduction at time and one-half, or $10/hr	...	$177,970	$177,970	$203,370
Labor escalation:				
Average labor escalation, 7%/year	8.1%	4.67%	8.1%	5.87%
Labor escalation	$487,296	$280,947	$487,296	$317,215
Labor-escalation cost reduction	...	$206,349	...	$170,081
Plant and equipment comparison after salvage:				
Construct adit	...	...	$+150,000	$+150,000
Rail equipment:				
1 additional Jacobs floor	...	$+110,000	...	$+110,000
1 additional drill jumbo	...	+150,000	...	+150,000
1 additional mucker	...	+ 36,000	...	+ 36,000
25 additional muck cars	...	+ 50,000	...	+ 50,000
additional specialty cars	...	+ 10,000	...	+ 10,000
additional compressors	...	+ 40,000	...	+ 40,000
Rubber-tired equipment	...	−175,000	−175,000	
Savings in track material	...	...	− 54,000	
Savings in vent line	...	...	− 46,000	
Savings in fans	...	...	− 15,000	
Savings in piping	...	...	− 42,000	
Increased cost, additional portal	...	+ 70,000		
Cost reduction in plant and equipment	...	...	$−182,000	
Cost increase in plant and equipment	...	$+291,000	...	$+546,000

Summary of comparative costs

Cost reductions:				
Overhead	...	$216,000	...	$ 144,000
Labor	...	...	...	612,000
Supplies	...	...	...	153,000
Travel time	...	178,000...	$178,000	203,000
Labor escalation	...	206,000	...	170,000
Plant and equipment	...	...	182,000	
Subtotal	...	$600,000	$360,000	$1,282,000
Cost increases:				
Overhead	...	...	36,000	
Plant and equipment	...	291,000	...	546,000
NET REDUCTION	...	$309,000	$324,000	$ 736,000

preliminary estimate of the deletions or additions in cost compared with Method 1 are given in Exhibit 6.

Based on this preliminary comparison, Method 4 will result in the least cost and the least construction time; so this method will be used in the estimate.

VIII. SELECTION OF EQUIPMENT

The minimum-size construction adit that can furnish clearance for haul trucks, a crawler-mounted overshot loader, vent pipe, and rail equipment is a 14-ft-wide vertical-side-wall horseshoe tunnel. This section will be overexcavated to provide truck passage clearance at two locations. The total length of adit to be excavated will be greater than 650 lin ft because Y branches are required in each heading direction. This Y-branch excavation makes the excavated adit equivalent to a length of 688 lin ft.

The adit and 1,000 lin ft of tunnel in each direction from the adit will be excavated by an Eimco overshot crawler-loader mucking into Koehring Dumptors and drilling will be done with a truck jumbo. This will give space in each heading for the erection of the main tunnel-driving equipment.

Then the Eimco mucker and rubber-tired haulage equipment will be moved to the inlet portal and 200 ft of tunnel will be driven to allow the shaft to be constructed. After excavation of the shaft, the tunnel section under the shaft will be enlarged to full diameter with this equipment.

Each heading of the main tunnel will then be driven with a Jacobs floor and with a Conway 102 mucker loading into 13 cu yd cars side-boarded to 15 cu yd capacity. Drilling will be done with 4½-in.-bore drifters plus one large drill for drilling the burn cut, all mounted on a gantry jumbo.

To determine the amount of equipment required, it is assumed that 80 holes will be required in the granite and 70 holes in the greenstone. The granite will control the number of drills.

The square feet of face per hole is:

Area of face $= 24.33^2 \times 0.8293 = 491$ sq ft
Granite 491 sq ft $\div 80 = 6.13$ sq ft per hole
Greenstone 491 sq ft $\div 70 = 7.01$ sq ft per hole

Ten drifter drills plus one burn-cut drill will be used, that is, one drill for each eight holes, which should result in a balanced cycle.

The compressed air required at 1,600-ft elevation is computed as follows:

1 burn-cut drill	600 cfm
10 4½-in.-bore drifters at 330 cfm	3,300 cfm
Air required for one heading	3,900 cfm
Air required for two headings	7,800 cfm
Shops and miscellaneous	500 cfm
	8,300 cfm
Altitude corrections, 1.05	8,715 cfm
Therefore, provide nine 1,075-cfm compressors	9,675 cfm

To obtain 4,000 cfm at each heading: A 6-in. pipeline will have a pressure drop of 0.94 lb in 1,000 ft, or on the longest heading of 12,700 ft, a total pressure loss of 12 lb. A 10-in. pipeline will have a pressure drop of 0.28 lb in 1,000 ft, or 3.6 lb in 12,700 ft. Therefore, 12-in. air pipe to the end of the construction adit and then 10-in. pipe in both headings will be used.

A 10-lin-ft round will be pulled which will require the following number of muck cars per round:

Rock in place per lineal foot of tunnel, including overbreak	20 cu yd
Rock in place per round	200 cu yd
Muck, assuming 50% swell	300 cu yd
Capacity of one 15 cu yd car, loaded to 80% of capacity	12 cu yd
Required number of cars per round = 300 ÷ 12	25 cars
For two-heading operation with allowance for spares, provide	60 cars

To find the number of locomotives for operating up the 0.1 percent grade:

Weight of car:	
Weight of empty car, 15 × 1,150 lb	17,250 lb
Rock, 12 cu yd broken at 2,600 lb	31,200 lb
Total weight of one loaded car	48,450 lb
Or	24.23 tons
Resistance to movement:	
Rolling resistance	20 lb/ton
Grade resistance	2 lb/ton
Acceleration at 0.2 mph per sec	18 lb/ton
Total	40 lb/ton

To start seven cars, a locomotive with the following drawbar pull is needed:

$$24.23 \text{ ton} \times 40 \times 7 = 6{,}784 \text{ lb}$$

A 15-ton locomotive will start the train, as its starting drawbar pull is 25 percent of its weight, or 7,500 lb.

To find the horsepower of a locomotive required to accelerate seven cars upgrade to 10 mph,

$$\text{hp} = \frac{\text{tractive effort} \times \text{speed in miles per hour}}{375 \times 0.80}$$

Tractive effort is the weight of the train multiplied by the resistance.

Train weight:	
7 cars at 24.23 ton	170 tons
Locomotive	25 tons
Total	195 tons

$$\text{hp} = \frac{195 \times 40 \times 10}{375 \times 0.80} = 260 \text{ hp}$$

Purchase 25-ton locomotive with Caterpillar diesel D 333A turbo-charged after-cooled engines which develop 255 hp.

To determine ventilation, assume two locomotives switching cars at each heading and one on the main haul in each heading.

Total hp = 3 × 255	765 hp
At 75 cfm/hp	57,375 cfm
Use 48-in. pipe and space:	
First fan at	520 ft
Others at	1,120 ft
Total fans required	20

In constructing the shaft, a 6- by 6-ft raise will be excavated with an Alimak Raise Climber. The muck will be allowed to fall down the shaft into the tunnel and will be picked up by the Eimco loader and loaded into trucks. The shaft will then be sunk from the top with Air Trac drills and a small crawler dozer to push the material down the raise.

IX. ESTIMATED PROGRESS AND PREPARATION OF A CONSTRUCTION SCHEDULE

To determine tunnel excavation progress, it is necessary to determine the length of time required to excavate rounds in the different types of formations (Exhibit 7). Then by using this progress, the number of excavation crew days can be determined.

Concreting crew days are then determined from estimated progress figures.

Exhibit 7

SIERRA TUNNEL ESTIMATE

Tunnel-round Calculations

	With rubber-tired equipment				With rail equipment and Jacobs floor					
Location	Adit	Main tunnel			Main tunnel					
Type of rock	Granite	Granite	Granite	Granite	Granite	Granite	Granite	Greenstone	Greenstone	Greenstone
Required supports	Unsupported	Supported	Unsupported	Unsupported	Supported	Unsupported	Unsupported	Supported	Unsupported	Unsupported
Length of round	8 ft	4 ft	8 ft	10 ft	4 ft	8 ft	10 ft	4 ft	8 ft	10 ft
Excavation, cu yd/lin ft:										
Pay	6.5 cu yd	18.18 cu yd								
Nonpay	1.0 cu yd	1.85 cu yd								
Total	7.5 cu yd	20.03 cu yd								
Excavation, cu yd/round:										
Solid	60 cu yd	80 cu yd	160 cu yd	200 cu yd	80 cu yd	160 cu yd	200 cu yd	80 cu yd	160 cu yd	200 cu yd
Broken	90 cu yd	120 cu yd	240 cu yd	300 cu yd	120 cu yd	240 cu yd	300 cu yd	120 cu yd	240 cu yd	300 cu yd
Number of loads	12 Each	15 Each	30 Each	38 Each	10 Each	20 Each	25 Each	10 Each	20 Each	25 Each
Drilling:										
Drill holes/round	40	80	80	80	80	80	80	70	70	70
Lin ft of drilling	360 lin ft	400 lin ft	720 lin ft	880 lin ft	400 lin ft	720 lin ft	880 lin ft	350 lin ft	630 lin ft	770 lin ft
Number of drills	4	8	8	8	10	10	10	10	10	10
Lin ft/drill	90 lin ft	50 lin ft	90 lin ft	110 lin ft	40 lin ft	72 lin ft	88 lin ft	35 lin ft	63 lin ft	77 lin ft
Drilling speed/hour	60 lin ft	60 lin ft	60 lin ft	60 lin ft	60 lin ft	60 lin ft	60 lin ft	70 lin ft	70 lin ft	70 lin ft
Time required for drilling	1 hr 30 min	50 min	1 hr 30 min	1 hr 50 min	40 min	1 hr 12 min	1 hr 28 min	30 min	54 min	1 hr 6 min
Number of holes/miner	10	10	10	10	8	8	8	7	7	7
Cycle time:										
Move drill jumbo in	5 min	5 min	5 min	5 min	5 min	5 min	5 min	5 min	5 min	5 min
Set steel	0 min	45 min	0 min	0 min	45 min	0 min	0 min	45 min	0 min	0 min
Drill	1 hr 30 min	50 min	1 hr 30 min	1 hr 50 min	40 min	1 hr 12 min	1 hr 28 min	30 min	54 min	1 hr 6 min
Load	40 min	40 min	40 min	40 min	32 min	32 min	32 min	28 min	28 min	28 min
Move jumbo out	5 min	5 min	5 min	5 min	10 min	10 min	10 min	10 min	10 min	10 min
Shoot and ventilate	15 min	15 min	15 min	15 min	15 min	15 min	15 min	15 min	15 min	15 min
Move mucker in	5 min	5 min	5 min	5 min	5 min	5 min	5 min	5 min	5 min	5 min
Muck 3 min/car, 2½ min/truck	25 min	38 min	1 hr 15 min	1 hr 35 min	30 min	1 hr 0 min	1 hr 15 min	30 min	1 hr 0 min	1 hr 15 min
Cleanup and bar down	15 min	15 min	15 min	15 min	15 min	15 min	15 min	15 min	15 min	15 min
Move mucker out	5 min	5 min	5 min	5 min	0 min	0 min	0 min	0 min	0 min	0 min
Delays	10 min	10 min	10 min	10 min	10 min	10 min	10 min	10 min	10 min	10 min
Total cycle	3 hr 25 min	3 hr 53 min	4 hr 25 min	5 hr 5 min	3 hr 27 min	3 hr 44 min	4 hr 15 min	3 hr 13 min	3 hr 22 min	3 hr 49 min
Decimal equivalent	3.41	3.88	4.41	5.1	3.45	3.73	4.25	3.22	3.37	3.82
Cycles in 23.25 hr	6.82	5.99	5.27	4.56	6.74	6.26	5.42	7.53	6.90	6.09
Lin ft excavated per day	54.56 lin ft	23.96 lin ft	42.16 lin ft	45.60 lin ft	26.96 lin ft	50.08 lin ft	54.20 lin ft	30.12 lin ft	35.20 lin ft	60.90 lin ft
USE IN ESTIMATE	45 lin ft†	24 lin ft	....	45 lin ft	27 lin ft	....	54 lin ft	30 lin ft	....	60 lin ft

† Production in adit is reduced because of crew training.

Excavation Crew Days

Adit construction	Length, lin ft	Time, days
First 100 lin ft in 15 days at one shift	100	15
Next 500 lin ft at 45 lin ft/day	500	11
Y section, including branch	50	4
	650	30

Tunnel excavation	Toward outlet		Toward inlet	
	Length, lin ft	Time, days	Length, lin ft	Time, days
Rubber-tired equipment in granite:				
First 160 lin ft from Y	160	8	160	8
10-ft rounds unsupported at 45 lin ft/day	760	17	760	17
4-ft rounds supported at 24 lin ft/day	80	3	80	3
Subtotal	1,000	28	1,000	28
Inlet construction in greenstone:				
First 100 lin ft	......	...	100	5
Next 100 lin ft	......	...	100	5
Enlarging section	......	...	......	5
Total rubber-tired	1,000	28	1,200	43
Rail equipment in granite:				
Alternating heading:				
80% of two-heading production				
4-ft rounds at 22 lin ft/day	200	9	200	9
10-ft rounds at 43 lin ft/day	1,800	42	1,800	42
Total	2,000	51	2,000	51.
Rail equipment in granite:				
Double-heading operation:				
4-ft rounds at 27 lin ft/day	837	31	270	10
10-ft rounds at 54 lin ft/day	7,452	138	2,280	42
2-ft rounds at 12 lin ft/day	......	...	30	3
Breastboarding	......	...	20	3
Subtotal	8,289	169	2,600	58
Rail equipment in greenstone:				
Double-heading operation:				
Breastboarding	......	...	20	3
2-ft rounds at 15 lin ft/day	......	...	30	2
4-ft rounds at 30 lin ft/day	......	...	1,488	49
10-ft rounds at 60 lin ft/day	......	...	3,412	57
Subtotal	......	...	4,950	111
Total double heading	8,289	169	7,550	169
Rail equipment in granite:				
Single-heading operation:				
4-ft rounds at 27 lin ft/day	213	8		
10-ft rounds at 54 lin ft/day	1,398	26		
Total single heading	1,611	34		
GRAND TOTAL	12,900	...	10,750	

The main-tunnel driving days which will be used in the estimate and in the preparation of the construction schedule are shown below in summary.

	Toward outlet, days	Toward inlet, days	Total days
Single heading, rubber-tired	28	43	71
Alternating heading, rail, excavate in both directions	...	...	51
Double heading, rail, excavate in both directions	...	...	169
Single heading, rail	...	34	34

Concreting Crew Days

Concreting done from adit toward portals			
	From adit to outlet	From adit to inlet	Total
Tunnel without sets, lin ft	11,570	8,532	20,102
Tunnel with sets, lin ft	1,330	2,218	3,548
Total lin ft	12,900	10,750	23,650
	In days	*In days*	*In days*
1. Remove vent line at 1,000 lin ft/day	13	11	24
Allowance for start-up	1	1	2
Total	14	12	26
2. Retimber supported ground at 200 lin ft/day	7	12	19
Allowance for start-up	1	1	2
Total	8	13	21
3. Primary cleanup at 500 lin ft/day	26	22	48
Allowance for enlarged station under shaft	...	1	1
Allowance for start-up	1	1	2
Total	27	24	51
4. Invert concrete at 750 lin ft/day (cu yd/day = 750 × 2 = 1,500)	17	15	32
Allowance for enlarged section	...	1	1
Allowance for equipment setup, moving, and start-up	3	2	5
Total	20	18	38
5. Arch concrete at 300 lin ft/day (cu yd/day = 300 × 4.48 = 1,344)	43	36	79
Allowance for section at base of shaft	...	3	3
Allowance for equipment setup, moving and start-up	4	3	7
Total	47	42	89
6. Low-pressure grout at 300 lin ft/day	43	36	79
Allowance for start-up	1	1	2
Total	44	37	81
7. Final cleanup at 1,000 lin ft/day	13	11	24
Allowance for start-up	1	1	2
Total	14	12	26
Adit plug at 600 cu yd at 5-ft lifts	...	...	5

Construction Schedule

Excavation crew days and concreting crew days have now been determined. Crew working days are then converted to calendar days and are plotted on the construction schedule. In determining the total excavation time, allowances have to be made for portaling-in; for assembling the crews and training them; for constructing the adit Y; and for slow progress in the main tunnel near the Y section because of restricted working space. Slow progress must be allowed in the closely supported ground and in the breastboarded section.

Portaling-in and driving the first 100 lin ft of tunnel will be done one shift per day, and because of the portal construction and crew training, it is estimated that this will take 15 days.

Constructing the Y and driving the first 160 lin ft of main tunnel from the Y in each direction will be slow work, and it is estimated that it will take approximately 4 days to construct the Y and 16 days to drive the 320 lin ft of main tunnel.

When the excavation is in ground supported on 2-ft centers, it is estimated that the production will be 20 ft a day. When excavation is in ground requiring breastboarding, it is estimated that only an average of 8 ft a day will be obtained.

In the preparation of the construction schedule, it is assumed that the work will be bid on the first of May and work will be awarded on the first of June. The rubber-tired driving equipment can be secured in 2 months, so adit driving can start on August 1.

When the main tunnel has been driven 1,000 ft in the direction of the outlet with the use of rubber-tired equipment, this equipment will then be moved to drive 1,000 ft on the gate shaft leg. While this is being done, the Jacobs floor and rail equipment can be installed in the outlet leg. Upon completion of the 1,000-ft section in the gate shaft leg, the rubber-tired equipment will be moved to the inlet portal and 200 ft of tunnel will be driven. Then the shaft-raising operations can be started.

Meanwhile the outlet leg will be excavated with rail equipment on a single heading until the Jacobs floor can be erected in the gate shaft leg.

After erection of this second Jacobs floor, alternate-heading operations can be started. The remainder of the tunnel will be excavated in the manner shown on the construction schedule.

Concreting operations have been arranged on the schedules so some of the cleanup can be performed while other work is being done. Since only one invert and one arch concreting setup was planned, this equipment must be transferred from one leg to the other.

EXHIBIT 8A
SIERRA TUNNEL CONSTRUCTION SCHEDULE

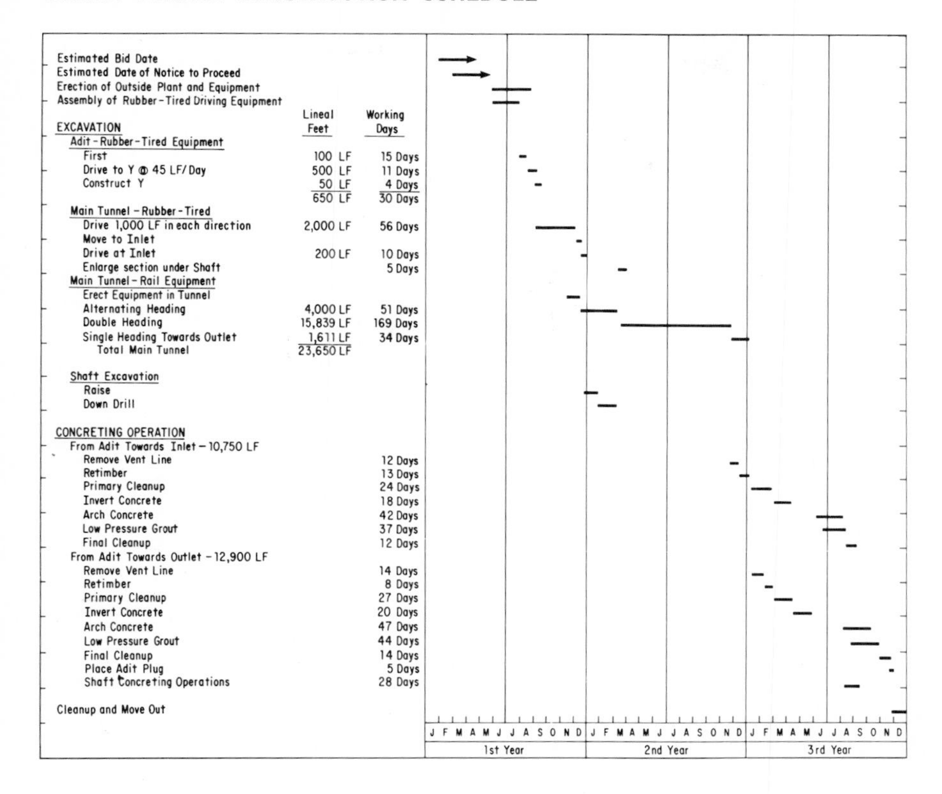

Two types of schedules are shown in Exhibits 8*A* and *B*. The bar chart schedule shows a later date of completion than the critical path schedule because the bar chart was prepared with built-in delay time. Critical path schedules do not take delay time into account. The critical path schedule for the Sierra Tunnel departs in some respects from the usual practice for critical path diagramming. It will be noted that there are four sequences of activities, grouped by location. The schedule can thus show how work begins at the adit and then, after the adit has been driven, proceeds in two parallel operations from the adit toward the outlet and from the adit toward the inlet. The construction of the gate shaft, which is to a large degree independent of work on the tunnels, is shown on a separate sequence. It will also be noted that the schedule is arranged so that durations and dates are drawn to scale, which permits one to determine by inspection which activities are proceeding simultaneously.

Exhibit 8B

DRAWING SHOWING CRITICAL PATH SCHEDULE

Heavy line indicates critical path

AWARD
June 1ST
1ST Year

COMPLETE
888 Days
Nov. 8TH
3RD Year

Mobilize rubber tired Equip.
60
60
Excavate Adit.
650'
45
105
1000'
42
147
Excavate with rubber
Mobilize Rail Equipment
Erect Floor
15
189
15
Single Rail heading
204
480 L.F.
2000'
77
Alternate heading Ex.
281
8289'
254
Double heading Ex.
Tunnel from adit to outlet 12900 L.F.
535
Single heading Excavation
1131'
35
570
Remove Fan Line
21
591
Retimber
12
603
Invert cleanup
40
643
7
650
Invert Concrete
30
680
746
Arch Concrete
71
817
15
832
Final Cleanup
18
850
Pour Adit Plug
858
8
888
30
Cleanup & move out
Contact
66
grout
Move Arch setup
3

1000'
42
Mobilize Rail Equipment
15
204
2000'
77
281
7550 L.F.
254
Tunnel from adit to gate shaft 10550 L.F.
535
Remove fan line
18
557
Retimber
19
576
Invert cleanup
36
612
Erect invert Equip.
4
616
Invert Concrete
27
643
Move Invert Setup
Erect Arch Equip.
10
Arch concrete
63
743
15
758
Contact
56
grout
785
Final Cleanup
18
803
Float
47
Mobilize Invert Concrete Equip.
Mobilize Arch Concr. Equip.

Move Rubber Equip.
23
196
Excavate with rubber
200'
219
Shaft Excavation
71
290
Shaft excavation float time
453
Gate shaft and 200 L.F. tunnel at inlet.
42
Shaft Concrete

X. COST OF OUTSIDE DEVELOPMENT

The majority of the outside work will be done by others, including the access roads, construction of power and water distributing lines, the opencut work, and the construction of the inlet and outlet structures. The cost of the remaining outside work is readily estimated and is included with the plant and equipment.

XI. COST OF TUNNEL EXCAVATION LABOR

Bid Item 1

The number of men and the daily cost to the contractor for these men will be estimated for each type of excavation crew. This daily crew cost times the crew days computed in Step IX is the cost of excavation labor. Part of this labor will be charged to steel supports, part to timber, and the remainder to excavation.

Crew Cost per Day in Adit—Rubber-tired Equipment

One-shift Operation

	No. of men/ shift or day	Rate	Total
Shifter	1	$79.14	$ 79.14
Miners	5	73.38	366.90
Eimco operator	1	89.39	89.39
Koehring Dumptor operator	1	80.62	80.62
Compressor operator	1	76.70	76.70
Mechanic foreman	1	92.43	92.43
Mechanics	1	89.39	89.39
Electricians	2	92.95	185.90
Tractor operator	1	80.96	80.96
Powderman	1	66.16	66.16
Warehouseman	1	67.16	67.16
Crane operator	1	83.62	83.62
Surveyors	2	......	166.02
Total	19	......	$1,524.39
Average cost per man-day	...	......	$ 80.23

Three-shift Operation

	No. of men/shift	No. of men/day	Rate	Total
Walkers	...	2	$85.00	$ 170.00
Shifters	1	3	79.14	237.42
Miners	5	15	73.38	1,100.70
Eimco operator	1	3	89.39	268.17
Koehring Dumptor operator	2	6	80.62	483.72
Compressor operator	1	3	76.70	230.10
Mechanic foreman	...	1	92.43	92.43
Mechanics, incl. drill "doctor" and bit grinder	...	4	89.39	357.96
Electricians	...	2	92.95	185.90
Tractor operator	...	1	80.96	80.96
Powderman	...	1	66.16	66.16
Warehouseman	...	1	67.16	67.16
Crane operator	...	1	83.62	83.62
Surveyors	...	2	......	166.02
Outside laborer	...	1	65.04	65.04
Total per day	...	46	......	$3,655.36
Average cost per man-day	...	...	......	$ 79.47

Single-heading Crew Cost per Day in Main Tunnel—Rubber-tired Equipment

	No. of men/shift	No. of men/day	Rate	Total
Walkers	...	2	$85.00	$ 170.00
Shifters	1	3	79.14	237.42
Miners	9	27	73.38	1,981.26
Nipper	1	3	71.54	214.62
Mucker operator	1	3	89.39	268.17
Truck drivers	3	9	80.62	725.58
Compressor operators	1	3	76.70	230.10
Mechanic foreman	...	1	92.43	92.43
Mechanics	...	5	89.39	446.95
Electricians	...	4	92.95	371.80
Tractor operator	...	1	80.96	80.96
Powderman	...	1	66.16	66.16
Warehouseman	...	1	67.11	67.11
Crane operator	...	1	83.62	83.62
Surveyors	...	2	......	166.02
Outside laborer	...	1	65.04	65.04
Total per day	...	67	......	$5,267.24
Average cost per man-day	...	...	......	$ 78.62

Single-heading Crew Cost per Day in Main Tunnel—Rail Equipment

	No. of men/shift	No. of men/day	Rate	Total
Walkers	...	2	$85.00	$ 170.00
Shifters	1	3	79.14	237.42
Miners	11	33	73.38	2,421.54
Nippers	1	3	71.54	214.62
Mucker operator	1	3	89.39	268.17
Motormen	4	12	79.42	953.04
Brakemen	2	6	75.52	453.12
Bull gang foreman	...	1	74.89	74.89
Bull gang laborers	...	6	70.33	421.98
Dumpmen	1	3	65.04	195.12
Swamper	...	1	70.33	70.33
Compressor operator	1	3	76.70	230.10
Mechanic foreman	...	1	92.43	92.43
Mechanics, incl. drill doctor and bit grinder	...	6	89.39	536.34
Electricians	...	4	92.95	371.80
Tractor operator	...	1	80.96	80.96
Powderman		1	66.16	66.16
Warehouseman	...	1	67.11	67.11
Crane operator	...	1	83.62	83.62
Surveyors	...	2	......	166.02
Cleanup, bull cook	...	1	65.04	65.04
Total per day	...	94	......	$7,239.81
Average cost per man-day	...	...	......	$ 77.02
Average crew cost per heading/hr worked: 7.75 × 3 = 23.25 hr/day $7,239.81 ÷ 23.25 = $311.39				

Alternating-heading Crew Cost per Day in Main Tunnel—Rail Equipment

	No. of men/shift	No. of men/day	Rate	Total
Walkers	...	2	$85.00	$ 170.00
Shifters	2	6	79.14	474.84
Miners, drilling	11	33	73.38	2,421.54
Nippers, drilling	1	3	71.54	214.62
Mucker operator	1	3	89.39	268.17
Cable tender	1	3	71.54	214.62
Miner on face	1	3	71.54	214.62
Car switching	2	6	71.54	429.24
Motormen	4	12	79.42	953.04
Brakemen	2	6	75.52	453.12
Bull gang foreman	...	1	74.89	74.89
Bull gang crew	...	8	70.33	562.64
Dumpman	1	3	65.04	195.12
Swamper	...	1	70.33	70.33
Compressor operator	1	3	76.70	230.10
Mechanic foreman	...	1	92.43	92.43
Mechanics, incl. drill doctor and bit grinder	...	8	89.39	715.12
Electricians	...	4	92.95	371.80
Tractor operator	...	1	80.96	80.96
Powderman	...	1	66.16	66.16
Warehouseman	...	1	67.11	67.11
Crane operator	...	1	83.62	83.62
Surveyors	...	2	......	166.02
Cleanup, bull cook	...	1	65.04	65.04
Total per day	...	113	......	$8,655.15
Average cost per man-day	...	...	......	$ 76.59
Average cost of heading crew/hr worked at 23.25 hr/day	...	...	......	$ 372.26

Double-heading Crew Cost per Day in Main Tunnel—Rail Equipment

	No. of men/shift	No. of men/day	Rate	Total
Walkers	...	2	$85.00	$ 170.00
Shifters	2	6	79.14	474.84
Miners	22	66	73.38	4,843.08
Nippers	2	6	71.54	429.24
Mucker operators	2	6	89.39	536.34
Motormen	...	21	79.42	1,667.82
Brakemen	...	12	75.52	906.24
Bull gang foremen	...	2	74.89	149.78
Bull gang	...	10	70.33	703.30
Dumpmen	1	3	65.04	195.12
Swamper	...	1	70.33	70.33
Compressor operator	1	3	76.70	230.10
Mechanic foreman	...	1	92.43	92.43
Mechanics, incl. drill doctor and bit grinder	...	10	89.39	893.90
Electricians	...	4	92.95	371.80
Tractor operator	...	1	80.96	80.96
Powderman	...	1	66.16	66.16
Warehouseman	...	1	67.11	67.11
Crane operator	...	1	83.62	83.62
Surveyors	...	2	......	166.02
Cleanup, bull cook	...	1	65.04	65.04
Total per day	...	160	......	$12,263.23
Average cost/man-day	...	...	......	$ 76.65
Average cost per crew/heading	...	......	......	$ 6,131.62
Average cost of heading crew/hr worked at 23.25 hr/day	...	...	......	$ 263.73

Summary of Excavation Labor

Excavation Labor in Adit to Be Charged to Plant and Equipment

15 Single-shift days at $1,524.39	$22,864
15 Triple-shift days at $3,655.36	54,830
Total excavation labor charged to adit	$77,694

Excavation Labor Charged to Tunnel Excavation, Bid Item 1

	Total	Per cu yd takeoff, 430,842 cu yd
Total excavation labor:		
71 Crew days, rubber-tired, single heading, at $5,267.24	$ 373,974	
51 Crew days, rail, alternate heading, at $8,655.15	441,413	
169 Crew days, rail, double heading, at $12,263.23	2,072,485	
34 Crew days, rail, single heading at $7,239.81	246,154	
Weekend maintenance, 71 weekends at $670 each	47,570	
	$3,181,596	
Less labor charged to supports:		
Cost per lb:		
Cost per ½ hr/heading on double-heading crew ... $131.86		
Lb of steel, one set ... 2,510 lb		
Labor cost per lb ... $0.05		
Total weight:		
912 Sets at 2,510 lb = 2,289,120 lb		
Labor for 2,289,120 lb at $0.05	$ 114,456	
Timber 404 MBM at $50.00	20,200	
Labor charge to tunnel excavation	$3,046,940	$7.07

XII. COST OF EXCAVATION SUPPLIES

Bid Item 1

a. *Powder and Exploders*

	Adit and Y	Main tunnel	
		Granite	Greenstone
Lin ft of tunnel	688	18,500	5,150
Number of rounds	92	2,143	760
Number of holes/round	40	80	70
Number of exploders, std tunnel	3,680	171,440	53,200
Added number under shaft	......	....	100
Total number of exploders	3,680	171,440	53,300
Lb of primer powder at ½ lb/hole	1,840	85,720	26,650
Pay cu yd of excavation	4,472	336,330	94,512
Lb of AN/cu yd	6	5	4
Lb of AN total	26,832	1,681,650	378,048

	Adit and Y	Main tunnel	
		Granite	Greenstone
Cost:			
Caps at $0.31 ea	$1,141	$ 53,146	$16,523
Powder at $0.22 lb	404	18,858	5,863
AN at $0.06	1,610	100,899	22,683
Wire and misc. at $1.00/lin ft	688	18,500	5,150
Total cost	$3,843	$191,403	$50,219
Cost per cu yd of pay excavation	$0.86	$ 0.57	$ 0.53
Cost per lin ft of tunnel	$5.59	$10.35	$ 9.75
Combining two main tunnel types:			
Total cost		$241,622	
Cost per cu yd on 430,842 cu yd		0.56	
Cost per lin ft		10.22	

b. *Steel and Bits*

	Adit and Y	Main tunnel
From above:		
Lin ft of tunnel	688	23,650
Number of rounds	92	2,903
Average length round, lin ft	7.5	8.15
Average drilling length of round, lin ft	8.5	9.15
Number of holes	3,680	224,640
Lin ft of standard drilling	31,280	2,055,456
At two holes/round:		
Burn-cut drilling, lin ft	1,564	53,125
Total drilling, lin ft	32,844	2,108,581
With bit life of 200 lin ft:		
Number of standard bits	157	10,277
Number of burn-cut bits	8	266
Estimated cost:		
Steel cost = $24.00 each piece		
One piece of steel has life of 1,000 lin ft		
At 1,000 lin ft = $0.024/lin ft	$ 789	$ 50,616
Standard bits at $18.70	2,936	192,180
Burn-cut bits at $207.00	1,656	55,062
Total cost	$5,381	$297,858
Cost per lin ft of drilling	$0.16	$0.14
Cost per cu yd of excavation	$1.20	$0.69

c. *Power*

	Rubber		Rail	
	Adit	Tunnel	Single and alternating heading	Double heading
Power load:				
Horsepower:				
Muckers	...	.....	165	330
Fans, average	200	400	450	1,000
Compressors	500	1,000	1,250	2,250
Shops	25	50	50	50
Pump	...	25	50	50
Misc. (shops, office, etc.)	100	100	100	100
Total hp	825	1,575	2,065	3,780
Kilowatts	615	1,175	1,540	2,820
At 50% load factor, kw	308	588	770	1,410
Cost per hr at $0.015/kwhr	$4.62	$8.82	$11.55	$21.15
Cost per day	$111	$212	$277	$508
Equivalent number of days	20	71	85	169
Total cost	$2,220	$15,052	$23,545	$85,852
Increase for Saturday and Sunday	220	1,505	2,355	8,585
	$2,440	$16,557	$25,900	$94,437
			Adit	Tunnel
Regroup cost			$2,440	$136,894
Cost per cu yd			$0.55	$0.32

d. *Electrical Supplies*

Based on past experience, cost without drag-cable replacements on mucker is $3.85 per lin ft of tunnel. Cost including drag-cable replacements is $4.35 per lin ft of tunnel.

Adit cost:	
688 lin ft at $3.85	$2,649
Cost per cu yd on 4,472 cu yd	$0.59
Tunnel cost:	
2,000 lin ft at $3.85	$ 7,700
21,650 lin ft at $4.35	94,178
Total cost	$101,878
Cost per cu yd based on 430,842 cu yd	$0.24

e. *Cost of Fuel, Lube, and Repair Parts*

	Unit cost per hr	Rubber-tired equipment				Rail equipment in tunnel					
		Adit		Tunnel		Single heading		Alternating heading		Double heading	
		Oper. hr	Daily cost	Oper. hr	Daily cost	Oper. hr	Daily cost	Oper. hr	Daily cost	Oper. hr	Daily cost
Eimco mucker	$15.00	12	$ 180.00	12	$ 180.00						
Conway mucker	15.00	...	....	...	....	12	$ 180.00	12	$ 180.00	24	$ 360.00
Truck for drill jumbo	4.50	3	13.50	3	13.50						
Drill jumbo	0.50	12	6.00	12	6.00	12	6.00	12	6.00	24	12.00
Drills	0.50	60	30.00	108	54.00	132	66.00	132	66.00	264	132.00
Floor	2.00	...	....	...	....	24	48.00	48	96.00	48	96.00
Haul trucks	5.00	24	120.00	36	180.00						
Locomotives	3.00	...	....	...	....	96	288.00	96	288.00	168	504.00
Cars	0.05	...	....	...	....	720	36.00	720	36.00	1,440	72.00
Fans	0.10	48	4.80	72	7.20	120	12.00	144	14.40	240	24.00
Pumps	0.50	...	....	24	12.00	38	19.00	24	12.00	76	38.00
Compressors	0.80	48	38.40	96	76.80	120	96.00	120	96.00	216	172.80
Car dumpers	1.00	...	....	...	....	12	12.00	12	12.00	24	24.00
Tractor	8.00	8	64.00	8	64.00	8	64.00	8	64.00	8	64.00
Front-end loader	8.00	8	64.00	8	64.00	8	64.00	8	64.00	8	64.00
Welding supplies	......	...	8.00	...	10.00	...	15.00	...	20.00	.....	25.00
Miscellaneous	......	...	20.00	...	30.00	...	50.00	...	75.00	.....	100.00
Total	......	...	$ 548.70	...	$ 697.50	...	$ 956.00	...	$ 1,029.40	.....	$ 1,667.80
Equivalent number of three-shift days	......	...	20 days	...	71 days	...	34 days	...	51 days	.....	169 days
Total cost	......	...	$10,974.00	...	$49,522.50	...	$32,504.00	...	$52,499.40	.....	$281,858.20
Total cost of tunnel	......	...	....	...	....	...	....	...	....	.....	$416,384.10
Pay yardage	......	...	4,472 cu yd	...	....	...	....	...	....	.....	430,842 cu yd
Cost per cu yd	......	...	$2.45/cu yd	...	....	...	....	...	....	.....	$0.97/cu yd

f. *Roadway Gravel, Ballast and Miscellaneous RR Supplies*

	Adit	Tunnel
Length, lin ft	688	23,650
Cost at $2.00/lin ft	$1,376	$47,300
Cu yd of excavation	4,472	430,842
Cost per cu yd	$0.31	$0.11

g, h, i. *Supply Cost Based on Manpower*

	Rubber		Rail		
	Adit	Main tunnel	Single heading	Alternating heading	Double heading
Crew size	46	67	94	113	160
Cost per day:					
g. Hard hats, raingear, safety at $0.50/man-day	$23	$33.50	$47	$56.50	$80
h. Misc. supplies and sanitation at $3.00/man-day	$138	$201	$282	$339	$480
i. Small tools and misc. at $2.00/man-day	$92	$134	$188	$226	$320
Number of equivalent three-shift days	20	71	34	51	169
Total cost:					
g. Hard hats, etc	$ 460	$ 2,379	$1,598	$ 2,882	$13,520
h. Misc. supplies, etc	2,760	14,271	9,588	17,289	81,120
i. Small tools and misc	1,840	9,514	6,392	11,526	54,080

Combining:	Adit, 4,472 cu yd		Tunnel, 430,842 cu yd	
	Total	Per cu yd	Total	Per cu yd
g. Hard hats, etc	$ 460	$0.10	$ 20,379	$0.05
h. Misc. supplies, etc	2,760	0.62	122,268	0.28
i. Small tools and misc	1,840	0.41	81,512	0.19

Summary of Excavation Supplies

	Adit, 4,472 cu yd	Main tunnel, 430,842 cu yd
	Cost per cu yd	
a. Powder and exploders	$0.86	$0.56
b. Steel and bits	1.20	0.69
c. Power	0.55	0.32
d. Electrical supplies	0.59	0.24
e. Fuel, lube, repair parts	2.45	0.97
f. Gravel, ballast, RR supplies	0.31	0.11
g. Hard hats, raingear, safety	0.10	0.05
h. Misc. supplies and sanitation	0.62	0.28
i. Small tools and misc. supplies	0.41	0.19
Total	$7.09	$3.41

Total Cost of Supplies for Adit This Cost To Be Tabulated in Cost of Plant and Equipment

Supplies from above	
4,472 cu yd at $7.09/cu yd	$31,706
Supports	
12 Sets at 810 lb at $0.12/lb	1,166
Timber	
3.7 MBM at $100.00	370
Portal protection	1,651
Total	$34,893

XIII. COST OF CONCRETE-LINING LABOR

Bid Item 9

Takeoff quantity 110,453 cu yd
Bid quantity 110,000 cu yd

This labor is divided into eight different operations. Crew days for each operation were computed in Step IX.

a. *Remove Vent Line—26 Days*

Labor	No. of men/shift	No. of men/day	Rate/ manshift	Total
Shifters	1	3	$79.14	$ 237.42
Miners	3	9	73.38	660.42
Crane operators	1	3	83.62	250.86
Locomotive operators	2	6	79.42	476.52
Brakemen	1	3	75.52	226.56
Mechanics	1	3	89.39	268.17
Total per day	...	27	......	$ 2,119.95
For 26 days	...	...	......	$55,119

b. *Retimber—21 Days*

Labor	No. of men/shift	No. of men/day	Rate/ manshift	Total
Walkers	...	2	$85.00	$ 170.00
Shifters	1	3	79.14	237.42
Miners	8	24	73.38	1,761.12
Locomotive operators	1	3	79.42	238.26
Brakemen	1	3	75.52	226.56
Crane operators	1	3	83.62	250.86
Compressor operators	1	3	76.70	230.10
Swamper	...	1	70.33	70.33
Mechanic	...	1	89.39	89.39
Electrician	...	1	92.95	92.95
Surveyors	...	2	......	166.02
Warehouseman	...	1	67.11	67.11
Total per day	...	47	......	$ 3,600.12
For 21 days	...	...	......	$75,603

c. *Primary Cleanup—51 Days*

Labor	No. of men/shift	No. of men/day	Rate/ manshift	Total
Walkers	...	2	$85.00	$ 170.00
Shifters	1	3	79.14	237.42
Mucker operators	1	3	89.39	268.17
Miners	12	36	73.38	2,641.68
Locomotive operators	2	6	79.42	476.52
Brakemen	1	3	75.52	226.56
Electricians	...	4	92.95	371.80
Mechanic foreman	...	1	92.43	92.43
Mechanics	...	3	89.39	268.17
Compressor operators	1	3	76.70	230.10
Crane operators	1	3	83.62	250.86
Outside labor	1	3	65.04	195.12
Warehouseman	...	1	67.11	67.11
Surveyors	...	2	......	166.02
Total per day	...	73	......	$ 5,661.96
For 51 days	...	...	......	$206,718

d. *Invert Concrete—38 Days*

Labor	No. of men/shift	No. of men/day	Rate/ manshift	Total
Walkers	...	2	$85.00	$ 170.00
Aggregate reclaim	1	3	79.14	237.42
Mix-plant operators	1	3	83.62	250.86
Concrete loaders	1	3	65.04	195.12
Mix-plant laborers	1	3	65.04	195.12
Shifters	1	3	79.15	237.45
Locomotive operators	4	12	79.42	953.04
Brakemen	1	3	75.52	226.56
Conveyor operators	1	3	77.84	233.52
Bridge operators	1	3	77.84	233.52
Invert screed operators	1	3	77.84	233.52
Vibrator operators	4	12	70.33	843.96
Finishers	4	12	73.91	886.92
Bridge setup	3	9	70.33	632.97
Pipemen and pump	3	9	70.33	632.97
Track crew foreman	1	3	74.89	224.67
Track crew	4	12	70.33	843.96
Compressor operators	1	3	76.70	230.10
Mechanic foreman	...	1	92.43	92.43
Mechanics	3	9	89.39	904.51
Electricians	...	4	92.95	371.80
Warehouseman	...	1	67.11	67.11
Surveyors	...	2	......	166.02
Change house	...	1	61.73	61.73
Total per day	...	119	......	$ 9,125.28
For 38 days	...	...	......	$346,761
Forms under shaft, 78 sq ft at $2.00 for labor	...	...	......	156
Total	...	...	......	$346,917

e. *Arch Concrete—89 Days*

Labor	No. of men/shift	No. of men/day	Rate/manshift	Total
Walkers	...	2	$85.00	$ 170.00
Aggregate reclaim	1	3	79.14	237.42
Mix-plant operators	1	3	83.62	250.86
Concrete loaders	1	3	65.04	195.12
Mix-plant laborers	1	3	65.04	195.12
Shifters	1	3	79.15	237.45
Locomotive operators	4	12	79.42	953.04
Brakemen	1	3	75.52	226.56
Conveyor operators	1	3	85.44	256.32
Gun operators	1	3	84.65	253.95
Nozzlemen	1	3	73.38	220.14
Pipemen	2	6	70.33	421.98
Vibrator operators	4	12	70.33	843.96
Finish and cure	2	6	73.91	443.46
Form foreman	1	3	74.89	224.67
Form movers	4	12	70.33	843.96
Pipe movers	2	6	70.33	421.98
Compressor operators	1	3	76.70	230.10
Mechanical foreman	...	1	92.43	92.43
Mechanics	...	9	89.39	804.51
Electricians	...	4	92.95	371.80
Warehouseman	...	1	67.11	67.11
Surveyors	...	2	.....	166.02
Change house	...	1	61.73	61.73
Total per day	...	107	......	$ 8,189.69
For 89 days	...	...	......	$728,882
Bulkhead forms:				
20 Bulkheads = 1,540 sq ft at $2.00 for labor	...	...	......	3,080
Forms under shaft and at adit:				
4,936 sq ft at $2.00 for labor	...	...	......	9,872
Total	...	...	......	$741,834

f. *Low-pressure Grout—80 Days*

Assume 3 cu ft/lin ft of tunnel. If grout progresses 300 lin ft/day, the same progress as arch, then 900 cu ft/day, working 16 hr = 56 cu ft/hr.

Labor	No. of men/shift	No. of men/day	Rate/manshift	Total
Shifters	1	2	$79.15	$ 158.30
Drillers	2	4	73.38	293.52
Connectors	2	4	70.33	281.32
Grout-pump operators	1	2	84.65	169.30
Laborers	2	4	70.33	281.32
Locomotive operators	1	2	79.42	158.84
Outside laborers	1	2	65.04	130.08
Mechanics	1	2	89.39	178.78
Total per day	...	22	......	$ 1,651.46
For 80 days	...	...	......	$132,117

g. *Final Cleanup—25 Days*

Labor	No. of men/shift	No. of men/day	Rate/manshift	Total
Walkers	1	2	$85.00	$ 170.00
Shifters	1	3	79.15	237.45
Track crew foremen	1	3	74.89	224.67
Track crew	6	18	70.33	1,265.94
Pipe crew	4	12	70.33	843.96
Finishers	1	3	73.91	221.73
Cleanup labor	4	12	70.33	843.96
Locomotive operators	3	9	79.42	714.78
Brakemen	1	3	75.52	226.56
Compressor operators	1	3	76.70	230.10
Mechanic foreman	...	1	92.43	92.43
Mechanics	2	6	89.39	536.34
Electricians	...	4	92.95	371.80
Warehouseman	...	1	67.11	67.11
Crane operators	1	3	83.62	250.86
Outside laborers	1	3	65.04	195.12
Change house	...	1	65.04	65.04
Total per day	...	87	......	$ 6,557.85
For 25 days	...	...	......	$163,946

h. *Weekend Maintenance Labor—37 Weekends*

at $670 . . . . $24,790

Summary of Labor Cost for Concrete Tunnel Lining, Bid Item 9

a. Remove vent line	$ 55,119
b. Retimber	75,603
c. Primary cleanup	206,718
d. Invert concrete	346,917
e. Arch concrete	741,834
f. Low-pressure grout	132,117
g. Final cleanup	163,946
h. Weekend maintenance	24,790
Total labor, bid item 9	$1,747,044

Cost per cu yd based on takeoff quantity of 110,453 cu yd . . . . $15.82/cu yd

XIV. COST OF CONCRETE LINING SUPPLIES

Bid Item 9

Takeoff quantity	110,453
Bid quantity	110,000

The supplies are consumed in seven different operations. Crew days for each operation were computed in Step IX.

a. *Remove Vent Line—26 Days*

			Cost per day
Supplies:			
Power and water (charged to other items)			
Fuel, oil, lube, repair parts, etc.:			
Locomotives	48 hr at $3.00	$144.00	
Crane	24 hr at $6.00	144.00	
Misc		40.00	$ 328.00
Other supplies:			
Misc. supplies	27 men at $3.00/day		81.00
Small tools, etc	27 men at $2.00/day		54.00
Rubber, raingear, safety	27 men at $0.50/day		13.50
Total per day			$ 476.50
For 26 days			$12,389

b. *Retimber—21 Days*

Supplies:			
Power, 650 hp = 484 kw:			
At 50% load factor = 242 kw			
At 24 hr/day = 5,808 kwhr at $0.015			$ 87.12
Electrical supplies			40.00
Fuel, lube, oil, repair parts, etc.:			
Compressors	48 hr at $0.80	$ 38.40	
Locomotives	24 hr at $3.00	72.00	
Crane	24 hr at $6.00	144.00	
Misc		30.00	284.40
Miscellaneous supplies	47 men at $3.00/day		141.00
Small tools and supplies	47 men at $2.00/day		94.00
Rubber, raingear, safety	47 men at $0.50/day		23.50
Total per day			$ 670.02
For 21 days			$14,070

c. *Primary Cleanup—51 Days*

			Cost per day
Supplies:			
Power, connected load of 1,300 hp			
970 kw at 50% load and 24 hr/day			
11,640 kwhr at $0.015			$ 174.60
Electrical supplies			50.00
Fuel, oil, lube, repair parts, etc.:			
Mucker	24 hr at $15.00	$360.00	
Locomotive	48 hr at $ 3.00	144.00	
Compressors	96 hr at $ 0.80	76.80	
Crane	24 hr at $ 6.00	144.00	
Pumps and misc		50.00	774.80
Misc. supplies	73 men at $3.00/day		219.00
Small tools and supplies	73 men at $2.00/day		146.00
Rubber, raingear, safety	73 men at $0.50/day		36.50
Total per day			$ 1,400.90
For 51 days			$71,446

d. *Invert Concrete—38 Days*

Item	Rate		Amount
Supplies, except aggregate, cement and admix:			
Power:			
Connected load—3,100 hp			
Connected load—2,312 kw			
At 25% load factor for 24 hr, 13,872 kwhr			
At $0.015/kwhr			$ 208.08
Electrical supplies			50.00
Track supplies at $0.40 lin ft for 23,560 lin ft = $9,424:			
Cost per day for 38 days			248.00
(These supplies used for relaying the track on the invert.)			
Fuel, lube, oil, repair parts, etc.:			
Mix plant	24 hr at $3.00	$ 72.00	
Agitator cars	384 hr at $0.20	76.80	
Locomotives	96 hr at $3.00	288.00	
Belts		50.00	
Bridge		20.00	
Screed		20.00	
Compressors	96 hr at $0.80	76.80	
Vibrators at $0.10 cu yd		100.00	
Misc		50.00	753.60
Misc. supplies	119 men at $3.00/day		357.00
Small tools, etc	119 men at $2.00/day		238.00
Rubber, raingear, safety	119 men at $0.50/day		59.50
Total per day			$ 1,914.18
For 38 days			$72,739
Forms under shaft, 78 sq ft at $2.00 for supplies			156
Total supplies			$ 72,895

e. *Arch Concrete—89 Days*

Item	Rate		*Cost per day*
Supplies, except aggregate, cement, and admix:			
Power			$ 208.08
Electrical supplies			50.00
Form hardware, 5,124 sq ft day at $0.10			512.40
Fuel, oil, lube, repair parts, etc.:			
Mix plant	24 hr at $3.00	$ 72.00	
Agitator cars	384 hr at $0.20	76.80	
Locomotives	96 hr at $3.00	288.00	
Belt		50.00	
Press Weld and pipe	24 hr at $1.00	24.00	
Vibrators at $0.10 cu yd		134.40	
Compressors	96 hr at $0.80	76.80	
Misc		50.00	772.00
Misc. supplies	107 men at $3.00/day		321.00
Small tools, etc	107 men at $2.00/day		214.00
Rubber, raingear, safety	107 men at $0.50/day		53.50
Total per day			$ 2,130.98
For 89 days			$189,657
Bulkhead forms:			
20 Bulkheads, 1,540 sq ft at $2.00 for supplies			3,080
Forms under shaft and at adit:			
4,936 sq ft at $2.00 for supplies			9,872
Total			$202,609

f. *Low-pressure Grout—80 Days*

Supplies:			
Cement by owner			
Sand, 450 cu ft at $0.20			$ 90.00
Oil, lube, repair parts, etc.:			
Drills	48 hr at $0.50	$24.00	
Grout pump	24 hr at $2.00	48.00	
Locomotive	24 hr at $3.00	72.00	
Grout hose and pipe		10.00	154.00
Misc. supplies	22 men at $3.00/day		66.00
Small tools, etc	22 men at $2.00/day		44.00
Rubber, raingear, safety	22 men at $0.50/day		11.00
Total per day			$ 365.00
For 80 days			$29,200

g. *Final Cleanup—25 Days*

			Cost per day
Supplies:			
Power			$ 174.60
Electrical supplies			20.00
Fuel, oil, lube, repair parts, etc.:			
Locomotives	72 hr at $3.00	$216.00	
Compressor	48 hr at $0.80	38.40	
Crane	24 hr at $6.00	144.00	
Other		50.00	448.40
Misc. supplies	87 men at $3.00/day		261.00
Small tools, etc	87 men at $2.00/day		174.00
Rubber, raingear, safety	87 men at $0.50/day		43.50
Total per day			$ 1,121.50
For 25 days			$28,038

Summary of Cost of Supplies for Concrete Tunnel Lining, Bid Item 9

Cost of supplies as detailed:		
a. Remove vent line	$ 12,389	
b. Retimber	14,070	
c. Primary cleanup	71,446	
d. Invert concrete	72,895	
e. Arch concrete	202,609	
f. Low-pressure grout	29,200	
g. Final cleanup	28,038	
Subtotal	$430,647	
Other supplies:		
Cement waste:		
154,263 cu yd of concrete at $0.05/cu yd	7,713	
Admixture:		
154,263 cu yd at $0.10/cu yd	15,426	
Total supplies	$453,786	
Cost per cu yd, based on takeoff quantity of 110,453 cu yd		$4.11

Cost of Aggregate

Total yards of concrete, incl. overbreak concrete	154,263 cu yd
Tonnage aggregate at 1.65 tons/cu yd	254,534 tons
Cost of aggregate at $2.10/ton	$534,521
Cost per cu yd of concrete, based on takeoff yardage of 110,453 cu yd	$4.84

XV. DIRECT COST OF OTHER BID ITEMS

Bid Item 2—Steel Sets

Labor/lb (see bid item 1)	$0.05
Permanent materials/lb	0.12
Total per lb	$0.17

Bid Item 3—Timber

Pay timber is within 4 in. of outside flange of sets. Assume one-half of timber is pay timber.

Labor/MBM from bid item 1	$ 50.00
Pay timber/MBM	80.00
Nonpay timber supplies/MBM	80.00
Total per MBM	$210.00

Bid Item 4—Roof Bolts

Takeoff = 1,520 lin ft of tunnel has four roof bolts across crown on 4-ft centers, or one roof bolt per lineal foot of tunnel; 1,520 roof bolts of 8-ft length = 12,160 lin ft. Use two men on rear-end jumbo to drill and set roof bolts. Time to go through roof-bolt section is 1,520 lin ft ÷ 60 = 25.33 days; 25.33 days at 6 men/day = 152 man-days.

		Total	For 12,160 lin ft
Labor for 152 man-days at $73.38/day		$11,154	$0.91
Supplies:			
Drill maintenance:			
2 Drills at 12 hr/day = 24 hr/day			
24 × 25.33 = 608 hr			
608 hr at $0.50	$ 304		
Misc. cost:			
152 man-days at $5.50	836		
Bit and steel cost for 12,160 lin ft of drilling:			
Steel at $0.02/lin ft	243		
Bits at $18.70/200 = $0.0935/lin ft	1,137	2,520	0.21
Permanent materials		4,864	0.40
Total cost		$18,538	$1.52

Bid Item 5—Drill Feeler Holes ahead of Tunnel Excavation

Assume a length of 24 lin ft. Therefore, at a 60 lin ft/hr drilling rate, the heading crew will be delayed 24 min, or 0.4 hr. On a double heading, crew cost of one-half the crew per hour is $263.73

Labor = $263.73 × 0.4 ÷ 24	$4.40/lin ft
Supplies	2.12/lin ft
Total cost	$6.52/lin ft

Bid Item 6—Drill Grout Holes as an Aid to Tunnel Driving

To be used when indications show that grouting-off in front of tunnel driving should be used. Drill 10 holes of 60-ft length with drifters. Because of drill-hole length, cut drilling speed down to 40 lin ft/hr.

Number of holes	10		
Number of drills	10		
Lin ft drilled	60		
Time required	60 ÷ 40 = 1½ hr		
Cost per hr for ½ crew of double heading		$263.73	
Cost for 1½ hr		$395.60	
Cost per lin ft of labor = $395.60 ÷ 10 × 60			$0.66
Supplies			0.21
Total cost per lin ft			$0.87

Bid Item 7—Grout as an Aid to Tunnel Driving

To be done when indications show that grouting-off in front of tunnel driving should be done. Assume grout holes per round will take 100 cu ft and to place this 100 cu ft will take 2 hr.

Labor for 100 cu ft = 2 × $263.73, or $527.46

Labor cost per cu ft	$5.27
Misc. supplies	2.58
Cement	1.50
Total cost per cu ft	$9.35

Bid Item 8—Shaft Excavation

Takeoff quantities:

Shaft	214 lin ft
Excavation	5,299 cu yd

Raise

Excavate a 6-ft-diameter raise from tunnel; let muck fall into bottom of tunnel, and pick it up with front-end loader and truck. Average progress in raise is 5 ft/shift, or 15 ft/day.

Cu yd/lin ft in raise	1.05	cu yd
For total raise	225	cu yd
Per day	15	cu yd
Broken yd/day	22.5	cu yd
Number of days = 214 ÷ 15	14.25	days
Allowance for start-up	2.75	days
	17	days
Number of rounds = 214 ÷ 5	43	rounds

Crew Cost per Day for Shaft Raising

	No. of men/shift	No. of men/day	Rate/ manshift	Total
Shifters	1	3	$82.19	$ 246.57
Miners	2	6	76.41	458.46
Nippers	1	3	74.54	223.62
Front-end loader operator	...	1	89.39	89.39
Compressor operators	1	3	76.70	230.10
Mechanic	...	1	89.39	89.39
Electrician	...	1	92.95	92.95
Total per day	...	18	......	$1,430.48
Average cost per man-day	...	...	......	$ 79.47

Cost of Shaft Raising

			Total	*Cost/lin ft*
Labor:				
17 days at $1,430.48			$24,318	$113.64
Supplies:				
Drill steel and bits:				
5-ft round = 7-ft holes at 18 holes/round = 126 lin ft round × 43 = 5,418 lin ft				
Steel, 5,418 lin ft at $0.03		$163		
Bits, 5,418 lin ft ÷ 200 × $18.70		507	670	3.13
Powder and exploders:				
Exploders, 774 at $0.31		$240		
Powder, 225 cu yd at 8 lb at $0.22		396	$ 636	$ 2.97
Power, $25 day for 17 days			425	1.99
Electrical supplies			213	1.00
Fuel, lube, equipment repair parts, etc.:				
	Cost/hr	*Cost/day*		
Drills, 24 hr	$1.00	$ 24.00		
Alimak, 24 hr	2.00	48.00		
Front-end loader, 8 hr	8.00	64.00		
2 Portable compressors, 48 hr	2.80	134.40		
Total		$270.40		
For 17 days			$ 4,597	21.48
Misc. supplies:				
Rubber, raingear, safety	$0.50 man-day			
Misc. supplies and sanitation	3.00 man-day			
Small tools, etc	2.00 man-day			
	$5.50 man-day			
Daily cost for 18 men	$99.00			
For 17 days			1,683	7.86
Total supplies			8,224	38.43
TOTAL COST			$32,542	$152.07

Downdrill

Take down in 5-ft rounds:

Total yardage	5,299
Less yardage in raise	225
Remainder	5,074
Average cu yd/lin ft	23.71

Average 80 holes/round at 7 lin ft/hole
Total drilling .... 560 lin ft/round

Use drill jumbo mounting four drifter drills:

Lin ft drilled/drill each round	140 lin ft
At 30 lin ft/hr	4⅔ hr
Set up jumbo	⅓ hr
Remove jumbo	⅓ hr
Load holes	1⅓ hr
Shoot and ventilate	½ hr
Muck 180 cu yd of broken material at 30 cu yd/hr	6 hr
Hand clean up bottom	1 hr
Total cycle	14.16 hr = 2 shifts

Therefore, base production on 7½ lin ft for three shifts:

214 ÷ 7½ lin ft	28.5 days
Allow for start-up	1.5 days
Total	30 days

Crew Cost per Day of Downdrilling

	No. of men/shift	No. of men/day	Rate/manshift	Total
Walker	...	1	$85.00	$ 85.00
Shifters	1	3	82.19	246.57
Miners	3	9	76.41	687.69
Nippers	1	3	74.54	223.62
Mucker operators	2	6	89.39	536.34
Truck drivers	1	3	80.62	241.86
Compressor operators	1	3	76.70	230.10
Crane operators	1	3	83.62	250.86
Mechanics	1	3	89.39	268.17
Electrician	...	1	92.95	92.95
Warehouseman	...	1	67.11	67.11
Total per day	...	36	......	$2,930.27
Average cost per man-day	...	...	......	$ 81.40

Estimated cost:		Total	Per yd, 5,074 cu yd
Labor, 30 days at $2,930.27		$ 87,908	$17.33
Supplies:			
Steel:			
Total lin ft in 80 holes of 7 lin ft/hole for 43 rounds = 24,080 lin ft			
24,080 lin ft at $0.03	$ 722		
Bits at 24,080 lin ft ÷ 200 × $18.70	2,251	2,973	0.59
Exploders and powder:			
80 × 43 = 3,440 exploders at $0.31	$ 1,066		
Powder, 5,074 cu yd at 4 lb at $0.22	4,465	5,531	1.09
Power, $50/day for 30 days		1,500	0.30
Electrical supplies		428	0.08
Fuel, lube, and equipment repair parts:			
Cost per day:			
Crane . . . 24 hr at $6.00	$144.00		
Drills . . . 48 hr at $0.50	24.00		
Compressor . . . 48 hr at $2.80	134.40		
Small mucker . . . 12 hr at $4.00	48.00		
Eimco 115 mucker . . . 8 hr at $8.00	64.00		
Truck . . . 8 hr at $5.50	44.00		
Pumps and fan	10.00		
Misc	25.00		
Total per day	$493.40		
For 30 days		14,802	2.92
Misc. supplies:			
Cost per man-day			
Hard hats, raingear, safety	$ 0.50		
Misc. supplies and sanitary	3.00		
Small tools and misc	2.00		
Cost per man-day	$ 5.50		
Cost per day for 36 men	$198.00		
For 30 days		5,940	1.18
Total cost of supplies		31,174	6.14
TOTAL COST		$119,082	$23.47

Summary of Cost of Shaft Excavation

	Labor	Supplies	Total
Raise	$ 24,318	$ 8,224	$ 32,542
Downdrill	87,908	31,174	119,082
Total	$112,226	$39,398	$151,624
Cost per cu yd for 5,299 cu yd	$21.18	$7.43	$28.61

Bid Item 10—Shaft Concrete

Bid Quantity	1,900 cu yd
Takeoff Quantity:	
Pay	1,894 cu yd
Overbreak	496 cu yd
Total	2,390 cu yd

Average cubic yard per lineal foot = 2,390 ÷ 214 = 11 cu yd/lin ft. With slip forms, pour 1 lin ft/hr. Pour at the same time as the tunnel arch is poured toward the outlet.

Use two trains, one car per train. Total hours of pour rate for slip forms is 1 lin ft/hr.

From Elev. 3626 to 3647, four pours	allow 4 shifts
From Elev. 3647 to 3802 = 155 lin ft, 155 hr	allow 19 shifts
From Elev. 3802 to 3806	allow 1 shift
From Elev. 3806 to 3840 = 34 lin ft, 34 hr	allow 4 shifts
Delays and start-up	allow 3 shifts
Total	31 shifts

Mixing-plant operation and cost of power and other utilities will not be charged to this operation as cost is absorbed in tunnel arch concrete.

To clean up shaft and remove tights, allow five shifts.

Labor Cost per Shift

	No. of men/shift	Cost of man/shift	Total shift
Shifter	1	$82.19	$ 82.19
Crane operator	1	83.62	83.62
Crane oiler	1	70.33	70.33
Miners	4	76.14	304.56
Front-end-loader operator	1	89.39	89.39
Total per shift	8	......	$ 630.09
For 5 shifts	...	......	$3,150

Supply Cost per Shift

	Unit	Cost/unit	Cost/shift
1 Crane	8 hr	$6.00	$ 48.00
1 Front-end loader	8 hr	8.00	64.00
Misc. supplies	8 men	3.00	24.00
Small tools	8 men	2.00	16.00
Rubber and safety	8 men	0.50	4.00
Misc	8 men	.....	10.00
Total per shift	.....	.....	$166.00
For 5 shifts	.....	.....	$830

Concrete Placing

	No. of men/shift	Cost of man/shift	Total shift
Labor for placing:			
Shifter	1	$82.19	$ 82.19
Locomotive operators	2	79.42	158.84
Concrete transfer	1	70.33	70.33
Crane operator	1	83.62	83.62
Crane oiler	1	70.33	70.33
Chute operator	1	77.84	77.84
Vibrator men and laborers	4	70.33	281.32
Finisher	1	73.91	73.91
Mechanic	1	89.39	89.39
Total	13	......	$ 987.77
For 31 shifts	...	......	$30,621

Placing supplies:			
Fuel, oil, lube, repair parts:			
Locomotives	16 hr at $3.00	$48.00	
Crane	8 hr at $6.00	48.00	
Misc.		22.00	$ 118.00
Misc. supplies	13 men/shift at $3.00		39.00
Small tools	13 men/shift at $2.00		26.00
Rubber, safety	13 men/shift at $0.50		6.50
Total			$ 189.50
For 31 shifts			$5,875

Slip Forms

	Labor	Supplies	Total
155-ft section ... 72.33 sq ft/lin ft			
34-ft section ... 89.00 sq ft/lin ft			
161.33 sq ft/lin ft			
Purchase 3 lin ft of each size = 484 sq ft at $8.00	......	$ 3,872	$ 3,872
Wood lining, 8 ft long, 1,291 sq ft at $4.00	......	5,164	5,164
Superstructure	$1,000	1,000	2,000
Jack rental	......	7,500	7,500
Platform rental	......	2,500	2,500
Labor for raising, 20 shifts for 2 men = 40 shifts at $70.33	2,813	....	2,813
Supervising	550	....	550
Misc. supplies	......	500	500
Total for slip forms	$4,363	$20,536	$24,899

Other Forms

	Labor	Supplies	Total
2,107 sq ft	$2,107	$ 2,107	$ 4,214

Contact Grout—4 Shifts

	No. of men/shift	Cost of man/shift	Total shift
Labor cost per shift:			
Shifter	1	$82.19	$ 82.19
Crane operator	1	83.62	83.62
Crane oiler	1	70.33	70.33
Grout-pump operator	1	84.65	84.65
Laborer	1	70.33	70.33
Miners	2	76.14	152.28
Locomotive operator	1	79.42	79.42
Mechanic	1	89.39	89.39
Cost per shift	9	......	$ 712.21
For 4 shifts	...	......	$2,849

Supply Cost per Shift

	Unit	Cost/unit	Cost/shift
Crane	8 hr	$6.00	$ 48.00
Locomotive	8 hr	3.00	24.00
Grout pump	8 hr	2.00	16.00
Misc. supplies	9 men	3.00	27.00
Small tools	9 men	2.50	22.50
Rubber and safety	9 men	0.50	4.50
Misc	.....	.....	10.00
Total per shift	.....	.....	$152.00
For 4 shifts	.....	.....	$608
Sand	.....	.....	50
Total supplies	.....	.....	$658

Final Cleanup

Use the same crew as for first cleanup, for two shifts.

Labor	$630.09 × 2	$1,260
Supplies	166.00 × 2	$ 332

Summary of Cost of Shaft Concrete
Bid Item 10

	Labor	Supplies	Subcontract	Total Direct
Clean shaft, remove tights	$ 3,150	$ 830	......	$ 3,980
Aggregates, 2,390 cu yd at 1.65 tons = 3,944 tons at $2.10	....	....	$8,282	8,282
Cement waste, 2,390 cu yd at $0.05	....	120	......	120
Admix, 2,390 cu yd at $0.10	....	239	......	239
Placing cost	30,621	5,875	......	36,496
Slip forms	4,363	20,536	......	24,899
Other forms	2,107	2,107	......	4,214
Contact grout	2,849	658	......	3,507
Final cleanup	1,260	332	......	1,592
Total cost	$44,350	$30,697	$8,282	$83,329
Per cu yd based on 1,894 cu yd	$ 23.42	$ 16.21	$ 4.37	$ 44.00

Bid Item 11—Cement for Concrete and Low-pressure Grout

Bid quantity 163,000 bbl

Our takeoff:

Tunnel lining:

Pay .... 110,453 cu yd

Nonpay .... 43,810 cu yd

Shaft lining:

Pay .... 1,894 cu yd

Nonpay .... 496 cu yd

Total cu yd of concrete .... 156,653 cu yd

Cement at 1 bbl/cu yd for concrete; grouting cement at $1\frac{1}{2}$ sacks/lin ft of tunnel

Total cement .... 162,565 bbl

Assumed price/bbl delivered to mix plant $5.00

Sales tax at 5% 0.25

Total cost per bbl $5.25

Bid Item 12—Steel Reinforcing

Bid quantity 285,000 lb

Assumed price/lb from subcontractor $0.13

Allow for servicing of the subcontractor 0.01

Total cost per lb $0.14

Bid Item 13—Embedded Anchor Bolts

Assumed price/lb for material $0.38

Sales tax at 5% 0.02

Total cost of material/lb $0.40

Estimated cost of installation:

Labor $0.50

Supplies 0.10

Total cost per lb $1.00

Bid Item 14—Embedded Vent Pipe

Assumed price/lb for material	$0.22	
Sales tax at 5%	0.01	
Total cost of material/lb	$0.23	
Estimated cost of installation:		
Two man-days to install, or $144; for 1 lb	0.24	
Misc. supplies	0.03	
Total cost per lb		$0.50

Bid Items 15, 16, and 17—Consolidation Grouting

Assumed prices from subcontractor:	
Drilling grout holes, per lin ft	$4.00
Consolidation grouting, per cu ft	4.00
Cement for grouting, per sack	1.25

Adit-plug Concrete

Adit-plug concrete will be charged to plant and equipment. Total concrete is 600 cu yd. Pour in 5-ft lifts or 5 days at one shift per day. Crew will be the same as for arch pour, less form movers and pipe movers.

		Labor	Supplies	Total
Arch-pour crew per day	107 men	$ 8,189.69	$2,130.98	$10,320.67
Less form movers and pipe movers	21 men	1,490.61	115.50	1,606.11
Remainder for three shifts	86 men	$ 6,699.08	$2,015.48	$ 8,714.56
Cost for one shift	29 men	$ 2,233.03	$ 671.83	$ 2,904.86
Cost for pouring plug, 5 shifts		$11,165	$3,359	$14,524

Summarizing Cost of Adit-Plug Concrete

	Labor	Supplies	Total
Aggregates, 990 tons at $2.10	....	$2,079	$ 2,079
Admix, 600 cu yd at $0.10	....	60	60
Cement, 600 bbls at $5.25	....	3,150	3,150
Placing cost	$11,165	3,359	14,524
Forms, 176 sq ft at $4.00	440	264	704
Total cost to plant and equipment	$11,605	$8,912	$20,517

XVI. SPREAD SHEET SUMMARIZING DIRECT COST

Exhibit 9

SIERRA TUNNEL

Bid item	Description	Quantity	Labor		Supplies		Permanent materials		Subcontracts		Total direct cost	
			Unit	Amount	Unit	Amount	Unit	Amount	Unit	Amount	Unit	Amount
Tunnel excavation:												
1	Tunnel excavation	431,000 cu yd	$ 7.07	$3,047,170	$ 3.41	$1,469,710					$10.48	$4,516,880
2	Steel sets	2,290,000 lb	0.05	114,500			$ 0.12	$ 274,800			0.17	389,300
3	Timber	400 MBM	50.00	20,000	80.00	32,000	80.00	32,000			210.00	84,000
4	Roof bolts	12,000 lin ft	0.91	10,920	0.21	2,520	0.40	4,800			1.52	18,240
5	Drill exploratory holes	300 lin ft	4.40	1,320	2.12	636					6.52	1,956
6	Drill grout holes as aid to tunnel driving	2,400 lin ft	0.66	1,584	0.21	504					0.87	2,088
7	Grout as aid to tunnel driving	400 cu ft	5.27	2,108	4.08	1,632					9.35	3,740
	Total tunnel excavation			$3,197,602		$1,507,002		$ 311,600				$5,016,204
Shaft excavation:												
8	Shaft excavation	5,300 cu yd	21.18	112,254	7.43	39,379					28.61	151,633
Concrete:												
9	Concrete tunnel lining	111,000 cu yd	15.82	1,756,020	4.11	456,210			$4.84	$537,240	24.77	2,749,470
10	Shaft concrete	1,900 cu yd	23.42	44,498	16.21	30,799			4.37	8,303	44.00	83,600
11	Cement for concrete and low-pressure grout	163,000 bbl					5.25	855,750			5.25	855,750
12	Steel reinforcement in shaft	285,000 lb	0.01	2,850					0.13	37,050	0.14	39,900
13	Embedded anchor bolts	3,200 lb	0.50	1,600	0.10	320	0.40	1,280			1.00	3,200
14	Embedded vent pipe	600 lb	0.24	144	0.03	18	0.23	138			0.50	300
	Total concrete			$1,805,112		$ 487,347		$ 857,168		$582,593		$3,732,220
Consolidation grouting:												
15	Drilling grout holes	4,000 lin ft							4.00	16,000	4.00	16,000
16	Consolidation grouting	10,000 cu ft							4.00	40,000	4.00	40,000
17	Cement for grouting	5,000 sacks							1.25	6,250	1.25	6,250
	Total grouting									$ 62,250		$ 62,250
	TOTAL DIRECT COST			$5,114,968		$2,033,728		$1,168,768		$644,843		$8,962,307

XVII. PLANT AND EQUIPMENT COST

	Quantity	Cost/unit	Freight and move-in cost	Labor	Equipment invoice	Other invoice	Total estimated cost	Salvage	Net cost P and E*	Rent		
										No. of months	Rent/ month	Total rent
Rubber-tired excavation equipment:												
1 Truck-mounted jumbo	1	$ 20,000	$ 1,000	......	......	$ 20,000	$ 21,000	$ 6,000	$ 15,000			
G-D 123 drifter drills	10	5,800	......	......	$ 58,000	......	58,000	17,400	40,600			
G-D 143 burn-cut drill	1	11,345	......	......	11,345	......	11,345	3,400	7,945			
Jibs	10	5,280	......	......	52,800	......	52,800	15,840	36,960			
Drill positioners	9	2,760	......	......	24,840	......	24,840	7,450	17,390			
Hydraulic pump and misc.	3	1,210	......	......	3,630	......	3,630	1,090	2,540			
Line oilers	9	150	......	......	1,350	......	1,350	......	1,350			
Eimco mucker, rent for 4 mo.	1	......	1,500	......	......	......	1,500	......	1,500	4	$2,500	$10,000
Koehring Dumptors	3	15,800	2,850	......	47,400	......	50,250	23,700	26,550			
Portable 1,200-cfm compressors, rent for 3½ mo.	3	......	600	......	......	......	600	......	600	10½	1,500	15,750
Total rubber-tired excavation equipment	......	......	$ 5,950	......	$ 199,365	$ 20,000	$ 225,315	$ 74,880	$150.435	....	......	$25,750
Rail-mounted excavation equipment:												
Jacobs floor	2	125,000	$20,000	$40,000	$ 250,000	$ 10,000	$ 320,000	$100,000	$220,000			
Gantry jumbos:												
Structural frame	2	30,000	2,000	......	......	60,000	62,000	18,000	44,000			
G-D 123 drills	24	5,800	......	......	139,200	......	139,200	41,760	97,440			
G-D 143 drills	2	11,345	......	......	22,690	......	22,690	6,800	15,890			
Jibs	24	5,280	......	......	126,720	......	126,720	38,160	88,560			
Positioners	22	2,760	......	......	60,720	......	60,720	18,220	42,500			
Hydraulic pumps	6	1,210	......	......	7,260	......	7,260	2,180	5,080			
Liner oilers	22	150	......	......	3,300	......	3,300	......	3,300			
Conway 102 muckers, new	2	68,000	4,000	......	136,000	......	140,000	68,000	72,000			
Conway 102 muckers, standby, used	1	34,000	1,000	......	34,000	......	35,000	20,000	15,000			
15 cu yd muck cars	60	4,000	12,000	......	240,000	......	252,000	120,000	132,000			
Flat cars	8	1,500	1,600	......	12,000	......	13,600	6,000	7,600			
Man cars	6	2,000	1,200	......	12,000	......	13,200	6,000	7,200			
Vent-line cars	2	7,000	500	......	14,000	......	14,500	7,000	7,500			
Locomotives, 25-ton	8	36,000	16,000	......	288,000	......	304,000	144,000	160,000			
Powder car	2	4,000	400	......	8,000	......	8,400	4,000	4,400			
Hand-held drills anp spades	......	......	......	......	5,000	......	5,000	......	5,000			
Total rail-mounted excavation equipment	......	......	$58,700	$40,000	$1,358,890	$ 70,000	$1,527,590	$600,120	$927,470			

* Plant and equipment.

Shaft excavation:												
Alimak Raise Climber	1	$ 23,500	$ 5[illegible]		$ 23,500		$ 24,000	$ 11,750	$ 12,250			
Stopers	2	1,720			3,440		3,440	1,030	2,410			
Rent 50-ton truck crane, 2 mo, 3 shifts	1		500				500		500	2	$7,550	$15,100
Drill jumbo (drills from truck jumbo)	1			$ 2,500		$ 2,500	5,000		5,000			
Man and material cages				1,000		1,000	2,000		2,000			
Rent 630 mucker, 3 mo	1		500				500		500	3	1,000	3,000
Total			$ 1,500	$ 3,500	$ 26,940	$ 3,500	$ 35,440	$ 12,780	$ 22,660			$18,100
Tunnel service equipment:												
70 lb rail, 26,000 track ft	606 ton	190				$115,140	$ 115,140	$ 57,570	$ 57,570			
Rail hardware	26,000 TF	0.50				13,000	13,000		13,000			
Ties	15,000 ea	2.50				37,500	37,500		37,500			
Stringers on concrete under ties	26,000 TF	0.60				15,600	15,600		15,600			
48-in. vent pipe	24,000 lin ft	5.65				135,600	135,600	48,000	87,600			
Fans	20 ea	3,000	$ 1,000		$ 60,000		61,000	30,000	31,000			
12-in. drainage pipe	25,000 lin ft	2.40				60,000	60,000	15,000	45,000			
12-in. air line	1,000 lin ft	2.40				2,400	2,400	600	1,800			
10-in. air line	24,000 lin ft	2.00				48,000	48,000	12,000	36,000			
4-in. water line	25,000 lin ft	0.65				16,250	16,250	5,000	11,250			
Fittings						5,000	5,000		5,000			
Pumps					20,000		20,000	10,000	10,000			
Parkway cable	25,000 lin ft	2.60				65,000	65,000	32,500	32,500			
Drag cable	4,000 lin ft	4.00				16,000	16,000		16,000			
Light cable	25,000 lin ft	0.30				7,500	7,500		7,500			
Telephone	25,000 lin ft	0.50				12,500	12,500		12,500			
Blasting circuit	25,000 lin ft	0.50				12,500	12,500		12,500			
Transformers					40,000		40,000	20,000	20,000			
Outlets						1,500	1,500		1,500			
Total			$ 1,000		$ 120,000	$563,490	$ 684,490	$230,670	$453,820			
Tunnel concrete equipment:												
Aggregate reclaim conveyor			$ 1,000	$ 5,000		$ 14,000	$ 20,000	$ 5,000	$ 15,000			
Mix plant			5,000	5,000	$ 160,000	5,000	175,000	80,000	95,000			
Agitator cars, 8 cu yd	20 ea	9,000	6,000		180,000		186,000	90,000	96,000			
Invert bridge and conveyor			5,000	5,000		30,000	40,000	15,000	25,000			
Invert bridge supports						5,000	5,000		5,000			
Invert screed			500			5,000	5,500	2,500	3,000			
Arch forms	400 lin ft	400	12,000			160,000	172,000	40,000	132,000			
Arch-form traveler	1 ea	20,000	1,000		20,000		21,000	10,000	11,000			
Unloading conveyor			100		3,500		3,600	1,750	1,850			
Press Weld rental												$30,000
Pipe and slick line			200			5,000	5,200		5,200			
Pipe and jumbo				2,000		3,000	5,000		5,000			
Vibrators					5,000		5,000		5,000			
Grouting setup	1 ea		500		8,135		8,635	4,000	4,635			
Total			$31,300	$17,000	$ 376,635	$227,000	$ 651,935	$248,250	$403,685			$30,000

XVII. PLANT AND EQUIPMENT COST (continued)

	Quantity	Cost/unit	Freight and move-in cost	Labor	Equipment invoice	Other invoice	Total estimated cost	Salvage	Net cost P and E	Rent		
										No. of months	Rent per month	Total rent
Shaft concrete:												
50-ton crane rentals, 2 mo, 3 shifts	1	......	......	......	......	......	......	......	......	2	$ 7,550	$15,100
Concrete buckets	......	......	$ 300	......	$ 4,000	......	$ 4,300	$ 1,000	$ 3,300			
Swing spout	......	......	......	$ 1,000	......	$ 2,500	3,500	......	3,500			
Air hoist	2	$ 2,860	......	......	5,720	......	5,720	2,860	2,860			
Total	......	......	$ 300	$ 1,000	$ 9,720	$ 2,500	$ 13,520	$ 3,860	$ 9,660	....	......	$15,100
Other facilities:												
Office trailers	......	......	500	$ 2,000	$ 8,000	$ 2,000	$ 12,500	$ 4,000	$ 8,500			
Shop, warehouse, complete	......	......	......	4,000	......	12,000	16,000	......	16,000			
Bins in warehouse	......	......	......	1,000	......	1,000	2,000	......	2,000			
First aid trailer	1	......	250	200	4,000	300	4,750	2,000	2,750			
Change house trailers	2	......	500	1,000	16,000	1,000	18,500	8,000	10,500			
Cap and powder house	......	......	......	1,000	......	3,000	4,000	......	4,000			
Shop equipment	......	......	500	......	12,000	......	12,500	......	12,500			
950 Front-end loaders	1	28,000	1,100	......	28,000	......	29,100	14,000	15,100			
Yard grading and track laying	......	......	......	15,000	......	5,000	20,000	......	20,000			
1075-cfm compressors, stationary, electric	9	20,120	......	4,500	181,080	900	186,480	91,040	95,440			
Starters	9	2,630	......	......	23,670	......	23,670	11,835	11,835			
Air receivers	2	2,277	400	......	4,554	......	4,954	2,300	2,654			
Pickups and sedans	10	2,100	......	......	21,000	......	21,000	5,000	16,000			
Ambulance (used)	1	2,000	......	......	2,000	......	2,000	500	1,500			
Car passers and misc	......	......	......	......	8,000	......	8,000	2,000	6,000			
Total	......	......	$ 3,250	$28,700	$ 308,304	$ 25,200	$ 365,454	$140,675	$224,779			

Exhibit 10

SIERRA TUNNEL

Summary of Estimated Cost of Plant and Equipment

	Freight and move-in	Labor	Equipment invoice	Other invoice	Total estimated cost	Salvage	Net cost P and E	Rent	Net cost P and E plus rent
Rubber-tired excavation equipment	$ 5,950	....	$ 199,365	$ 20,000	$ 225,315	$ 74,880	$ 150,435	$25,750	$ 176,185
Rail-mounted excavation equipment	58,700	$ 40,000	1,358,890	70,000	1,527,590	600,120	927,470	....	927,470
Shaft excavation equipment	1,500	3,500	26,940	3,500	35,440	12,780	22,660	18,100	40,760
Tunnel service equipment	1,000	....	120,000	563,490	684,490	230,670	453,820	....	453,820
Tunnel concrete equipment	31,300	17,000	376,635	227,000	651,935	248,250	403,685	30,000	433,685
Shaft concrete equipment	300	1,000	9,720	2,500	13,520	3,860	9,660	15,100	24,760
Other equipment	3,250	28,700	308,304	25,200	365,454	140,675	224,779	....	224,779
Adit excavation (from direct cost details)	....	77,694	....	34,893	112,587	....	112,587	....	112,587
Adit concrete plug (from direct cost details)	....	11,605	....	8,912	20,517	....	20,517	....	20,517
Total plant and equipment	$102,000	$179,499	$2,399,854	$ 955,495	$3,636,848	$1,311,235	$2,325,613	$88,950	$2,414,563
Sales and use tax	....	....	119,993	47,775	167,768	....	167,768	4,448	172,216
TOTAL	$102,000	$179,499	$2,519,847	$1,003,270	$3,804,616	$1,311,235	$2,493,381	$93,398	$2,586,779

XVIII. INDIRECT COST

Exhibit 11

SIERRA TUNNEL

	Number	Months	Cost/month	Total
Labor:				
Project manager	1	32	$ 2,000	$ 64,000
Tunnel superintendent	1	31	1,700	52,700
Project engineer	1	32	1,500	48,000
Office engineer	1	31	1,200	37,200
Design engineer	1	6	1,300	7,800
Safety engineer and licensed first aid*	1	31	1,000	31,000
Accountant	1	32	1,200	38,400
Purchasing	1	31	1,200	37,200
Payroll clerks	2	54	750	40,500
Secretaries	2	62	550	34,100
Total	...	....	....	$390,900
Burden, 27.75%	...	....	....	108,475
Total	...	....	....	$499,375
Other costs:				
Vehicle maintenance	...	300 VM	150	$ 45,000
Office and engineering supplies	...	31	500	15,500
Telephone and telegraph	...	31	500	15,500
Entertainment and expense accounts	...	31	100	3,100
Licenses and fees	...	....	....	2,000
Blue prints, photostats, photographs	...	31	100	3,100
Office equipment	...	....	....	7,500
Engineering equipment	...	....	....	5,000
First aid and safety	...	....	....	7,000
Outside consultants	...	....	....	1,000
Legal	...	....	....	2,000
Audit	...	....	....	3,000
Move key personnel in and out	...	....	....	5,000
Heat and light for office	...	31	50	1,550
Signs	...	....	....	1,000
Misc. cost	...	31	250	7,750
Total other cost	...	....	....	$125,000

* Quartered in trailer at the portal.

Insurance:
- Value of insurable equipment and buildings 2,150,000
- Insurance per month at $0.10/$100 2,150
- Number of months 31
  - Total insurance .... $ 66,650

Property tax:
- Value of taxable plant and equipment 2,150,000
- Assessed valuation, 25% 537,500
- Yearly tax at $6/$100 32,250
- Number of years 3
  - Total tax .... $ 96,750

Bond premium	Amount of contract	Bond cost/ $1,000	Amount	Total
First	$ 100,000	$7.50	$ 750	
Next	2,400,000	5.25	12,600	
Next	2,500,000	4.50	11,250	
Remainder	10,370,000	4.00	41,480	
Total	$15,370,000	.....	$66,080	
Time premium, 8%	....	.....	5,286	
Total bond premium	....	.....	....	$ 71,366
TOTAL INDIRECT	....	.....	....	$859,141

XIX. CAMP COST

A camp is not required on this project.

XX. COMPUTATION OF ESCALATION

Exhibit 12

SIERRA TUNNEL

	June 1 of 1st Year to June 1 of 2nd Year	June 1 of 2nd Year to June 1 of 3rd Year	June 1 of 3rd Year to June 1 of 4th Year	Total
Labor:				
Direct:				
Tunnel excavation items	$1,700,000	$1,497,602	....	$3,197,602
Shaft excavation	112,254	....	....	112,254
Concrete	....	720,000	$1,085,112	1,805,112
Total direct	$1,812,254	$2,217,602	$1,085,112	$5,114,968
Plant and equipment labor	149,954	17,940	11,605	179,499
Indirect labor	183,000	200,000	116,375	499,375
Total labor	$2,145,208	$2,435,542	$1,213,092	$5,793,842
Escalation, 7% a year compounded	....	7%	14.5%	
Total labor escalation	....	$ 170,488	$ 175,898	$ 346,386
TOTAL LABOR	....	....	....	$6,140,228

Supplies, Permanent Materials, and Subcontracts

Assume quotations are good for the life of the contract so there will be no escalation for these items.

(In making an estimate, quotations should be checked, and if they are not good for the life of the contract, escalation amounts should be added.)

XXI. SUMMARY OF TOTAL COST

Exhibit 13

SIERRA TUNNEL

		Total	*Total Labor*
Direct cost:			
Labor	$5,114,968	....	$5,114,968
Supplies	2,033,728		
Permanent materials	1,168,768		
Subcontracts	644,843		
Total direct cost		$ 8,962,307	
Plant and equipment:			
Freight and move-in	$ 102,000		
Labor	179,499	....	179,499
Equipment invoice	2,519,847		
Other invoice	1,003,270		
Subtotal	$3,804,616		
Salvage	(1,311,235)		
Rent	93,398		
Total plant and equipment		2,586,779	
Indirect:			
Labor	$ 499,375	....	499,375
Other cost	125,000		
Insurance	66,650		
Property tax	96,750		
Bond	71,366		
Total indirect		859,141	
Labor escalation		346,386	346,386
TOTAL COST		$12,754,613	$6,140,228

Exhibit 14

SIERRA TUNNEL CASH FORECAST

		1st Year			2nd Year				3rd Year			
	Total	June	3rd Quarter July–Sept.	4th Quarter Oct.–Dec.	1st Quarter Jan.–Mar.	2nd Quarter Apr.–June	3rd Quarter July–Sept.	4th Quarter Oct.–Dec.	1st Quarter Jan.–Mar.	2nd Quarter Apr.–June	3rd Quarter July–Sept.	4th Quarter Oct.–Dec.
Revenue:												
Bid-item revenue (20% markup)	$15,305,000		$ 150,000	$1,350,000	$1,900,000	$1,900,000	$1,900,000	$1,800,000	$1,670,000	$1,700,000	$1,635,000	$1,300,000
Less retained percentage			15,000	135,000	190,000	190,000	190,000	45,250				765,250
Subtotal	$15,305,000		$ 135,000	$1,215,000	$1,710,000	$1,710,000	$1,710,000	$1,754,750	$1,670,000	$1,700,000	$1,635,000	$2,065,250
Salvage revenue	1,311,235								250,000	250,000	250,000	561,235
Total cash revenue	$16,616,235		$ 135,000	$1,215,000	$1,710,000	$1,710,000	$1,710,000	$1,754,750	$1,920,000	$1,950,000	$1,885,000	$2,626,485
Disbursements:												
Direct cost:												
Excavation items	$ 5,167,837		$ 120,837	$1,006,000	$1,006,000	$1,006,000	$1,006,000	$ 858,000	$ 165,000			
Concrete items	3,794,470							40,470	915,000	$1,050,000	$1,289,000	$ 500,000
Labor escalation	346,386					15,000	45,000	38,386	45,000	60,000	93,000	50,000
Plant and equipment:												
Necessary for excavation	3,136,014	$ 50,014	1,651,000	860,000	190,000	120,000	120,000	120,000	25,000			
Necessary for concrete	762,000						362,000	330,000	20,000	15,000	15,000	20,000
Indirect cost:												
Labor and supplies	624,375	15,375	61,000	61,000	61,000	61,000	61,000	61,000	61,000	61,000	61,000	60,000
Bond premium	71,366	71,366										
Insurance and taxes	163,400	11,400	8,000	26,000	8,000	26,000	8,000	26,000	8,000	26,000	8,000	8,000
Inventories			100,000	20,000	20,000		60,000				−100,000	−100,000
Total disbursements	$14,065,848	$148,155	$1,940,837	$1,973,000	$1,285,000	$1,228,000	$1,662,000	$1,473,856	$1,239,000	$1,212,000	$1,366,000	$ 538,000
Revenue less disbursements		−148,155	−1,805,837	−758,000	425,000	482,000	48,000	280,894	681,000	738,000	519,000	2,088,485
Accumulated revenue less disbursements	2,550,387	−148,155	−1,953,992	−2,711,992	−2,286,992	−1,804,992	−1,756,992	−1,476,098	−795,098	−57,098	461,902	2,550,387
Working capital required		196,845	496,008	498,008	493,008	495,008	493,008	493,902	504,902	492,902		
Cash required		$345,000	$2,450,000	$3,210,000	$2,780,000	$2,300,000	$2,250,000	$1,970,000	$1,300,000	$ 550,000		
Interest at 6% per annum	$ 253,875	$ 1,725	$ 36,750	$ 48,150	$ 41,700	$ 34,500	$ 33,750	$ 29,550	$ 19,500	$ 8,250		

Chapter

9 Joint Venturing and Bid Preparation

INTRODUCTION

This chapter discusses the reasons for forming joint ventures in heavy construction and how these joint ventures operate, and describes the prebid meetings held by the joint venture partners to arrive at a mutually agreed upon estimate. The steps necessary to prepare a bid then are described and illustrated.

If a bid is submitted by a single contractor, there will be no prebid meeting, but the steps necessary to work up the bid will be the same as those for a joint venture. In some cases the contractor employs an outside consultant to make a separate estimate with which he compares his own. The procedure in comparing the two estimates is similar to that of a joint venture prebid meeting.

JOINT VENTURES

On large construction jobs, in order that contractors may have enough capital, bonding capacity, and experienced personnel to bid the work, it is common practice to bid in a joint venture with other contractors. A joint venture is a partnership of two or more contractors who join together to bid a particular construction job. Joint ventures are formed for only one job and are disbanded after this job is bid or constructed. The advantages of joint venturing are:

1. Because of the number of partners, it is easier for each individual partner to secure a bond for his percentage of the contract than it would be if he had to bond the entire contract.

2. It is easier for each partner to raise a share of the capital necessary to finance the work than to raise the entire sum.

3. Since each major partner generally prepares an estimate and since an estimate comparison meeting is held before submitting a bid, it provides a check on the various estimates.

4. Special talents of any of the participating companies can be utilized.

5. The contracting risk is spread since one company is able to have an interest in many more projects than if it were bidding by itself, which decreases the financial loss should one project be unprofitable.

6. Joint venturing works to the benefit of the owner as well as the contractor, as it assures the owner of more competition on the large projects. If a large contract is put out for bids, the number of contractors with sufficient bonding capacity not committed to other construction work may be very few. By use of the joint venture practice, contractors without free bonding capacity to bid the complete work by themselves are able to join together in groups to submit bids in competition with other joint ventures similarly formed. Many large contracts receive 10 or more bids from 10 or more joint ventures. On the assumption that each joint venture is composed of 4 contractors, 40 or more contractors are interested in the project. This makes the heavy construction industry a very competitive field.

The formation of a joint venture is usually initiated when one contractor decides to bid on a certain project and contacts other contractors, with whom it has been associated in the past or with whom associations are desired, to determine if they are interested in participating in the joint venture. The initiating contractor is the sponsor; the other participating companies are partners in the joint venture. The sponsor also inquires what percentage each contractor desires in the joint venture. When enough contractors indicate interest to subscribe for 100 percent of the work, the joint venture is formed.

The sponsor takes the largest percentage of participation in the joint venture. In the majority of cases, the sponsor is in charge of the work and receives only advice on major decisions and financial help from the other partners. In some cases a committee composed of a member from each of the major partners may be formed to meet and decide on major decisions. In other joint ventures the work is divided among the partners with each partner responsible for certain phases of construction, but each shares in the common profit. Others are formed where one partner is responsible for one phase of the work and takes the profit on this phase and other partners are responsible for other phases and take the corresponding profits from their phases. It is the practice with some organizations that the sponsoring partner gets an additional percentage of profits for sponsoring and administering the work, but this is not commonly done. Usually, each partner puts up working capital in accordance with his subscribed percentage and shares in the profits accordingly; the sponsor does not receive any additional compensation for manning and directing the work.

A prebid joint venture agreement is signed by all the partners prior to the bid submission. If the bid is successful, then before the work is started on the project, a joint venture agreement and a power of attorney is signed by all the partners.

A prebid joint venture agreement usually:

1. Dates the agreement.
2. Lists names of all partners and states their agreement to form a joint venture.
3. States that the partners are agreeing to submit a construction bid and perform construction on a certain specified contract.
4. States that the bid shall be satisfactory to all partners.
5. Delegates authority to individuals to sign the bid, bid bond, and other bid documents.
6. Defines the percentage of participation, and states that each partner agrees to furnish his share of deposits or other security for bidding.
7. Designates the sponsoring company.
8. States that the partners agree that if the bid is successful, they shall enter into a joint venture agreement covering construction of the contract.
9. Is executed by each partner.

In general, the joint venture agreement and the power of attorney:

1. Designate the sponsoring partners' personnel who have been nominated as attorneys-in-fact for the joint venture, and state the authority that has been delegated to them.

2. Date the agreement.
3. List partners.
4. List particular work to be accomplished by the joint venture.
5. State the name of the joint venture and its legal position.
6. Designate the sponsor.
7. Give percentage of participation.
8. State that partners will put up their proportional share of working capital.
9. Provide for a separate accounting system for the joint venture.
10. Give joint venture power to purchase equipment, open bank accounts, etc.
11. List reasons for default by any partner and the consequences in case of default.
12. Specify how profits and losses shall be shared.
13. Provide for audits.

These instruments are executed by all partners.

A joint venture has the advantages and disadvantages of any other partnership and is entered into by contractors who have mutual trust in each other's construction and financial abilities and honesty.

ESTIMATORS' MEETING

Separate estimates are usually made by all or several of the various partners. To arrive at a mutually agreed upon estimate on which to base the bid, an estimators' meeting is held prior to bid submittal. At this meeting estimates are compared, construction methods discussed, and adjustments made in each participating partner's estimate for anything left out of his estimate, any mistakes, or any cost changes resulting from improved methods of construction that are brought out at the meeting by other estimators. The estimators then arrive at a mutually satisfactory estimate that is approved by each estimator present. This estimate is then presented to the principals, who have a meeting to set the markup. Many principals attend the estimators' meeting since this is one of the best methods for them to become acquainted with the job.

The chairman of the estimators' meeting is a representative of the sponsoring company, and as well as presenting his company's estimate, he moderates the opinions of the representatives of the other companies in order to arrive at an agreement.

In some cases the estimators do not come to an agreement. When this happens, a tabulation of the various estimates is presented to the principals, who then have to reach an agreement on bid price without having the advantage of an agreed estimate.

At the estimators' meeting there is a limited time available to reach an agreement; so in order to facilitate the comparison of estimates and take advantage of each estimator's approach, the sponsoring company sends out to each partner, as soon as the information is available, some or all of the following information:

1. Forms for comparison of estimates (See Exhibit 15 which is the estimate comparison form for Sierra Tunnel.)
2. The format for preparation of the estimate
3. Wage rates applicable to the job (See Exhibit 5, Chap. 8.)
4. Payroll burdens
5. Insurance rates
6. Bond rates
7. Cost of power and up and down charges for the power supply
8. "Plugged" or "bogie" prices for materials and subcontracts (See Exhibit 4, Chap. 8, which gives plugged prices for Sierra Tunnel.)
9. List and cost of used construction equipment, if available
10. Any geological or materials engineering reports on the project site or material sources

The partners' estimators also often circulate each firms' quantity takeoffs so that agreement on quantities is reached on these before the estimators' meeting. This leaves more time to resolve other differences.

The use by all estimators of the same plugged or bogie prices for permanent materials and subcontract items results in a prearranged agreed estimated cost for these items and saves time and effort at the prebid estimators' meeting. These plugged prices do not have any effect on the final bid estimate as the cost ultimately used for these items is secured from quotations submitted by suppliers and subcontractors just prior to bid submittal. Upon receipt of these quotations the sponsoring company substitutes the quotation prices for the plugged prices and adjusts the total estimate and the total bid accordingly. Therefore, the use of these plugged prices allows each estimator to arrive at a total estimate of cost without spending time on items that will change upon the receipt of final quotes. This practice also saves time in the prebid estimators' meeting as each estimate and the agreed estimate will contain identical amounts for these items.

The first order of business at the meeting is for each partner to read his estimated figures as tabulated on the estimate comparison sheets, while the other estimators write them down, as shown in Exhibit 15. After the figures have all been read, discussions on cost, progress, methods, and equipment are held, and each partner makes such adjustments to his estimate as he feels are proper after due considerations of the factors presented in the discussions. (Adjustments made to the Sierra Tunnel estimates are shown by Exhibit 16.) After adjustments have been made to each partner's estimate, adjustments are made to arrive at a mutually agreed upon estimate to be used as a basis for bid preparation. Estimators should prepare their estimates in accordance with the format sent out by the sponsoring company and should completely fill out all forms transmitted to them for comparison of estimates. Estimates should be arranged so that unit cost and total cost of each operation are readily available for comparison. The estimators should thoroughly know all the details of their estimate and have the construction schedule and construction procedure in an orderly form both in their estimate and in their memories. It happens too often that meetings are delayed while one estimator tries to find in his estimate the answer to some simple question asked him by another estimator. The estimate form used in Chap. 7 arranges all information so that it is readily available. If the sponsoring company sends out a different estimating format than the one the partner's estimator used, then the estimator should have enough estimating flexibility to adjust his estimate to suit the format.

The agreed estimate is somewhat of a compromise, but advantage should be taken at the prebid meeting of the best construction method presented and the best estimates of cost. Individual estimators should relinquish any pride of authorship and be willing to adjust their estimates to take into account any method or cost which is better than they originally had in their estimates. In the majority of cases the final agreed estimate will reflect the best method of construction and the closest approximation to the actual cost of doing the work. It should always be remembered that the final agreed estimate is only an estimate and that the final cost of doing the work will vary to some degree from this estimate. Contracting is more hazardous than most businesses since the contractor is the only manufacturer that prices his product before it is manufactured.

After the estimators have arrived at an agreed cost, they should discuss the amount of capital that will be required from the joint venture partners to finance the construction, and the amount of interest charges on this invested capital. These two amounts should be presented to the principals so that they can be included in the markup figure. For an illustration of the method of determining the amount of capital required and the interest expense on this capital, refer to Exhibit 14, Chap. 8, Cash Forecast for the Sierra Tunnel estimate.

The estimators should discuss the overall concept of the job to

Exhibit 15

SIERRA TUNNEL

Estimate Comparison Sheets

	ABC Contracting Co.		KLM Contracting Co.		XYZ Construction Co.		Agreed cost
	Original	Revised	Original	Revised	Original	Revised	
Direct cost:							
Labor	$ 5,114,968	$ 5,187,968	$ 5,897,000	$ 5,050,000	$ 5,737,000	$ 5,491,000	$ 5,187,968
Supplies	2,033,728	2,063,728	2,267,000	2,175,000	2,047,000	2,066,000	2,063,728
Permanent materials	1,168,768	1,168,768	1,134,000	1,134,000	1,149,000	1,149,000	1,168,768
Subcontracts	644,843	625,399	644,850	644,850	644,850	644,850	625,399
Total direct cost	$ 8,962,307	$ 9,045,863	$ 9,942,850	$ 9,003,850	$ 9,577,850	$ 9,350,850	$ 9,045,863
Plant and equipment:							
Freight and move-in	$ 102,000	....	$ 85,000	$ 90,000	$ 70,000	$ 70,000	
Labor	179,499	....	80,000	180,000	195,000	195,000	
Equipment cost	2,519,847	....	2,120,000	2,710,000	2,420,000	2,220,000	
Plant invoice	1,003,270	....	960,000	1,006,000	950,000	950,000	
Subtotal	$ 3,804,616	....	$ 3,245,000	$ 3,986,000	$ 3,635,000	$ 3,435,000	
Salvage	(1,311,235)	....	(1,060,000)	(1,355,000)	(968,000)	(1,110,000)	
Rent	93,398	....	....	100,000	....	100,000	
Total plant and equipment	$ 2,586,779	$ 2,586,779	$ 2,185,000	$ 2,731,000	$ 2,667,000	$ 2,425,000	$ 2,586,779
Indirect:							
Labor	$ 499,375	....	$ 724,000	$ 544,000	$ 700,000	$ 500,000	
Other cost	125,000	....	160,000	120,000	220,000	125,000	
Insurance	66,650	....	50,000	50,000	50,000	66,000	
Property tax	96,750	....	50,000	80,000	63,000	81,000	
Bond	71,366	....	80,000	70,000	70,000	71,000	
Total indirect	$ 859,141	$ 859,141	$ 1,064,000	$ 864,000	$ 1,103,000	$ 843,000	$ 859,141
Labor escalation	346,386	$ 300,386	308,000	301,000	298,000	322,000	300,386
TOTAL COST	$12,754,613	$12,792,169	$13,499,850	$12,899,850	$13,645,850	$12,940,850	$12,792,169
Summary of labor:							
Direct	$ 5,114,968	$ 5,187,968	$ 5,897,000	$ 5,050,000	$ 5,737,000	$ 5,491,000	$ 5,187,968
Plant and equipment	179,499	179,499	80,000	180,000	195,000	195,000	179,499
Indirect	499,375	499,375	724,000	564,000	700,000	500,000	499,375
Subtotal	$ 5,793,842	$ 5,866,842	$ 6,701,000	$ 5,794,000	$ 6,632,000	$ 6,186,000	$ 5,866,842
Labor escalation	346,386	300,386	308,000	301,000	298,000	322,000	300,386
Total	$ 6,140,228	$ 6,167,228	$ 7,009,000	$ 6,095,000	$ 6,930,000	$ 6,508,000	$ 6,167,228
Direct cost comparison:							
Items 1–7, tunnel excavation	$ 5,016,204	$ 5,078,204	$ 6,162,600	$ 5,097,600	$ 5,435,600	$ 5,207,600	$ 5,078,204
Item 8, shaft excavation	151,633	151,633	135,000	135,000	170,000	170,000	151,633
Items 9–14, concrete	3,732,220	3,753,776	3,583,000	3,709,000	3,910,000	3,911,000	3,753,776
Items 15–17, consolidation grouting	62,250	62,250	62,250	62,250	62,250	62,250	62,250
Total direct	$ 8,962,307	$ 9,045,863	$ 9,942,850	$ 9,003,850	$ 9,577,850	$ 9,350,850	$ 9,045,863

Breakdown of item 9:							
Aggregate	$ 538,444	$ 519,000 (1)*	$ 468,000	$ 526,000 (1)*	$ 492,000	$ 511,000 (1)*	
Cement loss and admix	23,420	23,420	20,000	20,000	25,000	25,000	
Remove vent line and retimber	157,181	157,181	130,000	130,000	170,000	170,000	
Primary cleanup	278,164	278,164	290,000	290,000	350,000	350,000	
Invert concrete	422,893	413,893 (4)*	390,000	422,000 (4)*	440,000	422,000 (4)*	
Arch concrete	951,277	1,001,277 (4)*	910,000	946,000 (4)*	980,000	980,000 (4)*	
Low-pressure grout	161,317	161,317	150,000	150,000	180,000	180,000	
Final cleanup	191,984	191,984	175,000	175,000	190,000	190,000	
Week end maintenance	24,790	24,790	25,000	25,000	30,000	30,000	
Total	$ 2,749,470	$ 2,771,026	$ 2,558,000	$ 2,684,000	$ 2,857,000	$ 2,858,000	$ 2,771,026
Statistics:							
Excavation of main tunnel:							
Portals used	Adit		Outlet		Adit		Adit
Number of single-heading days, rubber	71		...		...		71
Number of single-heading days, rail	34		480		90		31
Number of alternate-heading days, rail	51		...		...		51
Number of double-heading days, rail	169		...		210		169
Number of men, single heading, rubber	67		...		...		67
Number of men, single heading, rail	94		100		104		97
Number of men, alternate heading, rail	113		...		...		113
Number of men, double heading, rail	160		...		168		164
Average wage rate/shift	$80		$79		$80		$80
Concrete, main tunnel:							
Progress:							
Number of days, invert pour	38		40		42		40
Number of days, arch pour	89		95		90		90
Size crew:							
Men per day, invert pour	119		100		110		110
Men per day, arch pour	107		90		100		100
% of overbreak	40		20		30		35
Total no. of mo to complete all construction	31		39		33		31
Yearly increase in labor cost	7 %		4 %		5 %		6 %
% Escalation on total labor	5.1 %		4.6 %		4.5 %		5.2 %
Maximum capital required to finance job	$3,210,000						
Date last capital will be returned	25 months						
Interest at 6 % on capital invested	$253,875						

* (1) and (4) refer to the Description of Adjustments, Exhibit 16, which follows.

determine whether it is a good job to bid or one with a high percentage of risk. Jobs may be classified risky for the following reasons:

1. If payment is on a lump sum or lineal foot basis, all the costs resulting from encountering bad ground, water, support requirements, etc., are the contractor's responsibility.
2. The job may be in a remote area and therefore have problems in securing competent workers, maintaining access, and supplying camps and living accommodations.
3. The job may extend for a considerable period of time with a large exposure to raises in wages, changes in fringe benefits, subsistence increases, changes in working hours and working conditions, and strikes.
4. Relief from unforeseen conditions may not be present in the specifications, and the job may be in ground of such a geological nature that it is difficult to determine the type of rock that will be encountered.
5. Equipment or supervision may not be readily available due to many similar jobs being bid or being under construction.

All conclusions reached at the estimators' meeting should then be presented by each estimator to his principal.

Exhibit 16

SIERRA TUNNEL

Adjustments Made at Joint Venture Meeting by Participating Partners

	ABC Co.	*KLM Co.*	*XYZ Co.*
Description of adjustments			
1. Adjusted to 35% of concrete overbreak	\$−19,444	\$ +58,000	\$ +19,000
2. Adjusted to drive from adit:			
Labor	....	−800,000	
Supplies	....	−150,000	
Plant and equipment	....	+941,000	
Increased salvage	....	−395,000	
Indirect	....	−200,000	
3. Adjusted for alternate headings	....	....	−110,000
4. Adjusted for crew sizes and progress:			
Tunnel excavation	+62,000	−115,000	−118,000
Invert concrete	−9,000	+32,000	−18,000
Arch concrete	+50,000	+36,000	
5. Adjusted for escalation:			
Agreed 6% and 31-month job	−46,000	−7,000	+24,000
6. Adjusted for renting equipment	....	....	−100,000
7. Adjusted salvage to 50% of equipment	....	....	−142,000
8. Adjusted to sponsor's overhead	....	....	−260,000
Total adjustments	\$+37,556	\$−600,000	\$−705,000

PRINCIPALS' MEETING

After the estimators have concluded their meeting, the results of this meeting are submitted by the estimators to their respective principals. The principals then hold a meeting to determine the amount of markup to be added to the agreed estimate to arrive at the bid price.

Principals should be well informed about the various aspects of the job. This job information is secured by discussing the work with their estimators, reviewing the results of the estimators' meeting, and a study of the bidding documents and job description. Many principals attend the estimators' meetings where exposure to different construction methods and their estimated costs will assist them in evaluating the proposed project.

The markup determined by the principals is composed of the following elements:

1. A proportional share of each participating company's home office expense.
2. Interest cost of the capital required to finance the work.
3. Contingency. In setting the contingency, the principals start with the job risk information that is presented to them by their estimators and with knowledge they have formulated by job review or attendance at the estimators' meeting. The amount reflects their evaluation of whether the markup should contain allowance for job contingency or estimating contingency or both.

a. Job contingency, discussed in the section on the estimators' prebid meetings, includes a measure of the reliability of the forecast of ground conditions on which the estimate is based. The contingency for variations in ground conditions should be taken into account more on tunnel construction than on other types of construction since the progress and cost of tunnel excavation is largely dependent on the kind of material that will be encountered. Even if the tunnel line has been completely drilled, it is impossible for any geologist or engineer to determine accurately how ground conditions will affect tunnel driving. Compared with other types of construction, a large percentage of markup is used in tunnel work to offset the risk of unforeseen conditions.

b. Estimating contingency. On most divisions of estimated cost, such as materials, supplies, and subcontracts, the estimator has previous job records or quotes that he can use to check his estimate. With labor, he must rely to a large extent on his own judgment since he will not receive any quotes on labor, and labor cost varies greatly from job to job. For this reason, and also because labor in tunnel construction represents a larger percentage of the total cost than in any other types of construction, profitable tunnel work is more reliant on estimating judgment and should therefore carry a larger estimating contingency than other types of construction.

4. Profit. In setting the job profit, the principal is influenced by the following job requirements: the amount of the contractor's capital required to finance the job; how many of the contractor's key personnel will be required to supervise the job, and for how long; and the estimated salvage value of the plant and equipment. This salvage value is a matter of judgment since it must be predetermined for a future date when the equipment may or may not be marketable, depending on whether it will fit any tunnel being advertised. Sometimes tunnel equipment does not sell for several years after it has been placed on the market and therefore requires storage and care, and property taxes must be paid on the equipment until it is sold or junked.

If the bid documents have not been circulated and signed prior to the prebid meeting, they are signed at the principals' meeting. At the conclusion of this meeting, the markup and other bidding instructions are given to the chief estimator of the sponsoring company, who has the responsibility for the bid preparation.

For the Sierra Tunnel bid, it is assumed that the principals agreed to a 20 percent markup on the total cost, composed of the following elements:

6% interest on capital required	$ 254,000
1½% of the total cost as home office expense allocation	192,000
Contingency and markup represented by the salvage value of the equipment	1,311,000
Contingency and markup represented by a cash profit	801,434
Total markup, 20%	$2,558,434

EFFECT ON THE BID PRICE IF USED EQUIPMENT IS AVAILABLE

To illustrate the effect that used plant and equipment bears on the bid price, the bid price will be recomputed on the basis that one of the partners has used plant and equipment available. This equipment is to be furnished to the project for 50 percent of its replacement value. Under these conditions the following changes could result in a revised bid price:

1. Plant and equipment net charge to the job would be reduced. If job salvage of the used plant and equipment is valued at 25 percent of replacement cost, the net charge to the job for plant and equipment

is 25 percent where it is utilized. The following table illustrates the effect this may have on the bid price:

	Sierra estimate agreed cost for new equip.	Revised for used plant and equip.
Freight and move-in	$ 102,000	$ 102,000
Labor	179,499	179,499
Plant and equipment:		
Equipment that can be replaced with used	2,000,000	1,000,000
Remainder of equipment purchased new	519,847	519,847
Plant invoice that can be replaced with used	500,000	250,000
Remainder of plant invoice purchased new	503,270	503,270
Subtotal, equipment and plant invoice	$3,523,117	$2,273,117
Total	$3,804,616	$2,554,616
Salvage	(1,311,235)	(770,000)
Rent	93,398	93,398
Total	$2,586,779	$1,878,014
Net job savings on plant and equipment	....	$ 708,765

2. Job maintenance of equipment would increase as it costs more to maintain used equipment than new equipment. The approximate total cost of maintaining the equipment as tabulated in the Sierra Tunnel estimate is approximately $870,000. If it is assumed that the maintenance cost will increase 15 percent, additional maintenance labor and supplies will amount to $130,000.

3. Production would decrease on hard-rock, fast-production jobs (such as the Sierra Tunnel) because the older equipment will not have all the improvements that have been developed and incorporated in the newer equipment. After tunnel equipment has driven several jobs, obsolescence generally makes it more economical to buy new equipment. For this comparison, we shall assume the equipment considered was only used on one job and is relatively modern, so the loss in production will only be approximately 5 percent.

Increased cost of tunnel excavation due to decreased production would then be:

Cost of tunnel excavation labor and supplies for item 1, plus labor for items 2 and 3	$4,651,380
Cost of loss of production, 5%	232,570
Cost of additional overhead:	
18 months @ 0.05 = 0.9 month at $21,000	18,900
Total cost of loss of production	$ 251,470

4. Markup would be reduced. When used equipment is substituted in the estimate, the first cost of plant and equipment reduces by one-

third, from $3,804,616 to $2,554,616. By examination of the cash forecast, the maximum capital required is at the time when $2,561,000 has been spent for plant and equipment. If this plant and equipment valued at $2,561,000 were reduced in cost 33 percent because of used equipment to $1,716,000, then cash requirements would be reduced a corresponding amount, or $845,000. Similarly, interest would be reduced by shortening the time period during which the capital would be required and decreasing the money required per month. Again, by examining the cash forecast, plant and equipment expenditures amount to 80 percent of the cash required. If these expenditures were reduced by one-third, the total interest could be reduced by one-third of 80 percent, or by 26 percent. This should reduce the markup by the change in interest charges and influence the percentage of markup since there will be less capital required. The amount of markup represented by the salvage value for the used equipment would be reduced from $1,311,000 to $770,000. This should also reduce the percentage of markup.

To summarize these changes in a theoretical bid price, the reduction in bid could be as follows:

	Sierra tunnel agreed bid	Theoretical bid with used equipment
Maximum capital required to finance work	$ 3,210,000	$ 2,365,000
Agreed total cost	$12,792,169	$12,792,169
Changes in cost due to used equipment:		
Reduction in plant and equipment	....	−708,765
Increased cost of maintenance	....	+130,000
Increased cost due to slower progress	....	+251,470
Revised total cost	$12,792,169	$12,464,864
Markup:		
Home office expense 1½% total cost	192,000	187,000
Interest cost on capital invested	254,000	188,000
Profit and contingency represented by salvage value of plant and equipment	1,311,000	770,000
Profit and contingency represented by cash profit	801,434	1,098,676
Total markup	$ 2,558,434	$ 2,243,677
Total bid	$15,350,603	$14,708,540
Markup %	20%	18%

The reduction on markup from 20 to 18 percent is justified because of the greater amount of profit represented in cash.

In theory, with all other parts of the estimate being the same and with a consistency of markup, the contractor who has modern used equipment partly amortized can always submit a lower bid than one that has to purchase new equipment. In practice this does not occur since tunnel construction methods may cause much larger variations in cost than the savings from used equipment. For example, on the Sierra Tunnel, which is a relatively simple job, different methods resulted in a variation of $736,000. (See Exhibit 6, Chap. 8.) If one adds 20 percent markup to this, the total variation is $883,000. Most tunnel jobs are more complicated than the Sierra Tunnel and could be constructed by many more methods, with resulting greater cost differences. Furthermore, progress and crew sizes used vary so much among estimators that these factors also cause large differences in estimated cost, and there is no consistency in markup among contractors. Therefore, although a contractor with used equipment has an advantage in bidding, he may not be the low bidder because of other factors.

BID PREPARATION

General

It is the responsibility of the sponsoring company's estimator to prepare the final bid. The period immediately before bid submittal is a very hectic period. In the short time available, the estimator must spread all cost and markup to individual items, check all quotations and make quotation adjustments as necessary, prepare the bidding papers in final form, check all extensions and additions, and transmit the bid to the bid opening agency.

Spreading Cost

There often are discussions by owners and engineers about "balanced" and "unbalanced" bids without a good understanding of what a balanced bid is. In preparing a tunnel estimate, the direct cost is estimated for each bid item, but the other divisions of cost—namely, plant and equipment cost, camp cost, indirect cost, and escalation—are estimated for the total job and must then be divided or spread among the individual bid items.

A balanced bid is one on which these other divisions of cost and profit are spread to the individual bid items which cause this cost and profit to occur. To arrive at a truly balanced bid, a very detailed study is necessary, and this study would require much more time than there is available between the prebid meeting and bid submission time. Because of this time limitation, it is impossible to submit such a bid on heavy construction work. Cost spreading is therefore done by various approximations, with reliance on the experience of the estimator. The methods of spreading vary among companies, and since the human element is involved, no two estimators with similar cost to spread would spread the cost in the same manner.

The easiest method of cost spreading (but the one which takes the least recognition of where cost occurs) is to divide the total direct costs into the total bid price to secure a factor by which each direct unit cost is multiplied to get the unit bid price. By this method plant and equipment cost, indirect cost, labor escalation, etc., are spread against many items which would not incur this cost, which results in an unbalanced bid. If time becomes critical, every contractor must resort to this simplified method in order to submit the bid by the deadline. Some contractors, in order to simplify bid submission, use this method on every bid, but it is not recommended except in critical bid submission conditions.

The preferred cost-spreading method is to use experience and judgment in arbitrarily placing cost against the proper items so that as good a unit cost is produced as is possible in the time available. This will not be a truly balanced bid but only an approximation. True unit cost is very important if the final pay items overrun or vary in quantity from the estimated quantities shown on the bid comparison sheets, since the final pay amounts will then reflect the true cost of the work. For instance, if a tunnel is bid where it is hard to determine how much rock will be supported and how much of the tunnel will be driven without supports, spreading can be done so that the cost of driving an unsupported tunnel is placed against tunnel excavation and the additional cost of driving the tunnel in supported ground is placed against supports. Then, if the contractor drives a tunnel that is mostly unsupported, the final pay quantities charged to the owner will reflect the lesser cost of that type of tunnel work. On the other hand, if the tunnel is supported through the majority of the ground, the contractor will receive payment comparable with the cost he incurred.

By using this cost-spreading method then:

1. Plant and equipment cost after salvage is spread against the major bid items that cover the type of work which caused its purchase.
2. Indirect cost is spread primarily against prime contract work with only a small percentage placed against purchased materials and subcontracts.
3. Camp construction and operation is spread against prime contract work as a subcontractor must reimburse the prime contractor if he uses the camp.
4. Contingencies are spread against high-risk items.
5. Labor escalation is spread against those items that involve labor and are scheduled in the years that the labor escalation occurs.

6. Markup is spread primarily against prime contract work with a small percentage against purchased materials and subcontracts. Markup should also be spread to round out bid unit prices so that the extensions are even dollar amounts to facilitate their use. In spreading markup, the unit bid prices can be rounded out so that the extensions will always be in even dollar amounts and cents will not have to be tabulated.

7. After bid unit prices are established, they should be reviewed by the estimator and adjusted to be sure that the contractor is protected against high-risk items. For instance, if the roof bolts overrun, work may be delayed which will cause extra cost to the contractor. The estimator may therefore decide to increase the bid price on this item and lower the bid price on another item. At this point in bid preparation, the estimator has a fixed bid sum to adhere to, and any increase in one item necessarily means a corresponding decrease in other items or item.

These seven steps represent the preferred spread. There is seldom time to complete all these steps, so approximations are made and reliance placed on the experience of the man directing the spread.

As an example of a method of spreading cost, the spread sheets on Sierra Tunnel estimated in Chap. 8 are shown as Exhibits 17 and 18. The spread sheets used have been set up so that they have an arithmetical check. If all totals posted are computed by multiplying the quantity by the unit price and then the columns are all added down and checked by adding across, arithmetic errors should be eliminated.

In the Sierra Tunnel spread of plant and equipment, cost for the special shaft excavation equipment was placed against the shaft excavation item, concrete equipment was spread against concrete, and all other plant and equipment was charged against tunnel excavation as this remaining equipment would be required for driving the tunnel even if the tunnel was not concreted.

Indirect cost was spread only to prime contract items.

Labor escalation was spread against concrete and excavation in accordance with the labor escalation computation.

Markup was spread at the rate of 5 percent to materials and subcontracts and the remainder at the rate of 21.2 percent to prime contract work. This combination of rates works out to the agreed 20 percent overall markup.

Bid prices were not adjusted for high-risk items as none occurred in this tunnel. If the tunnel were in soft ground, more cost might have been placed against tunnel supports in order to reimburse the contractor for delays in tunnel driving.

Exhibit 17

SIERRA TUNNEL

Spreading Plant and Equipment, Indirect, and Escalation to Arrive at Total Cost

Bid item	Description	Pay quantity	Agreed direct cost		Agreed plant and equipment		Agreed indirect		Agreed escalation		Agreed total cost	
			Unit	Amount	Unit	Amount	Unit	Amount	Unit	Amount	Unit	Amount
Tunnel excavation												
1	Tunnel excavation	431,000 cu yd	$ 10.62	$4,577,220*	$ 4.77	$2,055,870	$ 1.13	$487,030	$0.20	$ 86,200	$ 16.72	$ 7,206,320
2	Steel sets	2,290,000 lb	0.17	389,300	......	....	0.02	45,800	.....	....	0.19	435,100
3	Timber	400 MBM	210.00	84,000	......	....	21.70	8,680	.....	....	231.70	92,680
4	Roof bolts	12,000 lin ft	1.52	18,240	......	....	0.16	1,920	.....	....	1.68	20,160
5	Drill exploratory holes	300 lin ft	6.52	1,956	......	....	0.67	201	.....	....	7.19	2,157
6	Drill grout holes as an aid to tunnel driving	2,400 lin ft	0.87	2,088	......	....	0.09	216	.....	....	0.96	2,304
7	Grout as an aid to tunnel driving	400 cu ft	9.35	3,740	......	....	1.00	400	.....	....	10.35	4,140
	Total	....	....	$5,076,544	......	$2,055,870	......	$544,247	.....	$ 86,200	....	$ 7,762,861
Shaft excavation												
8	Shaft excavation	5,300 cu yd	28.61	151,633	8.18	43,354	2.84	15,052	....	....	39.63	210,039
Concrete												
9	Tunnel lining	111,000 cu yd	24.96	2,770,560*	4.16	461,760	2.63	291,930	1.93	214,230	33.68	3,738,480
10	Shaft concrete	1,900 cu yd	44.00	83,600	13.88	26,372	4.56	8,664	.....	....	62.44	118,636
11	Cement for concrete and low-pressure grout	163,000 bbl	5.25	855,750	......	....	......	....	.....	....	5.25	855,750
12	Steel reinforcing in shaft	285,000 lb	0.14	39,900	......	....	......	....	.....	....	0.14	39,900
13	Embedded anchor bolts	3,200 lb	1.00	3,200	......	....	0.10	320	.....	....	1.10	3,520
14	Embedded vent pipe	600 lb	0.50	300	......	....	0.05	30	.....	....	0.55	330
	Total	....	....	$3,753,310	......	$ 488,132	......	$300,944	.....	$214,230	....	$ 4,756,616
Consolidation grouting												
15	Drilling grout holes	4,000 lin ft	4.00	$ 16,000	......	....	......	....	.....	....	4.00	16,000
16	Consolidation grouting	10,000 cu ft	4.00	40,000	......	....	......	....	.....	....	4.00	40,000
17	Cement for grouting	5,000 sacks	1.25	6,250	......	....	......	....	.....	....	1.25	6,250
	Total	....	....	$ 62,250	......	....	......	....	.....	....	....	$ 62,250
	Totals from extensions†	....	....	$9,043,737	......	$2,587,356	......	$860,243	.....	$300,430	....	$12,791,766
	Totals from agreed estimate and instructions from principals†	....	....	$9,045,863	......	$2,586,779	......	$859,141	.....	$300,386	....	$12,792,169

* Totals adjusted from agreed direct cost to give even unit prices.

† It is not necessary to bid exactly the agreed amount as bid extensions can seldom be made to total the agreed bid.

Exhibit 18

SIERRA TUNNEL

Spreading Markup and Making Quotation Adjustments to Bid Items

Bid item	Description	Pay quantity	Total cost		Markup, 20%*		Bid price		Quote adjustments		Adjusted bid price	
			Unit	Amount	Unit	Amount	Unit	Amount	Unit	Amount	Unit	Amount
Tunnel excavation												
1	Tunnel excavation	431,000 cu yd	$ 16.72	$ 7,206,320	$ 3.54	$1,525,740	$ 20.26	$ 8,732,060	$+0.07	$ +30,170	$ 20.33	$ 8,762,230
2	Steel sets	2,290,000 lb	0.19	435,100	0.04	91,600	0.23	526,700	......	....	0.23	526,700
3	Timber	400 MBM	231.70	92,680	48.30	19,320	280.00	112,000	......	....	280.00	112,000
4	Roof bolts	12,000 lin ft	1.68	20,160	0.32	3,840	2.00	24,000	......	....	2.00	24,000
5	Drill exploratory holes	300 lin ft	7.19	2,157	1.51	453	8.70	2,610	......	....	8.70	2,610
6	Drill grout holes as an aid to tunnel driving	2,400 lin ft	0.96	2,304	0.24	576	1.20	2,880	......	....	1.20	2,880
7	Grout as an aid to tunnel driving	400 cu ft	10.35	4,140	2.65	1,060	13.00	5,200	......	....	13.00	5,200
	Total	....	......	$ 7,762,861	......	$1,642,589	......	$ 9,405,450	......	$ +30,170	......	$ 9,435,620
Shaft excavation												
8	Shaft excavation	5,300 cu yd	39.63	210,039	8.37	44,361	48.00	254,400	......	....	48.00	254,400
Concrete												
9	Tunnel lining	111,000 cu yd	33.68	3,738,480	7.19	798,090	40.87	4,536,570	+1.10	+122,100	41.97	4,658,670
10	Shaft concrete	1,900 cu yd	62.44	118,636	13.52	25,688	75.96	144,324	......	....	75.96	144,324
11	Cement for concrete and low-pressure grout	163,000 bbl	5.25	855,750	0.25	40,750	5.50	896,500	......	....	5.50	896,500
12	Steel reinforcing in shaft	285,000 lb	0.14	39,900	0.01	2,850	0.15	42,750	......	....	0.15	42,750
13	Embedded anchor bolts	3,200 lb	1.10	3,520	0.30	960	1.40	4,480	......	....	1.40	4,480
14	Embedded vent pipes	600 lb	0.55	330	0.15	90	0.70	420	......	....	0.70	420
	Total	....	......	$ 4,756,616	......	$ 868,428	......	$ 5,625,044	......	$+122,100	......	$ 5,747,144
Consolidation grouting												
15	Drilling grout holes	4,000 lin ft	4.00	16,000	0.20	800	4.20	16,800	......	....	4.20	16,800
16	Consolidation grouting	10,000 cu ft	4.00	40,000	0.20	2,000	4.20	42,000	......	....	4.20	42,000
17	Cement for grouting	5,000 sacks	1.25	6,250	0.05	250	1.30	6,500	......	....	1.30	6,500
	Total	....	......	$ 62,250	......	$ 3,050	......	$ 65,300	......	....	......	$ 65,300
	Total from extension	....	......	$12,791,766	......	$2,558,428	......	$15,350,194	......	$+152,270	......	$15,502,464
	Total from agreement	....	......	$12,792,169	......	$2,558,434	......	$15,350,603	......	$+152,175	......	$15,502,778

* Markup is spread at 5% on subcontracts and materials and 21.2% on remainder.

To be competitive in the bidding and to give the owner a lower price for the work, some contractors spread cost heavily to items done early in the contract. This gives the contractor early money, reduces his financing costs, which in turn reduces his interest expense, and permits a lower markup. This type of spreading may work to the advantage of both the owner and the contractor.

The owner often recognized the large sum of money that is required by the contractor to finance the work and to relieve the contractor of some of this financing includes a pay item for mobilization which partly reimburses the contractor for this expense. Such payment clauses often specify reimbursement for 75 percent of the equipment cost when this equipment arrives at the jobsite and is paid for by the contractor. This mobilization item helps the contractor to finance the work but is to his disadvantage if quantities overrun. If the contractor places his equipment cost in the mobilization item, the bid is "unbalanced" in that the bid prices for the various items do not include any charges for equipment write-off.

If there is a major overrun in quantities, the job will be extended in time, and the equipment will be older and have more hours of use, with a resulting decrease in salvage. This causes the net cost of equipment to the job to increase. But since equipment is a fixed sum under mobilization, the contractor is not reimbursed for this added equipment cost. If equipment write-off had been spread to the direct cost items, then as the work increased, the reimbursement for its additional use would have been included in the payment for the additional quantities. To express this in another manner, placing equipment cost in mobilization fixes the equipment write-off irrespective of the amount of work required.

A contractor makes his own quantity takeoffs to check the accuracy of bid quantities furnished by the owner's engineers. If the bid-item quantities are incorrectly stated so that an underrun will occur when final pay quantities are determined, the contractor must increase the unit prices in order that he may properly recover his cost, since a large percentage of the cost spread over these items is fixed and varies only slightly with the amount of work performed. Such fixed costs will not be recoverable on the quantities of work bid but not done nor paid for unless the contractor increases the spread in proportion to the amount each item will underrun. This increase in unit prices will increase the bid total and, if the bid-quantity error is not caught by every contractor, there will be an error in bid preparation, with the low bidder receiving the work without sufficient compensation. Owner's engineers too often do not understand this principle of bidding and do not pay sufficient attention to the accuracy of the bid quantities. In one case, the engineers threw out all the original bids submitted, then completely redesigned the job with smaller quantities but readvertised the work with the original bid quantities. This made it impossible for the contractors to submit a bid that would add up to a proper total and still allow the contractor proper reimbursement. When such flagrant errors in bid quantities occur, it forces the contractor to place as much cost as possible against lump sum items or items for which quantities are correctly stated.

Spreading cost is an important item in bids, worthy of more attention than is generally given it by estimators, owners, and engineers.

BIDDING DOCUMENT PREPARATION AND ADJUSTMENTS FOR LOW QUOTES

As soon as the spread sheets are finished and bid prices computed, these units and extensions should be transferred to the bidding schedule. Sierra Tunnel contains only 17 bid items, and this posting procedure would be comparatively short and simple. Many tunnel jobs are quite complicated with hundreds of bid items. Posting of the bid may take hours and, in some cases, days. All permanent-material prices and estimated subcontract prices are still subject to last-minute quotation adjustments so one, two, or three large bid items are left open, with prices not written in the bidding papers, so that all final quotation adjustments can be made in these bid items. When this is done, the addition of all extensions written in should be made so that this total will be available when the total adjusted bid price is determined at the bid closing time.

It is very important that the bid prices be checked, that the extensions be checked, and that the additions be checked on the bidding papers. The unit bid price controls; if the extensions are wrong, they are corrected by the owner's representative and a new total developed. Some contracts are lost because of sloppy extensions or erroneous unit prices written in the bid. The need for accuracy in this portion of the bid cannot be overstressed.

Keeping track of the latest quotes on materials and subcontracts is very important as the receipt of a final low quote may make the difference between having the low bid or just being another bidder. There are many ways of keeping track of these quotations so that adjustments can be readily made to the bid. The estimator should decide on the method that suits him best and be familiar with its procedure. Exhibit 19 shows an "over and under" sheet which is a very simple and effective method by which a running total of adjustments may be kept and the total adjustment to the agreed bid may be determined

Exhibit 19

SIERRA TUNNEL

Adjustments to Bid Price for Final Permanent-material and Subcontract Quotes

Bid item	Description	Pay quantity	In estimate incl. sales tax		Lowest quotation incl. sales tax		Plus	Minus	Name of supplier or subcontractor
			Unit	Amount	Unit	Amount			
2	Steel sets	2,290,000 lb	$ 0.12	$ 274,800	$ 0.13	$ 297,700	$ +22,900	....	Steel Fabrication Co.
3	Timber	800 MBM	80.00	64,000	75.00	60,000	....	$ −4,000	North Woods Lumber Co.
4	Roof bolts	12,000 lin ft	0.40	4,800	0.50	6,000	+1,200	....	True Steel Co.
9	Aggregate in tunnel lining	247,143 tons	2.10	519,000	2.50	617,858	+98,858	....	Crusher Aggregate Producers
10	Aggregate in shaft concrete	3,944 tons	2.10	8,282	2.50	9,860	+1,578	....	Crusher Aggregate Producers
11	Cement for concrete and low-pressure grout	163,000 bbl	5.25	855,750	5.30	863,900	+8,150	....	Kilm Cement Co.
12	Steel reinforcement in shaft	285,000 lb	0.13	37,050	0.12	34,200	....	−2,850	Sutter Steel Co.
13	Embedded anchor bolts	3,200 lb	0.40	1,280	0.35	1,120	....	−160	Sutter Steel Co.
14	Embedded vent pipe	600 lb	0.23	138	0.28	162	+24	....	Sutter Steel Co.
15	Drilling grout holes	4,000 lin ft	4.00	16,000	5.00	20,000	+4,000	....	Hardrock Drilling Co.
16	Consolidation grouting	10,000 cu ft	4.00	40,000	3.50	35,000	....	−5,000	Hardrock Drilling Co.
17	Cement for grouting	5,000 sacks	1.25	6,250	1.50	7,500	+1,250	....	Kilm Cement Co.
	Aggregate in tunnel plug	990 tons	2.10	2,079	2.50	2,475	+396	....	Crusher Aggregate Producers
	Total	....	......	$1,829,429	......	$1,955,775	$ 138,356	$−12,010	
	Net change due to quotations	....	......	....	......	....	+126,346		
	Markup, 20%	....	......	....	......	....	+25,269		
	Subtotal	....	......	....	......	....	$ +151,615		
	Adjust bond premium	....	......	....	......	....	+560		
	Additions to agreed bid price	....	......	....	......	....	$ 152,175		
	Agreed bid price	....	......	....	......	....	15,350,603		
	Adjusted bid price	....	......	....	......	....	$15,502,778		

Bid price adjustments: All bid prices and extensions had been written in the bid except for item 1, Tunnel excavation, and item 9, Tunnel concrete, so the bid adjustment was made in these two items. If the bid is successful and a budget estimate is prepared, each adjustment should be worked back into the estimate.

at any time. In using this method, the lowest quote for any item is posted and compared with the amount in the agreed cost, and the adjustment is tabulated. Any new quotation received is compared with the one posted; if it is higher, it is put aside; if lower, the one on the "over and under" sheet is erased and the new one posted, extensions are made, and the new adjustment is made. This is a foolproof method as each quote needs to be handled only once.

The receipt of quotes must be halted sufficiently ahead of bid closing time to allow time for entering the final adjusted bid figures on the bidding documents and to allow time for the transportation of the bidding documents to the point of submission. In order to reduce this bid closing time to a minimum, a temporary office can be used near the location where the bid must be submitted. Hotel rooms are commonly used for this purpose. To close the bids, the adjustments to the total bid price must be totaled on the "over and under" sheet. The bid items left open on the bidding papers have to be adjusted to reflect this adjusted total, the adjusted bid total has to be written in, these computations should be checked, the bid envelope containing all the bidding documents must be sealed, and the bid must be carried and deposited at the location stated in the bidding instructions. After bid closing time, bids are opened by the owner's representative, read, and the apparent low bidder announced. The owner's representative then checks all bids for any errors in extensions or additions and determines the low bidder. As previously stated, the unit prices control and the apparent low bidder may not be low when the extensions are verified and the additions are checked on all the bids.

BUDGET ESTIMATE

If the bid is successful, the sponsoring company's estimator should then prepare a budget estimate. This budget estimate is used by the job management to compare the production and cost achieved during construction with the production and cost that was estimated for the work. The estimator should also make these comparisons so that he can reflect this work experience in his next estimate.

To prepare the budget estimate, the bid estimate must be adjusted to the agreed cost estimate. The detailed sheets in the estimate must also be changed to reflect the final quotations for materials and subcontracts.

The cash forecast should also be adjusted for major changes made at the prebid meeting by actual spread of plant and equipment, final markup, and final quotations so that it can be used for job control.

Glossary of Tunnel Terminology

"A" LINE Dimensioned line in a tunnel beyond which rock projections are not permitted.

ADIT A short length of tunnel driven from the surface and connecting to the main tunnel. Often driven to enable more headings to be driven in the main tunnel; sometimes used to provide permanent access to the tunnel.

AIR GUN A steel cylindrical-shaped vessel with gates for dropping concrete into it and with air connections and discharge pipe connections. After the gun is charged, the concrete is forced through the discharge pipe by air pressure.

AIR LEGS Air-activated, long pipe jacks used for positioning light drills and maintaining pressure on the drills during the drilling operation. Also known as *feed legs*.

AIR LOCKS Pressure chambers located in the air bulkhead of a tunnel driven under air pressure. Men, material, and equipment pass in and out of the tunnel through these locks. While they are in the locks, the air pressure is slowly adjusted to that which will next be encountered in the direction of travel. Separate locks are provided for personnel.

ALTERNATING CREW A crew of miners that is switched from one heading to another in a double-heading location; has the advantage of keeping drilling and mucking operations continuous with one crew of men for each operation.

ANFO Explosive. A mixture of ammonium nitrate prills and a carbonizing agent.

ARCH POUR All the tunnel lining except the bottom section; also, the process in which this lining is poured. See Invert pour.

"B" LINE Pay line for excavation in a tunnel.

BACK Top of the arch of a tunnel.

BACKFILL GROUT See Low-pressure grout.

BLOCKING (1) Wood blocks installed between the lagging (or steel sets or a collar bracing) and rock surfaces of a tunnel to transfer stress to the supports. (2) Any timbers with a thickness greater than 4 in. spanning the area between sets.

BLOW OUT Quick release of air from a heading driven under air pressure.

BOOTLEG Amount of drilled rock in the tunnel face not broken by the explosion.

BOTTOM HEADING The excavation of the bottom half of a tunnel after the top half has been excavated for the full tunnel length.

BREAK Fragmentation of solid rock as a result of the explosion of an explosive mixture in drill holes at the heading.

BREASTBOARDING Partial or complete, braced support across the tunnel face which holds back soft ground during tunnel driving. Breastboards are braced to steel sets or to a shield or are supported with hydraulic jacks mounted on a breastboard jumbo.

BULKHEAD FORMS Forms placed in the top and sides of the pour between the forms and the tunnel surface. These forms are placed in a vertical line to form a vertical construction joint.

BULKHEAD POUR Concrete placed in a short section of tunnel between two bulkhead forms or between another bulkhead pour and a bulkhead form.

BULL GANG Crew of laborers usually used on the day shift to lay rail track, install pipes, clean up the tunnel, and perform any other necessary work that is located in the tunnel but not at the face.

BURN CUT Drilling pattern of large "relief holes" drilled horizontally in the center of the face to provide space for the expansion of rock broken by a blasting agent.

BURN-CUT DRILL Large drill used for the large-diameter holes in the center of a burn cut.

CABLE TENDER Man who takes care of the power cable running to the mucker.

CAGE An enclosed platform, similar to an elevator car, used to transport men and miscellaneous material up and down a shaft.

CALIFORNIA SWITCH Portable platform that rides on a track in a tunnel and is used for passing cars and trains. It has space for two or more tracks, crossovers, and switches, and has sliding and tapered end rails that ride on main-line rails.

CAR PASSER Portable tracks used for switching cars. The portable tracks are of sufficient length to accommodate one car when the portable tracks are resting on top of the main-line track. The rails are knife-edged on each end so a car can be placed on them from the main track. Then these tracks and car can be manually rolled on other rails to the side a sufficient distance to clear the main track.

CHANGE HOUSE A building containing toilets, showers, lockers, and clothes-drying facilities for the tunnel crews.

CHERRY PICKER Any frame capable of lifting a car vertically so a train may pass beneath it; used for passing cars.

CHUCK TENDER Assistant to the driller. (Before the use of modern jibs, the driller's assistant had to help position the drill steel while starting the hole in the face; hence the term *chuck tender*.)

CLEANUP The operation of removing loose muck, water, and other material from a tunnel prior to concreting.

COLLAR BRACING Struts installed between sets, capable of taking compressive forces.

COMPETENT GROUND Ground that does not require support when a tunnel is excavated through it.

CONCRETE PLACER Concrete pump or air gun for forcing concrete through a pipe line.

CONCRETE PUMP A pump that mechanically forces concrete through a pipeline into forms. (One type of concrete placer.)

CONTINUOUS POUR Process in which a concrete pour in a tunnel is poured as a continuous operation. The only shutdowns are for unforeseen delays and weekends.

COVER Amount of rock or soil over the arch of a tunnel.

CROWN BARS Timbers or other members installed in tunnel roof above sets.

CURBS Small pours made on the bottom and at each side of a tunnel and generally located outside the minimum concrete line; used as a reference point and support for invert and arch pour in the tunnel.

CUT A drilling pattern in the tunnel face which provides relief for an explosive charge. See also Burn cut.

DAY SHIFT Shift that extends from 8:00 A.M. to 4:00 P.M. See Swing shift, Graveyard shift.

DELAY CAPS Exploders used in the tunnel face, that have delay provisions resulting in the charges' firing in rotation. Delay caps are used so that the rock will be exploded into an area into which it can expand.

DIAMOND CUT Inclined short drill holes near the center of the tunnel face, so arranged that when the first shots are exploded in the round, a diamond-shaped wedge of rock is removed, which allows relief for the remaining rock when the delay exploders set off the charges in the other drill holes.

DOUBLE HEADING Two headings in a tunnel that can be driven from one plant location. Double headings are possible, for example, when a tunnel passes through and daylights in a depression or canyon or when two headings are driven from one adit.

DOUBLE-HEADING CREW Crew of men, located at one entrance to the tunnel, who drive two headings simultaneously from this entrance.

DRIFT A short section of tunnel not connecting to another tunnel nor daylighting at one end.

DRIFTER A heavy drill for drilling nearly horizontal holes in the tunnel face. Drifters require support from jibs.

DRILL Machine that transmits striking or rotating force (or both) to the drill steel and bits; used to drill holes which can be loaded with powder in rock tunnels.

DRILL JUMBO Movable frame on which drill positioners, jibs, and drills are mounted.

DRILL POSITIONERS Mechanical control for moving, rotating, and controlling jibs.

DRY PACKING When solid lagging is used in a supported tunnel, pea gravel or other material may be blown in between the lagging and the excavated surface to furnish support.

ERECTOR ARM Swing arm on boring machine or shield, used for picking up supports and setting them in position.

FACE Vertical wall at the end of the excavation in a tunnel.

FEED LEGS See Air legs.

FEELER HOLES Holes driven ahead of the excavation for exploratory purposes.

FINISH JUMBO Traveling support for the concrete finishers when repairing concrete and applying curing compound to cure and repair arch concrete.

FLOOR Self-propelled platform used in tunnel excavation (see Chap. 2).

FORCE MAJEURE Clause in the specifications that relieves the contractor of financial responsibility for certain events not under his control. Examples include acts of God, war, earthquakes, floods, and strikes.

FOREPOLING Round poles or steel driven underneath the second rib from the face and above the first rib from the face to provide support around the excavated area. See Spiling.

FORM TRAVELER Traveling frame used to strip, collapse, transport, and erect full-circle or arch forms.

FULL-CIRCLE POUR Process in which the complete concrete lining in a tunnel is poured in one operation. See Arch pour, Invert pour.

FULL FACE Tunnel blasted out to full bore size with each round.

GANTRY JUMBO Drill jumbo which has an open space in the center large enough for muckers, cars, and locomotives to pass through the jumbo; supported by separate rails, tracks, or tires.

GOUGE Finely ground up material found in fault areas.

GRASSHOPPER Traveling frame with hinged ends, riding on separate wide-gauge rail track and used for car passing. Cars are run up on this frame to permit trains to pass beneath.

GRAVEYARD SHIFT Shift that extends from midnight to 8:00 A.M. See Day shift, Swing shift.

GROUND The material through which a tunnel is driven, whether it is solid rock or running mud.

GROUT A mixture of water and cement or water, cement, and sand. See Low-pressure grout, High-pressure grouting.

GUNITE Pneumatically placed mortar, used to prevent air slacking of a tunnel's excavated surface; also applied as a support either directly on the excavated surface or over other supports in order to strengthen them.

HEADFRAME Tower built over a shaft to support the ropes for raising and lowering men, equipment, and material in the shaft.

HEADING Space adjacent to the face of a tunnel where the excavation crew works.

HEAVY GROUND Ground requiring strong supports.

HIGH-PRESSURE GROUTING Consolidation grouting used to strengthen rock or cut off water inflows.

HOG RODS A steel turnbuckle rod installed horizontally across a shield driven tunnel and fastened on each side to the liner plate, remains in position until the shield tail void is filled with pea gravel and grouted; prevents deflection of the liner plate.

HOLING THROUGH That point in excavation when a tunnel face daylights at a portal or meets another face which gives a continuous tunnel.

INCOMPETENT GROUND Ground that requires support when a tunnel is excavated through it.

INVERT On a circular tunnel, the invert is approximately the bottom 90° of the arc of the tunnel. On a square-bottom tunnel, it is the bottom of the tunnel.

INVERT POUR Process in which the invert of a tunnel is poured separately. See Arch pour.

INVERT STRUTS When tunnel ribs tend to move inward at the tunnel invert, compression struts are installed across the invert to resist this movement. These are the invert struts.

JACKHAMMER Light, hand-held percussion drill.

JIB Horizontal support for drifter drills bolted to a jumbo. These arms allow mechanical positioning of the drill at the tunnel face. Some jibs allow rotation of the drills so that side holes and lifters can be drilled closer to the final grade.

JIM CROW Manual or hydraulic rail bender.

JUMBO Any traveling frame used to support other items, such as drills, men, pipe for conveying concrete, conveyors, etc.

JUMP SET Tunnel rib (support) installed between two previously placed ribs.

LAGGING Wood or other structural members spanning the area between the ribs.

LIFTER HOLES Holes drilled in the bottom of the invert to fragment the rock in the invert. Because drills cannot be positioned to drill on the invert line, they have to be pitched slightly down in order to prevent tights.

LINER PLATE Pressed-steel plates with turned-back edges on each side containing bolt holes so that the plates can be bolted together to support the arch, sides, and in some cases the invert of a tunnel. Liner-plate sections can also be fabricated from steel plates and structural members, or they can be of cast iron, cast steel, or precast concrete.

LONG-HOLE DRILLING Procedure of drilling long holes to contain powder for breaking the rock in underground excavation. As an illustration, a tunnel may be excavated by first driving a pilot drift near the center of the tunnel. Then approximately 10-ft lengths of this drift are enlarged to full tunnel dimensions at intervals of 100 to 200 ft. These excavated areas are used as working chambers to drill holes in the remaining rock to the next enlarged section. Holes are then loaded and exploded, with relief for the explosion provided by the pilot drift.

LOW-PRESSURE GROUT Grout pumped through the concrete lining under low pressure to fill any voids between the concrete lining and the tunnel surface or between steel tunnel liners and backfill concrete.

MAIN-LINE JUMBO Drill jumbo that travels on the main rail line; has man platforms on the sides that can be folded back when not in use. After drilling out the round, the jumbo has to be moved back from the face to a passing track before the mucker can be moved in.

MIXED FACE The situation when the tunnel passes through both rock and unconsolidated material and both are exposed simultaneously at the face.

MOLE A tunnel-boring machine.

MUCK Broken rock or other material produced at the face of a tunnel by the excavation process.

MUCKER Machine for loading excavated material into haulage units.

MUDSILL Continuous horizontal member installed along the side of a tunnel at the lowest excavation line to support sets or take the load of the supports from the wall plate.

MULTIPLE DRIFT Excavation of a tunnel by driving two small drifts along each side of the tunnel, which allow the side support to be placed. A top drift is then driven and widened out slowly to take the roof support.

NIPPER Laborer on the drilling crew who handles drill steel replacements and bits and does general housekeeping.

NONTELESCOPIC FORMS Full-circle or arch forms that when stripped and collapsed, will not pass through other forms erected in place.

OVERBREAK Excavation that occurs back of the B, or pay, line of a tunnel owing to the irregular pattern of rock breakage; in lined tunnels also describes concrete required to fill this overexcavated position.

OVERBURDEN The mantle of earth overlying rock formations.

PANNING The channeling of water down the sides of a tunnel behind metal strips before concreting. After concrete is placed, these channels can be grouted off.

PIPE JUMBO Traveling support for the discharge line from a concrete placer.

PLENUM METHOD Excavating a tunnel under air pressure.

PORTAL Point where tunnel enters the earth's surface.

PORTAL-IN To start the tunnel excavation at the portal face.

POT A steel pressure vessel used for transporting concrete. At the point of placement, the concrete is ejected from the pot by use of compressed air.

POWDER FACTOR Number of pounds of powder per cubic yard of rock.

PRESS WELD Brand name of an air-activated concrete placer.

PULL Length of rock broken when a round is shot at the face. In estimating, it is assumed to be at least 1 ft shorter than the length of the drill holes.

RIB Section of tunnel between the spring line and back. Also an H- or I-beam steel support. See Set.

ROCK THROW The distance broken rock will be thrown down the tunnel when the round is exploded.

ROOF BOLTS Bolts equipped with an expandable anchor at one end and a nut and washer at the other. Installed in drilled holes to tie rock together. Also known as *rock bolts.*

ROUND The length of tunnel that is drilled and shot in one operation.

RUN-INS Flow of material into the tunnel from the tunnel face or from the tunnel circumference.

RUNNING GROUND Fine particles of material which flow into the excavated area while the tunnel is being excavated. Water is usually present in the material.

SAND HOG Miner who works in a tunnel driven under air pressure.

SCREED A slip form used on an invert pour; anything used to strike off a concrete pour.

SCRUBBER The equipment required to be installed on diesel engines, whose purpose is to dissolve or neutralize exhaust gases.

SET One structural support for the sides and roof of a tunnel; used more when tunnel supports were built up with wood members (post and crown). See Rib.

SHIELD Steel tube shaped to fit excavation line of the tunnel and used to provide support for the tunnel, provide space within its tail for erecting supports, protect the men excavating and erecting supports, and if breastboards are required, provide supports for them.

SHIFTER Foreman of heading crew.

SHOTCRETE Method under development for applying concrete lining on tunnel arch immediately after excavation. This lining would replace tunnel supports and also serve as the permanent lining.

SILICOSIS A lung disease caused by breathing dust from rock drills over a long period of time. Rocks with high silica content are the most harmful.

SINGLE-HEADING CREW Crew of men located at one entrance to the tunnel who only excavate one heading at any one time for this entrance.

SKIP Container used in hoisting muck from a shaft.

SLASHING The operation of enlarging a pilot shaft to full diameter by conventional methods.

SLICK LINE Section of the discharge line from a concrete placer that is embedded in the fresh concrete during arch or full-circle pour.

SLIDING CROWN BARS Crown bars that are slid forward over sets as mucking advances, in order to protect the workmen and support the back.

SLUSHER TRAIN A muck train composed of a locomotive and articulated muck cars. During the mucking cycle, the locomotive furnishes power to operate a scraper which runs along the top of the train; as the lead car is loaded by the mucking machine, the scraper drags the material back from the lead car and loads the others.

SPILING Supporting wood or steel members driven in front of the second set and in back of the first set from the face; support the sides and roof of the tunnel. See Forepoling.

SPRING LINE Point on the side of a tunnel where tunnel or set starts curving into the arch.

SQUEEZING GROUND Material that exerts heavy pressure on the circumference of the tunnel after excavation has passed through that area; may cause inward movement of sets, rising of invert, breaking of blocking, etc., and may necessitate the installation of invert struts and jump sets and further excavation to relieve pressure.

STEMMING Inert material packed in a drilled hole on top of the explosive charge. Its purpose is to contain the force of the explosion in the rock.

STOPERS Drills designed for drilling overhead holes.

STRUTS Compression supports placed between tunnel sets.

SWELL Increase in rock volume when it passes from the solid to the broken state.

SWING SHIFT Shift that extends from 4:00 P.M. to midnight. See Day shift, Graveyard shift.

TELESCOPIC FORMS Full-circle or arch forms that, when stripped and collapsed, will pass through other forms that are erected in place.

TIE RODS Tension members between sets to maintain spacing. These pull the sets against the struts.

TIGHT Projection of rocks in a tunnel past the A line.

TOP HEADING Upper section of the tunnel. Also, a tunnel excavation method where the complete top one-half of the tunnel is excavated before the bottom section is started.

TOP HEADING AND BENCH Method of tunnel driving where the top heading is carried about 1½ times the length of one round ahead of the lower heading or bench.

TUNNEL-BORING MACHINE Machine that excavates a tunnel by drilling out the heading to full size in one operation.

V CUT Inclined short drill holes near the center of the tunnel face, drilled so that when the first shots are exploded in the round, a wedge of rock is removed, which allows relief for the remaining rock when the delay exploders set off the charges in the other drill holes.

WALKER Shift superintendent.

WALL PLATES Continuous horizontal members installed along the sides of the tunnel at or near the spring line, when a top heading or multiple heading is driven to support arch sets. Often two I beams are used for wall plates. After excavating the bottom heading, supports are installed to support the wall plate from the mud sill.

WALKER Shift superintendent.

so that blocking will seat firmly against tunnel roof or sides.

INDEX

Index